W9-BNH-249

A Book
of
Short Stories - 1

PERSPECTIVES IN LITERATURE

A Book of Short Stories—1
A Book of Poetry—1
A Book of Nonfiction—1
A Book of Drama—1

A Book of Short Stories—2
A Book of Poetry—2
A Book of Nonfiction—2
A Book of Drama—2

Modern American Prose
A Book of Modern American Poetry
A Book of Drama—3

Modern British Prose
A Book of Modern British Poetry
A Book of Drama—4

PERSPECTIVES IN LITERATURE

A Book of
Short Stories - 1

SARAH E. LAUBACHER

ROBERT A. LODGE

HARCOURT BRACE JOVANOVICH

New York   Chicago   San Francisco   Atlanta   Dallas   *and*   London

Cover Photo: A detail from the sculpture Mayflower *by Marisol. From the collection of Mr. and Mrs. Charles B. Benenson, New York, N. Y. Courtesy Sidney Janis Gallery, New York, N. Y. Photograph by Jack Mitchell.*

Printed in the United States of America.

ISBN 0-15-336800-4

Contents

INTRODUCTION

IN THE COLLECTION *The Arabian Nights' Entertainments*,[1] we read the tales of beautiful Scheherezade, who saved her life by recounting to her husband, the king, a new story each night until her stories numbered a thousand and one. What an enviable skill—to invent such a multitude of tales. The modern short-story writer might well wish for a small share of Scheherezade's talent.

The history of the short story is old, although the name is relatively new. Centuries ago, biblical stories and parables and Greek myths and fables were enjoyed in much the same manner as the stories of today.

There is no prescribed length for a short story. It is often brief, but it does not necessarily have to be so. The average length of a short story is usually from 2,000 to 3,000 words, although it may run from 500 words up to 40,000 words. Sometimes a long or extended short story is referred to as a novelette.

The difference between a short story and other fictional forms, such as the novel, lies in its intensity: a conversation, an action, an emotional appeal will all deliberately focus on one desired effect. The short story strives for unified treatment of a single action.

Although two of the major reasons for reading short stories are enjoyment and entertainment, they provide more than mere escape from our surroundings and the realities of life. Good short stories permit us to examine our own lives, our own little worlds—and from different points of view.

Elements of the Short Story

Just as you need to know fabric and color names in sewing, or to understand such words as *foul, strike,* and *curve* for baseball, so too do you need a vocabulary for discussing the short story. Not all

1. *The Arabian Nights' Entertainments:* a group of Oriental stories (also called *The Thousand and One Nights*) dating from the tenth century, narrated by Queen Scheherezade (shə·her′ə·zäd′). The king postponed her death (the usual fate of his wives) from day to day so he could hear more of her interesting stories. Aladdin, Ali Baba, and Sinbad the Sailor are among the characters in these tales.

short stories contain all of the following elements. Depending on the author's purpose, some factors may receive more emphasis than others; some may not be used at all.

Suspense

Basic to every short story are curiosity and tension regarding the outcome. Many writers try to arouse the reader's curiosity in the first sentence. For example, notice the opening sentence of "Dog Star" by Arthur C. Clarke: "When I heard Laika's frantic barking, my first reaction was one of annoyance." The reader wonders: Why is the dog barking so urgently? What happens when the "I" of the story reacts? The writer keeps the reader in suspense by not answering these questions until later in the story.

Suspense is created as soon as we read of an uncertain or doubtful situation. The author increases the suspense by withholding information that would satisfy the reader's curiosity.

Conflict

The reason a story grows in tension and suspense as it moves is that the pressure of conflict, the struggle between two opposing forces, is increased by each event. Conflict in a story may be (1) man against man, (2) man against nature, (3) man against himself, (4) man against society, or (5) a combination of one or more of these types.

An example of man against man would be one man fighting another to win the hand of a pretty girl. Man against nature might involve a person caught in a storm at sea. An athlete debating the morality of accepting a bribe would illustrate man against himself. And a doctor who meets community opposition to a new medicine or vaccination would be an example of man against society. It is possible, obviously, to have more than one conflict within a story.

Conflict can be *external* or *internal*. Physical or external conflict is easy to recognize, especially in an adventure story which emphasizes a vivid physical struggle. Internal conflict may be represented by a character's struggle with himself or his conscience, or between what is and what should be. He might be struggling against an impulse to commit a crime, or a tendency to be cowardly, or a fear that something disastrous is going to happen. The best stories combine external and internal conflict.

The forces opposing each other in a conflict are labeled the *protagonist* and the *antagonist*. The protagonist is the hero or heroine who is faced with a basic problem or struggle. The antagonist is the person, place, idea, or physical force opposing the protagonist. To succeed, the protagonist must overcome the antagonist.

Plot

This is the plan of a story—the arrangement and sequence of incidents and details. Just as a building must be constructed from a blueprint, so must a short story have a pattern to follow.

The plot follows a pattern of related events. It begins with a *situation* or problem that is real and vital to the protagonist. The nature of the antagonist(s) may be made known. The introductory paragraphs in a short story should be read slowly to understand all the details of time, place, and situation.

The tension created in the opening situation cannot remain at the same level. To maintain our interest, *complications* are introduced. The goal that the hero wishes to attain does not appear as easy to reach as it first did, or his opponent may seem more formidable than he thought. Barriers and detours are presented, creating a need for new plans and decisions.

As the main character struggles with these conflicts, the reader begins to recognize a growing or rising action in the plot toward a particular high point of interest called the *climax*. This is the point of highest dramatic intensity. All action builds toward it.

Following the climax comes the *dénouement*, which is the final unraveling or solution of the plot. The outcome of the story is now made known. One side or the other triumphs, a main character meets success or failure, a mystery is solved, or some misunderstanding is cleared up. Some stories end, as conflicts in life often do, with no clear-cut answers or solutions.

Theme

Another important element is the theme, the central idea on which the story is based. Sometimes a theme is stated; sometimes it is implied.

Usually, the main idea—not a summary, not the plot—of a story can be stated in one or two sentences. For example, the theme might be a simple one such as "Honesty is the best policy," or "All that glitters is not gold." Or the theme might be that every man is a responsible being who must someday answer for his acts; still another might be that every young person must search for his own identity, painful and lonely as that search may be. In short, the theme is the total meaning of the story—the comment about life or the appraisal of life that the author is trying to convey to the reader.

Foreshadowing

This means exactly what the name implies—a hint of things to come. A word, a phrase, or a sentence can contain an important clue that has been purposely inserted by the author to prepare the reader for a later event. An alert reader stores such a clue in his mind and recalls it when the seemingly unexpected takes place or when a character reacts in a manner that at first appears strange or unreasonable.

Character Portrayal

There are a number of techniques an author can use to help his characters come alive. These include:

1. A physical description of a character and/or a description of the kind of person he is: the writer may tell you that a man is stingy and mean, or kind and considerate.

2. A description by another character.

3. Dialogue or presentation of a character's conversations.

4. An explanation of a character's inner thoughts.

5. The behavior or actions of a character.

6. The characters' responses and reactions to each other or to situations.

7. A combination of several of these methods.

Character and plot are obviously closely related because plot involves meaningful human action, which means that characters act consciously and deliberately. A plot is believable only if the characters in a story act in a reasonable, consistent, and natural way. If we do not believe in the characters, we cannot believe in the plot.

Everything you are told about a character should be significant. The good short-story writer is selective and includes only such information as he deems essential.

Setting and Atmosphere

The setting of a story, that is, the time and place of a story's action, is most often stressed in a story of *local color* which emphasizes the particular characteristics of a certain region and its inhabitants. It is also important in *science-fiction* stories, where the author has to create an impression of reality in order to make his imagined scientific changes of the future acceptable and real to his present-day readers. When evaluating the role of setting in a short story, ask yourself what, if anything, the setting contributes to the story and if it could possibly be eliminated as an essential element in the story.

As a rule, the setting is not a dominant element, but it does serve to establish or heighten atmosphere. This is especially evident in stories where the author wants to create a special feeling or mood.

Atmosphere, an integral part of plot, theme, and character, is something you sense or feel. Descriptive details give an emotional coloring to a story, but there are many other ways of obtaining atmosphere. For example, the author's choice of words, the kind and quantity of verbs, adjectives, and adverbs, and the length and rhythmical pattern of sentences all help to create atmosphere.

Point of View

There are basically two points of view from which a writer can tell a story:

1. **First-Person Narrator (Author Participant).** Here the writer usually has a major or a minor character tell the story in his or her own words ("I said," "I did," "I remember"). The author, through this first-person narrator, can reveal only what the narrator might reasonably be expected to know. If a ten-year-old boy tells the story, his powers of observation and expression are naturally limited. On the positive side, the use of the first person gives an illusion of immediacy and authority.

2. **Third-Person Narrator (Author Omniscient).** If an author feels that the reader should know more than any one person can tell, he may write from an omniscient, or all-knowing, point of view. He can tell his readers as much as he likes and can comment upon any character's actions. A disadvantage of this third-person writing ("he said," "he thought") is that it often calls attention to the fact that the events are "made up."

Sometimes an author, as third-person narrator, writes a story as if he had no insight into the behavior of his characters. Such writing is called *objective*, in contrast to *subjective*, in which the author's opinions and sympathies are obvious.

Symbol

A symbol is something which represents or suggests a relationship or association. For example, a flag symbolizes patriotism; a lamp represents knowledge; a cross stands for the Church.

In fiction, symbols are often concrete objects used to represent abstract ideas. A stack of gold coins might, during the course of a story, come to stand for greed, or a lovely rose, for beauty.

Characters' names may also be symbolic. "Red," for example, could be a name associated with a hotheaded boy. A "Mr. Oakwood" might manifest both physical and moral strength.

Tone

Tone is a writer's attitude toward his subject and characters. It may be sad or sorrowful, sentimental, angry, ironic, sympathetic, or objective and impersonal. Through his choice and selection of details and words, the writer helps to set the tone, thus indicating how he expects his reader to react to a particular character. To misjudge the tone of a work is to miss its full meaning.

Exposition

The presentation of background material uncovers, exposes, or conveys to the reader all the relevant facts that he should know in order to understand the problem to be solved. The exposition, usually imparted near the beginning of a story, may introduce one or more of the main characters, reveal the events leading up to the present situation, give the setting of the present action, and establish the tone.

The Commercial or Craft Story

Short stories may generally be classified as (1) the "commercial" or "craft" story and (2) the "quality" or "serious" story.

The word *commercial* refers to a story written for the mass market or the general public. The term *craft* means that a skill is involved and that a particular formula is followed.

Commercial short stories usually have stock characters and conventional themes that are generally accepted by a mass readership. Their plots have strong suspense, and the tone is often romantic.

Stock Characters

Goods or merchandise kept on hand and readily brought forth are "stock" items. You have heard "stock" jokes and "stock" phrases. And you are probably familiar with such "stock" characters of television and the movies as the sweet young girl, the cruel stepmother, the difficult mother-in-law, the bumbling but lovable father, the mad scientist, the vivacious blonde, the handsome and charming doctor, and the gangster and his moll. Such characters are not lifelike, always have the same character traits, require little or no imagination or insight from the writer, reader, or viewer, act in a predictable way, and sometimes even have a particular way of talking.

Conventional Themes

Like stock characters, conventional themes conform to approved and established practices and customs. One of the most common movie themes is the cliché "love conquers all." The story will usually deal with the love of a handsome young man and a beautiful girl. Various complications that prevent their being married are one by one eliminated, and they live "happily ever after."

Other traditional themes are: crime does not pay; all mothers love their children; old age brings wisdom (that others want to hear about); poverty can be bearable and even fun if one has endurance and inventiveness; good fortune always comes to those who do all the things they are supposed to do in life.

The Quality or Literary Story

A "quality" story, on the other hand, is written for those whose tastes are more inclined toward "serious" literature. There is no set formula for the quality story. There is usually more emphasis on the development of character and theme than on the development of plot.

The characters are individualized and true to life, and the theme is often a reversal or a renunciation of fashionable and established customs and ideas. For example, a story may refute the idea that honesty is the best policy: the business of an honest old shopkeeper may fail, while that of a cunning young man who cheats his customers may succeed.

Analysis of a Short Story

In order to discover the underlying meaning and not miss the point of a story, we need to learn to read more than just the exact printed words. Much of the pleasure of reading comes from being able to supply what the author does *not* say but only suggests. For example, when you read "The Secret Life of Walter Mitty," notice that Walter Mitty never says he is deathly tired of being nagged and henpecked, but listen as Mrs. Mitty talks at him. Every word is a pin in a balloon, a pop in his soap-bubble world.

The key to a story will most often be found by asking the question "Why?" Of each story, ask two *why's*. The first *why* is directed toward the characters' motivations. Why do the characters act and speak as they do? What motives do they have for their choices and decisions? These decisions are what bring the action or plot to its climax. The dénouement should be determined by the nature of the characters. You should be able to believe that certain characters would make the kinds of choices they do. Through their characters, authors are able to tell their readers something about human beings —what pressures they face and how they react, or what they will live or die for.

The second *why* will help relate the different parts or elements of the story. Short stories are limited. They do not include extras. Ask then, why the author used this type of setting, this kind of dialogue (a burly Texan does not say "Alas," nor does Goldilocks swear like a seaman's parrot at finding the porridge too hot), these events, these characters, this particular point of view? Asking these questions will help you to understand how the story's meaning is conveyed through the relationship of all the parts of the story: that is, the method of this particular writer in this particular story. In every good story there will be good reasons for the author's selection and arrangement of material.

Truman Capote

The critic and biographer Mark Schorer once said of Truman Capote that he writes "a prose of many moods, equally at ease in situations of black nightmarish horror and of high, often hilarious comedy." Two works which illustrate this statement are *In Cold Blood* (1966), a detailed factual account of a multiple murder case in Kansas; and *Breakfast at Tiffany's* (1958), a light-hearted story about the New York adventures of a heroine called Holly Golightly.

An English teacher at a high school in Connecticut first recognized Capote's prose talents and encouraged him to write short stories for the school newspaper. In general, he was not a distinguished student. He disliked school and had no thought of attending college.

Upon graduation from high school he returned to New Orleans, Louisiana, (where he was born in 1924) and began reading, writing short stories, and working on a novel. He drifted to New York and worked for a while at an office job, but was dissatisfied. Little else interested him except writing.

It was Capote's fiction which first brought him to the attention of the public. "Miriam," a short story published by *Mademoiselle* magazine when the author was nineteen, won an O. Henry Memorial Award in 1946. Widespread public acclaim came two years later with the publication of the novel *Other Voices, Other Rooms*. A second novel, *The Grass Harp*, published in 1951, was later adapted as a play.

Capote's efforts in the nonfiction field are also noteworthy. His impressions of such places as Spain, Haiti, and North Africa were published under the title *Local Color* (1950). Another nonfiction work, *The Muses are Heard* (1956), tells of his experiences while traveling in Russia with a cast of *Porgy and Bess* on a cultural exchange program.

"Jug of Silver" is one of the eight stories in *A Tree of Night* (1949), his first short-story collection.

* **Capote** (kə·pō′tē).

Jug of Silver

After school I used to work in the Valhalla [1]
drugstore. It was owned by my uncle, Mr. Ed Marshall. I call him Mr. Marshall because everybody,
including his wife, called him Mr. Marshall. Nevertheless he was a nice man.

This drugstore was maybe old-fashioned, but it
was large and dark and cool: during summer months
there was no pleasanter place in town. At the left,
as you entered, was a tobacco-magazine counter behind which, as a rule, sat Mr. Marshall: a squat,
square-faced, pink-fleshed man with looping, manly,
white mustaches. Beyond this counter stood the
beautiful soda fountain. It was very antique and
made of fine, yellowed marble, smooth to the touch
but without a trace of cheap glaze. Mr. Marshall
bought it at an auction in New Orleans in 1910 and
was plainly proud of it. When you sat on the high,
delicate stools and looked across the fountain you
could see yourself reflected softly, as though by
candlelight, in a row of ancient, mahogany-framed
mirrors. All general merchandise was displayed in
glass-doored, curiolike cabinets that were locked
with brass keys. There was always in the air the smell
of syrup and nutmeg and other delicacies.

The Valhalla was the gathering place of Wachata
County till a certain Rufus McPherson came to
town and opened a second drugstore directly across
the courthouse square. This old Rufus McPherson
was a villain; that is, he took away my uncle's trade.
He installed fancy equipment such as electric fans
and colored lights; he provided curb service and
made grilled-cheese sandwiches to order. Naturally,
though some remained devoted to Mr. Marshall,
most folks couldn't resist Rufus McPherson.

1. **Valhalla** (val·hal'ə): In Norse mythology, Valhalla was the hall of Odin (the
Norse god of war, wisdom, and poetry), where the souls of brave warriors slain
in battle were brought to feast. It may also mean a building where statues or
other memorials of a nation's heroes are placed.

For a while, Mr. Marshall chose to ignore him: if you were to mention McPherson's name he would sort of snort, finger his mustaches, and look the other way. But you could tell he was mad. And getting madder. Then one day toward the middle of October I strolled into the Valhalla to find him sitting at the fountain playing dominoes and drinking wine with Hamurabi.[2]

One effort to resolve conflict.

Beginning of central action.

Time established.

Hamurabi was an Egyptian and some kind of dentist, though he didn't do much business as the people hereabouts have unusually strong teeth, due to an element in the water. He spent a great deal of his time loafing around the Valhalla and was my uncle's chief buddy. He was a handsome figure of a man, this Hamurabi, being dark-skinned and nearly seven feet tall; the matrons of the town kept their daughters under lock and key and gave him the eye themselves. He had no foreign accent whatsoever, and it was always my opinion that he wasn't any more Egyptian than the man in the moon.

Introduction and description of a new major character.

Author casts doubt about Hamurabi.

Anyway, there they were swigging red Italian wine from a gallon jug. It was a troubling sight, for Mr. Marshall was a renowned teetotaler.[3] So naturally I thought: Oh, golly, Rufus McPherson has finally got his goat. That was not the case, however.

Narrator's observations of unusual situation arouse reader's curiosity.

Transition.

"Here, son," said Mr. Marshall, "come have a glass of wine."

"Sure," said Hamurabi, "help us finish it up. It's store-bought, so we can't waste it."

Much later, when the jug was dry, Mr. Marshall picked it up and said, "Now we shall see!" And with that disappeared out into the afternoon.

Suspense building.

"Where's he off to?" I asked.

"Ah," was all Hamurabi would say. He liked to devil me.

A half-hour passed before my uncle returned. He

2. **Hamurabi** (hä'mōō·rä'bē): Notice the similarity in spelling with Hammurabi, a king of Babylonia, a large empire of ancient Asia, who ruled about 2000 B.C. He is mainly noted for having established a systematic code of laws to be used in courts throughout his empire. In general, the laws were humanitarian; but the penalties were often severe, such as the principle of "an eye for an eye, a tooth for a tooth."

3. **teetotaler** (tē·tōt'lər): a person who abstains totally from alcoholic drinks.

was stooped and grunting under the load he carried. He set the jug atop the fountain and stepped back, smiling and rubbing his hands together. "Well, what do you think?"

"Ah," purred Hamurabi.

"Gee . . ." I said.

It was the same wine jug, God knows, but there was a wonderful difference; for now it was crammed to the brim with nickels and dimes that shone dully through the thick glass.

Introduction of jug of silver— and explanation of title of story.

"Pretty, eh?" said my uncle. "Had it done over at the First National. Couldn't get in anything bigger-sized than a nickel. Still, there's lotsa money in there, let me tell you."

"But what's the point, Mr. Marshall?" I said. "I mean, what's the idea?"

Narrator asks the logical question.

Mr. Marshall's smile deepened to a grin. "This here's a jug of silver, you might say. . . ."

"The pot at the end of the rainbow," interrupted Hamurabi.

". . . and the idea, as you call it, is for folks to guess how much money is in there. For instance, say you buy a quarter's worth of stuff—well, then you get to take a chance. The more you buy, the more chances you get. And I'll keep all guesses in a ledger till Christmas Eve, at which time whoever comes closest to the right amount will get the whole shebang."

Readers told that climax of story will be Christmas Eve.

Hamurabi nodded solemnly. "He's playing Santa Claus—a mighty crafty Santa Claus," he said. "I'm going home and write a book: *The Skillful Murder of Rufus McPherson*." To tell the truth, he sometimes did write stories and send them out to the magazines. They always came back.

It was surprising, really like a miracle, how Wachata County took to the jug. Why, the Valhalla hadn't done so much business since Station Master Tully, poor soul, went stark raving mad and claimed to have discovered oil back of the depot, causing the town to be overrun with wildcat prospectors. Even the poolhall bums who never spent a cent on any-

Gradual movement forward in time.

Use of local color.

thing not connected with whisky or women took to investing their spare cash in milk shakes. A few elderly ladies publicly disapproved of Mr. Marshall's enterprise as a kind of gambling, but they didn't start any trouble and some even found occasion to visit us and hazard a guess. The school kids were crazy about the whole thing, and I was very popular because they figured I knew the answer.

"I'll tell you why all this is," said Hamurabi, lighting one of the Egyptian cigarettes he bought by mail from a concern in New York City. "It's not for the reason you may imagine; not, in other words, avidity.[4] No. It's the mystery that's enchanting. Now you look at those nickels and dimes and what do you think? 'Ah, *so* much!'? No, no. You think: 'Ah, *how* much?' And that's a profound question, indeed. It can mean different things to different people. Understand?"

And oh, was Rufus McPherson wild! When you're in trade, you count on Christmas to make up a large share of your yearly profit, and he was hard pressed to find a customer. So he tried to imitate the jug; but being such a stingy man he filled his with pennies. He also wrote a letter to the editor of *The Banner*, our weekly paper, in which he said that Mr. Marshall ought to be "tarred and feathered and strung up for turning innocent little children into confirmed gamblers and sending them down the path to Hell!" You can imagine what kind of laughing stock he was. Nobody had anything for McPherson but scorn. And so by the middle of November he just stood on the sidewalk outside his store and gazed bitterly at the festivities across the square.

Conflict between merchants further developed.

Time advanced.

At about this time Appleseed[5] and sister made their first appearance.

Introduction of main character.

He was a stranger in town. At least no one could

4. **avidity** (ə·vid′ə·tē): greediness.
5. **Appleseed**: The name makes one think of Johnny Appleseed, the popular name for John Chapman (1775–1849), a Massachusetts-born pioneer. He is best known for planting apple seeds during his travels in present-day Ohio, Indiana, and Illinois. He also preached a type of mystical religion and read the Bible aloud to settlers wherever he went. After his death, legends grew up about the good fortune of starving pioneers who stumbled on his orchards.

recall ever having seen him before. He said he lived on a farm a mile past Indian Branches; told us his mother weighed only seventy-four pounds and that he had an older brother who would play the fiddle at anybody's wedding for fifty cents. He claimed that Appleseed was the only name he had and that he was twelve years old. But his sister, Middy, said he was eight. His hair was straight and dark yellow. He had a tight, weather-tanned little face with anxious green eyes that had a very wise and knowing look. He was small and puny and high-strung, and he wore always the same outfit: a red sweater, blue denim britches, and a pair of man-sized boots that went clop-clop with every step.

Background for Appleseed filled in by narrator.

Description of Appleseed, his clothing, and his first appearance at the Valhalla.

It was raining that first time he came into the Valhalla; his hair was plastered around his head like a cap and his boots were caked with red mud from the country roads. Middy trailed behind as he swaggered like a cowboy up to the fountain where I was wiping some glasses.

"I hear tell you folks got a bottle fulla money you fixin' to give 'way," he said, looking me square in the eye. "Seein' as you-all are givin' it away, we'd be obliged iffen you'd give it to us. Name's Appleseed, and this here's my sister, Middy."

Dialogue used for characterization; it is also intended to introduce Appleseed's need for money.

Middy was a sad, sad-looking kid. She was a good bit taller and older-looking than her brother: a regular bean pole. She had tow-colored hair that was chopped short, and a pale, pitiful little face. She wore a faded cotton dress that came way up above her bony knees. There was something wrong with her teeth, and she tried to conceal this by keeping her lips primly pursed like an old lady.

Physical description of Middy.

Teeth a noteworthy feature. First hint of their importance.

"Sorry," I said, "but you'll have to talk with Mr. Marshall."

So sure enough he did. I could hear my uncle explaining what he would have to do to win the jug. Appleseed listened attentively, nodding now and then. Presently he came back and stood in front of the jug and, touching it lightly with his hand, said, "Ain't it a pretty thing, Middy?"

Relationship between children revealed through tone of dialogue.

Middy said, "Is they gonna give it to us?"

"Naw. What you gotta do, you gotta guess how much money's inside there. And you gotta buy two bits' worth so's even to get a chance."

Simple statement of conflict.

"Huh, we ain't got no two bits. Where you 'spec we gonna get us two bits?"

Appleseed frowned and rubbed his chin. "That'll be the easy part, just leave it to me. The only worrisome thing is: I can't just take a chance and guess. . . . I gotta *know*."

Beginning of main conflict in story. Raises the questions of what does he want the money for and how can he *know*?

Well, a few days later they showed up again. Appleseed perched on a stool at the fountain and boldly asked for two glasses of water, one for him and one for Middy. It was on this occasion that he gave out the information about his family: ". . . then there's Papa Daddy, that's my mama's papa, who's a Cajun,[6] an' on accounta that he don't speak English good. My brother, the one what plays the fiddle, he's been in jail three times. . . . It's on accounta him we had to pick up and leave Louisiana. He cut a fella bad in a razor fight over a woman ten years older'n him. She had yellow hair."

Childlike family history shows simplicity and directness of character.

Middy, lingering in the background, said nervously, "You oughtn't to be tellin' our personal private fam'ly business thataway, Appleseed."

"Hush now, Middy," he said, and she hushed. "She's a good little gal," he added, turning to pat her head, "but you can't let her get away with much. You go look at the picture books, honey, and stop frettin' with your teeth. Appleseed here's got some figurin' to do."

Further character revelation and development of brother-sister relationship.

Second reference to Middy's teeth.

This figuring meant staring hard at the jug, as if his eyes were trying to eat it up. With his chin cupped in his hand, he studied it for a long period, not batting his eyelids once. "A lady in Louisiana told me I could see things other folks couldn't see 'cause I was born with a caul[7] on my head."

First reference to the caul and Appleseed's supposed supernatural talent.

6. **Cajun** (kā′jən): in Louisiana, a person said to be a descendant of the French settlers from a region in eastern Canada formerly known as Acadia.
7. **caul** (kôl): a portion of a membrane occasionally covering a child's head at birth, considered a lucky omen and charm against drowning.

"It's a cinch you aren't going to *see* how much there is," I told him. "Why don't you just let a number pop into your head, and maybe that'll be the right one."

"Uh, uh," he said, "too darn risky. Me, I can't take no sucha chance. Now, the way I got it figured, there ain't but one sure-fire thing and that's to count every nickel and dime."

"Count!"

"Count what?" asked Hamurabi, who had just moseyed inside and was settling himself at the fountain.

"This kid says he's going to count how much is in the jug," I explained.

Hamurabi looked at Appleseed with interest. "How do you plan to do that, son?"

"Oh, by countin'," said Appleseed matter-of-factly.

Hamurabi laughed. "You better have X-ray eyes, son, that's all I can say."

"Oh, no. All you gotta do is be born with a caul on your head. A lady in Louisiana told me so. She was a witch; she loved me and when my ma wouldn't give me to her she put a hex on her and now my ma don't weigh but seventy-four pounds."

"Ve-ry in-ter-esting," was Hamurabi's comment as he gave Appleseed a queer glance.

Middy sauntered up, clutching a copy of *Screen Secrets*. She pointed out a certain photo to Appleseed and said: "Ain't she the nicest-lookin' lady? Now you see, Appleseed, you see how pretty her teeth are? Not a one outa joint."

"Well, don't you fret none," he said.

After they left, Hamurabi ordered a bottle of orange Nehi and drank it slowly, while smoking a cigarette. "Do you think maybe that kid's OK upstairs?" he asked presently in a puzzled voice.

Small towns are best for spending Christmas, I think. They catch the mood quicker and change and come alive under its spell. By the first week in December house doors were decorated with wreaths, and store windows were flashy with red paper bells

Appleseed's attitude toward his problem explained, with his proposed solution.

Meeting of Hamurabi and Appleseed.

Reinforcement of supernatural element in story.

More concern with teeth.

Hamurabi questions Appleseed's mental stability.

Shortening of time as part of plot development.

and snowflakes of glittering isinglass.[8] The kids hiked out into the woods and came back dragging spicy evergreen trees. Already the women were busy baking fruitcakes, unsealing jars of mincemeat, and opening bottles of blackberry and scuppernong [9] wine. In the courthouse square a huge tree was trimmed with silver tinsel and colored electric bulbs that were lighted up at sunset. Late of an afternoon you could hear the choir in the Presbyterian church practicing carols for their annual pageant. All over town the japonicas [10] were in full bloom.

Atmosphere heightened by description.

The only person who appeared not the least touched by this heartwarming atmosphere was Appleseed. He went about his declared business of counting the jug-money with great, persistent care. Every day now he came to the Valhalla and concentrated on the jug, scowling and mumbling to himself. At first we were all fascinated, but after a while it got tiresome and nobody paid him any mind whatsoever. He never bought anything, apparently having never been able to raise the two bits. Sometimes he'd talk to Hamurabi, who had taken a tender interest in him and occasionally stood treat to a jawbreaker [11] or a penny's worth of licorice.

Contrast.

Tension increases as time passes.

Reactions of other characters.

Friendship growing.

"Do you still think he's nuts?" I asked.

"I'm not so sure," said Hamurabi. "But I'll let you know. He doesn't eat enough. I'm going to take him over to the Rainbow Café and buy him a plate of barbecue."

Concern and kindness of Hamurabi.

"He'd appreciate it more if you'd give him a quarter."

"No. A dish of barbecue is what he needs. Besides, it would be better if he never was to make a guess. A high-strung kid like that, so unusual, I wouldn't want to be the one responsible if he lost. Say, it would be pitiful."

Tension increased by Hamurabi's worry.

8. **isinglass** (ī′zən·glas′): a shiny mineral that can be separated into thin, flexible, often transparent sheets; also known as mica.
9. **scuppernong** (skup′ər·nông): a large, yellowish-green grape of the southern United States, or the sweet golden-colored wine made from it.
10. **japonica** (jə·pon′i·kə): an Asian shrub with bright red flowers.
11. **jawbreaker**: *here*, a round, hard candy. It can also mean a word that is hard to pronounce.

I'll admit that at the time Appleseed struck me as being just funny. Mr. Marshall felt sorry for him, and the kids tried to tease him, but had to give it up when he refused to respond. There you could see him plain as day sitting at the fountain with his forehead puckered and his eyes fixed forever on that jug. Yet he was so withdrawn you sometimes had this awful creepy feeling that, well, maybe he didn't exist. And when you were pretty much convinced of this he'd wake up and say something like, "You know, I hope a 1913 buffalo nickel's in there. A fella was tellin' me he saw where a 1913 buffalo nickel's worth fifty dollars." Or, "Middy's gonna be a big lady in the picture shows. They make lotsa money, the ladies in the picture shows do, and then we ain't gonna never eat another collard [12] green as long as we live. Only Middy says she can't be in the picture shows 'less her teeth look good."

Middy didn't always tag along with her brother. On those occasions when she didn't come, Appleseed wasn't himself; he acted shy and left soon.

Hamurabi kept his promise and stood treat to a dish of barbecue at the café. "Mr. Hamurabi's nice, all right," said Appleseed afterward, "but he's got peculiar notions: has a notion that if he lived in this place named Egypt he'd be a king or somethin'."

And Hamurabi said, "That kid has the most touching faith. It's a beautiful thing to see. But I'm beginning to despise the whole business." He gestured toward the jug. "Hope of this kind is a cruel thing to give anybody, and I'm damned sorry I was ever a party to it."

Around the Valhalla the most popular pastime was deciding what you would buy if you won the jug. Among those who participated were Solomon Katz, Phoebe Jones, Carl Kuhnhardt, Puly Simmons, Addie Foxcroft, Marvin Finkle, Trudy Edwards, and a colored man named Erskine Washington. And these were some of their answers: a trip to and a

---

12. **collard** (kol′ərd): a variety of cabbage.

Margin notes:

Another reference to Appleseed's wanting money.

Second reference to movie actresses.

Another reference to teeth; by now it's obviously foreshadowing.

Contrast reveals more of Appleseed's character.

Another doubt about Hamurabi.

Second reference to Hamurabi's concern over Appleseed and the contest.

Notice that the answers seem to indicate that each one wanted something for *himself*.

permanent wave in Birmingham, a secondhand piano, a Shetland pony, a gold bracelet, a set of *Rover Boys* [13] books, and a life insurance policy.

Once Mr. Marshall asked Appleseed what he would get. "It's a secret," was the reply, and no amount of prying could make him tell. We took it for granted that whatever it was, he wanted it real bad.

Suspense.

Honest winter, as a rule, doesn't settle on our part of the country till late January, and then it's mild, lasting only a short time. But in the year of which I write we were blessed with a singular cold spell the week before Christmas. Some still talk of it, for it was so terrible: water pipes froze solid; many folks had to spend the days in bed snuggled under their quilts, having neglected to lay in enough kindling for the fireplace; the sky turned that strange dull gray that it does just before a storm, and the sun was pale as a waning moon. There was a sharp wind: the old dried-up leaves of last fall fell on the icy ground, and the evergreen tree in the courthouse square was twice stripped of its Christmas finery. When you breathed, your breath made smoky clouds. Down by the silk mill where the very poor people lived, the families huddled together in the dark at night and told tales to keep their minds off the cold. Out in the country the farmers covered their delicate plants with gunny sacks and prayed; some took advantage of the weather to slaughter their hogs and bring the fresh sausage to town. Mr. R. C. Judkins, our town drunk, outfitted himself in a red cheesecloth suit and played Santa Claus at the five 'n' dime. Mr. R. C. Judkins was the father of a big family, so everybody was happy to see him sober enough to earn a dollar. There were several church socials, at one of which Mr. Marshall came face to face with Rufus McPherson: bitter words were passed but not a blow was struck.

Advance in time. Here's a hint that something unusual is going to happen; even the weather is different.

Reference to minor conflict.

Now, as has been mentioned, Appleseed lived on

13. *Rover Boys:* a series of stories for boys, often about school life.

a farm a mile below Indian Branches; this would be approximately three miles from town; a mighty long and lonesome walk. Still, despite the cold, he came every day to the Valhalla and stayed till closing time which, as the days had grown short, was after nightfall. Once in a while he'd catch a ride part way home with the foreman from the silk mill, but not often. He looked tired, and there were worry lines about his mouth. He was always cold and shivered a lot. I don't think he wore any warm drawers underneath his red sweater and blue britches.

Proves how determined he is and how much he is willing to endure.

Conflict telling on Appleseed.

It was three days before Christmas when out of the clear sky, he announced: "Well, I'm finished. I mean I know how much is in the bottle." He claimed this with such grave, solemn sureness it was hard to doubt him.

Climax approaching.

Critical moment.

"Why, say now, son, hold on," said Hamurabi, who was present. "You can't know anything of the sort. It's wrong to think so: You're just heading to get yourself hurt."

Contrast. Hamurabi arouses doubts.

"You don't need to preach to me, Mr. Hamurabi. I know what I'm up to. A lady in Louisiana, she told me . . ."

Repetition. Reader is reminded of Appleseed's faith in his supernatural gift.

"Yes yes yes—but you got to forget that. If it were me, I'd go home and stay put and forget about this . . . jug."

"My brother's gonna play the fiddle at a wedding over in Cherokee City tonight and he's gonna give me the two bits," said Appleseed stubbornly. "Tomorrow I'll take my chance."

Time of critical moment revealed.

So the next day I felt kind of excited when Appleseed and Middy arrived. Sure enough, he had his quarter: it was tied for safekeeping in the corner of a red bandanna.

The two of them wandered hand in hand among the showcases, holding a whispery consultation as to what to purchase. They decided finally on a thimble-sized bottle of gardenia cologne which Middy promptly opened and partly emptied on her hair. "It smells like . . . Oh, darlin' Mary, I ain't never

Purchase reflects Appleseed's love for his sister.

smelled nothin' as sweet. Here, Appleseed, honey, let me douse some on your hair." But he wouldn't let her.

Mr. Marshall got out the ledger in which he kept his records, while Appleseed strolled over to the fountain and cupped the jug between his hands, stroking it gently. His eyes were bright and his cheeks flushed from excitement. Several persons who were in the drugstore at that moment crowded close. Middy stood in the background quietly scratching her leg and smelling the cologne. Hamurabi wasn't there.

Mr. Marshall licked the point of his pencil and smiled. "OK, son, what do you say?"

Appleseed took a deep breath. "Seventy-seven dollars and thirty-five cents," he blurted.

Critical moment.

In picking such an uneven sum he showed originality, for the run-of-the-mill guess was a plain round figure. Mr. Marshall repeated the amount solemnly as he copied it down.

"When'll I know if I won?"

"Christmas Eve," someone said.

"That's tomorrow, huh?"

"Why, so it is," said Mr. Marshall, not surprised. "Come at four o'clock."

During the night the thermometer dropped even lower, and toward dawn there was one of those swift, summerlike rainstorms, so that the following day was bright and frozen. The town was like a picture postcard of a Northern scene, what with icicles sparkling whitely on the trees and frost flowers coating all windowpanes. Mr. R. C. Judkins rose early and, for no clear reason, tramped the streets ringing a supper bell, stopping now and then to take a swig of whisky from a pint which he kept in his hip pocket. As the day was windless, smoke climbed lazily from various chimneys straightway to the still, frozen sky. By midmorning the Presbyterian choir was in full swing; and the town kids (wearing horror masks, as at Hallowe'en) were chasing one another

Setting again used to create atmosphere.

Notice the change from the "strange dull gray" sky to a day that's "bright and frozen" with "icicles sparkling whitely."

round and round the square, kicking up an awful fuss.

Hamurabi dropped by at noon to help us fix up the Valhalla. He brought along a fat sack of Satsumas,[14] and together we ate every last one, tossing the hulls into a newly installed potbellied stove (a present from Mr. Marshall to himself) which stood in the middle of the room. Then my uncle took the jug off the fountain, polished and placed it on a prominently situated table. He was no help after that whatsoever, for he squatted in a chair and spent his time tying and retying a tacky green ribbon around the jug. So Hamurabi and I had the rest to do alone: we swept the floor and washed the mirrors and dusted the cabinets and strung streamers of red and green crepe paper from wall to wall. When we were finished it looked very fine and elegant.

Focus narrows to the jug.

But Hamurabi gazed sadly at our work, and said: "Well, I think I better be getting along now."

"Aren't you going to stay?" asked Mr. Marshall, shocked.

"No, oh, no," said Hamurabi, shaking his head slowly. "I don't want to see that kid's face. This is Christmas and I mean to have a rip-roaring time. And I couldn't, not with something like that on my conscience. Hell, I wouldn't sleep."

Hamurabi still being used to cast doubt as to the outcome and to heighten suspense.

"Suit yourself," said Mr. Marshall. And he shrugged, but you could see he was really hurt. "Life's like that—and besides, who knows, he might win."

Hamurabi sighed gloomily. "What's his guess?"

"Seventy-seven dollars and thirty-five cents," I said.

"Now I ask you, isn't that fantastic?" said Hamurabi. He slumped in a chair next to Mr. Marshall and crossed his legs and lit a cigarette. "If you got any Baby Ruths I think I'd like one; my mouth tastes sour."

14. Satsuma (sä·tsōō·mä): a kind of mandarin orange, originally from China, and grown commercially in Florida and Alabama.

As the afternoon wore on, the three of us sat around the table feeling terribly blue. No one said hardly a word and, as the kids had deserted the square, the only sound was the clock tolling the hour in the courthouse steeple. The Valhalla was closed to business, but people kept passing by and peeking in the window. At three o'clock Mr. Marshall told me to unlock the door.

Within twenty minutes the place was jam full; everyone was wearing his Sunday best, and the air smelled sweet, for most of the little silk-mill girls had scented themselves with vanilla flavoring. They scrunched up against the walls, perched on the fountain, squeezed in wherever they could; soon the crowd had spread to the sidewalk and stretched into the road. The square was lined with team-drawn wagons and Model T Fords that had carted farmers and their families into town. There was much laughter and shouting and joking—several outraged ladies complained of the cursing and the rough, shoving ways of the younger men, but nobody left. At the side entrance a gang of colored folks had formed and were having the most fun of all. Everybody was making the best of a good thing. It's usually so quiet around here: nothing much ever happens. It's safe to say that nearly all of Wachata County was present but invalids and Rufus McPherson. I looked around for Appleseed but didn't see him anywhere.

Mr. Marshall harumphed, and clapped for attention. When things quieted down and the atmosphere was properly tense, he raised his voice like an auctioneer, and called: "Now listen, everybody, in this here envelope you see in my hand"—he held a manila envelope above his head—"well, in it's the *answer*—which nobody but God and the First National Bank knows up to now, ha, ha. And in this book"—he held up the ledger with his free hand—"I've got written down what you folks guessed. Are there any questions?" All was silence. "Fine. Now, if we could have a volunteer. . . ."

Not a living soul budged an inch: it was as if an

awful shyness had overcome the crowd, and even
those who were ordinarily natural-born show-offs
shuffled their feet, ashamed. Then a voice, Appleseed's, hollered, "Lemme by . . . Outa the way,
please, ma'am." Trotting along behind as he pushed
forward were Middy and a lanky, sleepy-eyed fellow
who was evidently the fiddling brother. Appleseed
was dressed the same as usual, but his face was
scrubbed rosy clean, his boots polished and his hair
slicked back skintight with Stacomb.[15] "Did we get
here in time?" he panted.

But Mr. Marshall said, "So you want to be our
volunteer?"

Appleseed looked bewildered, then nodded vig-
orously.

"Does anybody have an objection to this young
man?"

Still there was dead quiet. Mr. Marshall handed
the envelope to Appleseed who accepted it calmly.
He chewed his under lip while studying it a moment
before ripping the flap.

In all that congregation there was no sound except
an occasional cough and the soft tinkling of Mr.
R. C. Judkins' supper bell. Hamurabi was leaning
against the fountain, staring up at the ceiling;
Middy was gazing blankly over her brother's shoulder, and when he started to tear open the envelope
she let out a pained little gasp.

Appleseed withdrew a slip of pink paper and,
holding it as though it was very fragile, muttered to
himself whatever was written there. Suddenly his
face paled and tears glistened in his eyes.

Climax reached, but result withheld.

"Hey, speak up, boy," someone hollered.

Turning point begins.

Hamurabi stepped forward and all but snatched
the slip away. He cleared his throat and commenced
to read when his expression changed most comically.
"Well . . ." he said.

"Louder! Louder!" an angry chorus demanded.

"Buncha crooks!" yelled Mr. R. C. Judkins, who
had a snootful by this time. "I smell a rat and he

15. **Stacomb:** The brand name of this hair tonic is probably pronounced stay-comb.

smells to high heaven!" Whereupon a cyclone of catcalls and whistling rent the air.

Appleseed's brother whirled around and shook his fist. "Shuddup, shuddup 'fore I bust every one a your . . . heads together so's you got knots the size a muskmelons, hear me?"

"Citizens," cried Mayor Mawes, "citizens—I say, this is Christmas . . . I say. . . ."

And Mr. Marshall hopped up on a chair and clapped and stamped till a minimum of order was restored. It might as well be noted here that we later found out Rufus McPherson had paid Mr. R. C. Judkins to start the rumpus. Anyway, when the outbreak was quelled, who should be in possession of the slip but me . . . don't ask how.

Without thinking, I shouted, "Seventy-seven dollars and thirty-five cents." Naturally, due to the excitement, I didn't at first catch the meaning; it was just a number. Then Appleseed's brother let forth with his whooping yell, and so I understood. The name of the winner spread quickly, and the awed, murmuring whispers were like a rainstorm.

Oh, Appleseed himself was a sorry sight. He was crying as though he was mortally wounded, but when Hamurabi lifted him onto his shoulders so the crowd could get a gander, he dried his eyes with the cuffs of his sweater and began grinning. Mr. R. C. Judkins yelled, "Gyp! Lousy gyp!" but was drowned out by a deafening round of applause.

Middy grabbed my arm. "My teeth," she squealed. "Now I'm gonna get my teeth."

"Teeth?" said I, kind of dazed.

"The false kind," says she. "That's what we're gonna get us with the money—a lovely set of white false teeth."

But at that moment my sole interest was in how Appleseed had known. "Hey, tell me," I said desperately, "tell me, how in God's name did he know there was just exactly seventy-seven dollars and thirty-five cents?"

Middy gave me this *look*. "Why, I thought he told you," she said, real serious. "He counted."

Beginning of dénouement.

Appleseed's motivation is explained.

"Yes, but how—how?"

"Gee, don't you even know how to count?"

"But is that all he did?"

"Well," she said, following a thoughtful pause, "he did do a little praying, too." She started to dart off, then turned back and called, "Besides, he was born with a caul on his head."

And that's the nearest anybody ever came to solving the mystery. Thereafter, if you were to ask Appleseed "How come?" he would smile strangely and change the subject. Many years later he and his family moved to somewhere in Florida and were never heard from again.

Notice that Appleseed does not refer to his caul.

But in our town his legend flourishes still; and till his death a year ago last April, Mr. Marshall was invited each Christmas Day to tell the story of Appleseed to the Baptist Bible class. Hamurabi once typed up an account and mailed it around to various magazines. It was never printed. One editor wrote back and said "If the little girl really turned out to be a movie star, then there might be something to your story." But that's not what happened, so why should you lie?

Author concludes with subtle comment on what people want in stories.

Story Analysis

To understand a story and really get the most from it, you should probably read it twice. The first time you meet the characters, notice the setting and atmosphere, and watch the action build, peak, and fall. But when you reread a story, it is unlikely that the enjoyment of your first encounter with these characters is duplicated. Remember how you felt when you first heard, "Name's Appleseed, and this here's my sister, Middy"? However, on your second reading you will notice details that you missed the first time. Let's see how Truman Capote used some of the elements of the short story.

Plot

"Jug of Silver" has a major and a minor plot. The major plot concerns Appleseed and the winning of the jug; the minor plot deals with the business rivalry between the owners of two local drugstores.

We have mentioned that plot and conflict are closely related and that it is conflict which sets in motion a pattern or sequence of events. In "Jug of Silver" it is Appleseed's struggle against the incredible odds he sets up for himself that makes his conflict the central focus of the major plot. His fellow contestants from Wachata County leave their winning to chance, but Appleseed does not take that risk. He emphatically states, "I can't just take a chance and guess . . . I gotta *know*." Then he announces his "sure-fire" plan to count every coin. His sister, Middy, is the only one who seems to have faith in his special ability to do this.

In the minor plot, the conflict involves the *protagonist*, Mr. Marshall, and his *antagonist*, or competitor, Rufus McPherson. Because he has installed fancy equipment and provided new services, McPherson has lured the townsfolk away from the Valhalla drugstore.

The tension created by the opening *situation* of the minor plot increases when Mr. Marshall decides to take measures to destroy his competitor. *Complications* are introduced. To attract the townsfolk to his store, Mr. Marshall starts a contest for a jug of silver. The "catch" is that in order for a person to make a guess as to how much money is in the jug, he has to buy a quarter's worth of goods in the Valhalla. The results are astonishing. No one can resist the temptation to guess *how* much. "Even the poolhall bums who never spent a cent on anything not connected with whisky or women took to investing their spare cash in milk shakes."

As a result, McPherson finds that his trade diminishes to almost nothing. To remedy the situation, he fills a jug too—but with pennies. He also writes to the local paper condemning Mr. Marshall for "turning innocent little children into confirmed gamblers." This is the high point or *climax* of their feud. McPherson's efforts to sway public opinion only make him the "laughing stock" of the town. Mr. Marshall has succeeded. He will have the most customers during the Christmas season, the time when the most profit can be made.

Usually once the conflict is reached and the *outcome* made known, a story can conclude. Here, however, this minor plot serves as a tool for the presentation of the major plot.

The readers, therefore, are caught up in the major plot and the minor plot. We wonder if Appleseed will win the contest and, if so, *how*, and we are curious to see if McPherson will succeed in doing anything about the Valhalla's contest.

Character Portrayal

Did you recognize the "stock" characters involved in the minor plot? The narrator calls "old Rufus McPherson" a "villain," and the name itself sounds like "ruthless" and "fear." In contrast, he calls Mr. Marshall (note that Capote never puts Mr. before McPherson's name) a "nice" man, and his name could be a synonym for "officer." And Mr. Marshall tells the story of Appleseed to the Bible class every Christmas. The antagonist is a stingy man, and dishonest enough to bribe the town drunkard into starting a rumpus at the drawing.

One of the main characters in the story is Hamurabi. When Hamurabi is first introduced, the narrator gives us a few descriptive details. The name itself, with its similarity to that of a famous king of Babylonia, lends him an exotic air. He is quite handsome and extraordinarily tall, and his striking appearance complements his name. He claims he is an Egyptian, but the narrator doubts this, and adds that he is some kind of a dentist and an unsuccessful author. But there is no evidence of this, and Hamurabi's main occupation seems to be hanging around the Valhalla.

Capote never states directly how he wants the reader to react to Hamurabi. It is only by observing the details and words that describe his unusual ways, and by listening to the humor in the phrasing of his speeches, that the reader becomes aware of the author's half-amused attitude or *tone*.

The main character, of course, is the boy Appleseed, with his sister Middy playing a minor role. For characterizing Appleseed, the author uses a number of techniques:

1. He tells us how he looks and what his background is.
2. He presents Appleseed's conversations in the Valhalla.
3. He shows the reactions of Hamurabi, the narrator, and some of the other townsfolk to Appleseed's behavior, and in some instances gives their remarks and conversations about him.
4. He reveals his attitude toward others, particularly toward his sister, Middy.
5. He contrasts his attitude toward the Christmas season with that of the other townsfolk.
6. He describes his reactions at key moments in the story.

It is interesting to observe the incidents, speeches, and comments that pertain to Hamurabi. His speeches about the jug, which he calls "the pot at the end of the rainbow," reveal his philosophical nature.

It is Hamurabi, in a conversation with the narrator, who puts the talk about the jug on a higher level than mere greed:

"No. It's the mystery that's enchanting. Now you look at those nickels and dimes and what do you think? 'Ah, so much!'? No, no. You think: 'Ah, *how* much?' And that's a profound question, indeed. It can mean different things to different people. Understand?"

Hamurabi's responses and reactions to Appleseed involve him in the major plot. When he first meets Appleseed, who states matter-of-factly that he is going to count every coin, Hamurabi is amused and says, "You better have X-ray eyes, son, that's all I can say." As events progress, however, Hamurabi is puzzled, then concerned, and finally deeply upset by Appleseed's unshaken confidence in his ability to win. He grows to like the boy. To help Appleseed, he buys him a plate of barbecue instead of giving him the money to take a chance on the jug. It is after this meeting that Hamurabi states the conflict within his mind:

"That kid has the most touching faith. It's a beautiful thing to see. But I'm beginning to despise the whole business." He gestured toward the jug. "Hope of this kind is a cruel thing to give anybody, and I'm damned sorry I was ever a party to it."

He tries to resolve this conflict by telling Appleseed that he should give up, as he can't possibly know the right number just by counting. Finally, on the day of the drawing, he plans to leave the drugstore so he will not have Appleseed's disappointment "on his conscience."

We also learn something of Hamurabi by his actions at the time of the climax and outcome of the plot in which he again plays a major part. Before the results are revealed, Hamurabi snatches the paper out of Appleseed's hands. Somehow it travels from there to the narrator, who announces the winner. And it is Hamurabi who carries Appleseed in triumph on his shoulders. At the conclusion of the story, we learn that Hamurabi puts his thoughts about the entire episode into a magazine article.

Are Hamurabi's actions consistent and clearly motivated? How does he get involved in both plots? Capote clearly gives him a great deal of free time, and thus he can form close friendships with Mr. Marshall and Appleseed. He also aids, in one way or another, both of his friends. It also seems natural at the end to learn that he would write a story about Appleseed. Notice the reference on page 12 to

The Skillful Murder of Rufus McPherson. As has been pointed out, his sympathy for Appleseed is clearly motivated. On the day of the drawing the reader understands why Hamurabi doesn't want to be around when the results of the contest are announced.

When the narrator tells Hamurabi what Appleseed's guess is, Hamurabi decides to stay for the drawing. Neither this decision, nor his role in the action that follows, is ever clearly explained. Thus it is left for the reader to decide if Hamurabi had anything to do with Appleseed's winning the jug of silver. Was the winning figure really seventy-seven dollars and thirty-five cents? Or did Hamurabi switch the paper that held the winning number and, in the mad scramble that followed, give a different paper to the narrator? But if Hamurabi did rig the contest, wouldn't his action eventually be discovered by the First National Bank, which knew the correct amount in the jug?

Setting and Atmosphere

The setting is limited to the Valhalla drugstore; the time is from mid-October to Christmas Eve. The atmosphere of the story shifts from pleasant to humorous to tense to riotously exciting. This changing atmosphere is conveyed through the description of the interior of the Valhalla and of the weather, along with the narrator's comments on how everyone is feeling.

In addition, these factors should be considered in noting how atmosphere contributes to the total effect of the story:

1. The time setting of the climax is Christmas Eve. How does the holiday air add to the excitement of the drawing? Why is this holiday an appropriate background for Appleseed's success?

2. The narrator uses such clichés as "got his goat," "to tell the truth," "awful creepy feeling," "kicking up an awful fuss," "making the best of a good thing," "not a living soul budged an inch," "a dead quiet," and "a sorry sight." Do these expressions add to or detract from the small-town atmosphere?

Point of View

As indicated in the marginal notes, the author has used a first-person narrator. The storyteller is related to the owner of the Valhalla. Interestingly, you never find out the narrator's name, and only by one word in the story do you know that this is a nephew and not a niece of Mr. Marshall. The narrator is addressed as "son" when he is invited to have a glass of wine.

What effect is the author trying to create by limiting his narrator's scope of knowledge?

Levels of Interpretation

Most stories can be interpreted on more than one level. The first or basic level is simply the plot itself. The second level may be called the symbolic one, based perhaps on allusions or on what the characters represent.

"Jug of Silver" is an exciting story, well told and filled with suspense. It is also a kind of legend or fairy tale. One reason for this is that there is an air of mystery about Appleseed because he was born with a caul. He claims that a "witch" told him this caul gives him the ability to "see things other folks couldn't see." Still another reason is that Appleseed is befriended by Hamurabi, who may be a king of an ancient empire. And still another reason is that Appleseed's good luck takes place in a drugstore named Valhalla, the name, in Norse mythology, of the hall where the souls of brave warriors slain in battle were brought to feast.

And notice that Appleseed wins on Christmas Eve, a time when the miraculous can happen and when good deeds are rewarded. The season of Christmas is also in keeping with the *theme* of the story—that love, selflessness, and faith can overcome incredible odds.

The narrator tells us that Appleseed's "legend flourishes still" in his town. In some ways, Appleseed's simplicity, poverty, and faith recall the qualities of another legendary figure, Johnny Appleseed. His deeds, once historical fact, are no longer verifiable. Over the years each storyteller has exaggerated details to make his version better.

The basic story of a poor boy's good fortune is enhanced by Capote's addition of legendary and fairy-tale elements. If there were no atmosphere of mystery surrounding the characters and the events, and if there were no reason for interpreting this story as a legend or folk tale, then "Jug of Silver" would have to be interpreted simply as the story of a boy's winning a guessing contest.

Richard Connell

[1893–1949]

Like many other American short-story writers, Richard Connell had a background of newspaper work and college writing. As a boy in Poughkeepsie, New York, he reported baseball games for his father's newspaper. At Harvard, from which he was graduated in 1915, he wrote for the humor magazine and the college paper. He enlisted in the army during World War I and after his discharge became a professional writer.

Connell wrote not only short stories but also several novels and some scenarios for the movies. At the time of his death in Beverly Hills, California, he was at work on a play. His major talent, however, lay in creating stories of action.

"The Most Dangerous Game," an example of this kind of story, was chosen as an O. Henry Memorial Award story in 1924.

The Most Dangerous Game

"Off there to the right—somewhere—is a large island," said Whitney. "It's rather a mystery—"

"What island is it?" Rainsford asked.

"The old charts call it 'Ship-Trap Island,'" Whitney replied. "A suggestive name, isn't it? Sailors have a curious dread of the place. I don't know why. Some superstition—"

"Can't see it," remarked Rainsford, trying to peer through the dank tropical night that was palpable [1] as it pressed its thick warm blackness in upon the yacht.

"You've good eyes," said Whitney, with a laugh, "and I've seen you pick off a moose moving in the brown fall bush at four hundred yards, but even you can't see four miles or so through a moonless Caribbean night."

"Nor four yards," admitted Rainsford. "Ugh! It's like moist black velvet."

"It will be light enough in Rio," promised Whitney. "We should make it in a few days. I hope the jaguar guns have come from

1. **palpable** (pal′pə·bəl): capable of being touched or felt.

Purdey's.[2] We should have some good hunting up the Amazon. Great sport, hunting."

"The best sport in the world," agreed Rainsford.

"For the hunter," amended Whitney. "Not for the jaguar."

"Don't talk rot, Whitney," said Rainsford. "You're a big-game hunter, not a philosopher. Who cares how a jaguar feels?"

"Perhaps the jaguar does," observed Whitney.

"Bah! They've no understanding."

"Even so, I rather think they understand one thing—fear. The fear of pain and the fear of death."

"Nonsense," laughed Rainsford. "This hot weather is making you soft, Whitney. Be a realist. The world is made up of two classes—the hunters and the hunted. Luckily, you and I are hunters. Do you think we've passed that island yet?"

"I can't tell in the dark. I hope so."

"Why?" asked Rainsford.

"The place has a reputation—a bad one."

"Cannibals?" suggested Rainsford.

"Hardly. Even cannibals wouldn't live in such a Godforsaken place. But it's got into sailor lore, somehow. Didn't you notice that the crew's nerves seemed a bit jumpy today?"

"They were a bit strange, now you mention it. Even Captain Nielsen—"

"Yes, even that tough-minded old Swede, who'd go up to the devil himself and ask him for a light. Those fishy blue eyes held a look I never saw there before. All I could get out of him was: 'This place has an evil name among seafaring men, sir.' Then he said to me, very gravely: 'Don't you feel anything?'—as if the air about us was actually poisonous. Now, you mustn't laugh when I tell you this—I did feel something like a sudden chill.

"There was no breeze. The sea was as flat as a plate glass window. We were drawing near the island then. What I felt was a—a mental chill; a sort of sudden dread."

"Pure imagination," said Rainsford. "One superstitious sailor can taint the whole ship's company with his fear."

"Maybe. But sometimes I think sailors have an extra sense that tells them when they are in danger. Sometimes I think evil is a tangible thing—with wave lengths, just as sound and light have. An evil place can, so to speak, broadcast vibrations of evil. Anyhow, I'm

---

2. **Purdey's:** a well-known firm in London which sells a wide variety of guns and hunting equipment.

glad we're getting out of this zone. Well, I think I'll turn in now, Rainsford."

"I'm not sleepy," said Rainsford. "I'm going to smoke another pipe up on the afterdeck."

"Good night, then, Rainsford. See you at breakfast."

"Right. Good night, Whitney."

There was no sound in the night as Rainsford sat there but the muffled throb of the engine that drove the yacht swiftly through the darkness, and the swish and ripple of the wash of the propeller.

Rainsford, reclining in a steamer chair, indolently [3] puffed on his favorite brier.[4] The sensuous drowsiness of the night was on him. "It's so dark," he thought, "that I could sleep without closing my eyes; the night would be my eyelids—"

An abrupt sound startled him. Off to the right he heard it, and his ears, expert in such matters, could not be mistaken. Again he heard the sound, and again. Somewhere, off in the blackness, someone had fired a gun three times.

Rainsford sprang up and moved quickly to the rail, mystified. He strained his eyes in the direction from which the reports had come, but it was like trying to see through a blanket. He leaped upon the rail and balanced himself there to get greater elevation; his pipe, striking a rope, was knocked from his mouth. He lunged for it; a short, hoarse cry came from his lips as he realized he had reached too far and had lost his balance. The cry was pinched off short as the blood-warm waters of the Caribbean Sea closed over his head.

He struggled up to the surface and tried to cry out, but the wash from the speeding yacht slapped him in the face, and the salt water in his open mouth made him gag and strangle. Desperately he struck out with strong strokes after the receding lights of the yacht, but he stopped before he had swum fifty feet. A certain coolheadedness had come to him; it was not the first time he had been in a tight place. There was a chance that his cries could be heard by someone aboard the yacht, but that chance was slender, and grew more slender as the yacht raced on. He wrestled himself out of his clothes, and shouted with all his power. The lights of the yacht became faint and ever-vanishing fireflies; then they were blotted out entirely by the night.

Rainsford remembered the shots. They had come from the right, and doggedly he swam in that direction, swimming with slow, delib-

3. **indolently** (in'də·lənt·lē): lazily.
4. **brier** (brī'ər): a pipe.

erate strokes, conserving his strength. For a seemingly endless time he fought the sea. He began to count his strokes; he could do possibly a hundred more and then—

Rainsford heard a sound. It came out of the darkness, a high screaming sound, the sound of an animal in an extremity of anguish and terror.

He did not recognize the animal that made the sound; he did not try to; with fresh vitality he swam toward the sound. He heard it again; then it was cut short by another noise, crisp, staccato.[5]

"Pistol shot," muttered Rainsford, swimming on.

Ten minutes of determined effort brought another sound to his ears—the most welcome he had ever heard—the muttering and growling of the sea breaking on a rocky shore. He was almost on the rocks before he saw them; on a night less calm he would have been shattered against them. With his remaining strength he dragged himself from the swirling waters. Jagged crags appeared to jut up into the opaqueness; he forced himself upward, hand over hand. Gasping, his hands raw, he reached a flat place at the top. Dense jungle came down to the very edge of the cliffs. What perils that tangle of trees and underbrush might hold for him did not concern Rainsford just then. All he knew was that he was safe from his enemy, the sea, and that utter weariness was on him. He flung himself down at the jungle edge and tumbled headlong into the deepest sleep of his life.

When he opened his eyes he knew from the position of the sun that it was late in the afternoon. Sleep had given him new vigor; a sharp hunger was picking at him. He looked about him, almost cheerfully.

"Where there are pistol shots, there are men. Where there are men, there is food," he thought. But what kind of men, he wondered, in so forbidding a place? An unbroken front of snarled and ragged jungle fringed the shore.

He saw no sign of a trail through the closely knit web of weeds and trees; it was easier to go along the shore, and Rainsford floundered along by the water. Not far from where he had landed, he stopped.

Some wounded thing, by the evidence a large animal, had thrashed about in the underbrush; the jungle weeds were crushed down and the moss was lacerated; one patch of weeds was stained crimson. A small, glittering object not far away caught Rainsford's eye and he picked it up. It was an empty cartridge.

5. **staccato** (stə·kä′tō): having a sharp, abrupt, disjointed quality.

"A twenty-two," he remarked. "That's odd. It must have been a fairly large animal, too. The hunter had his nerve with him to tackle it with a light gun. It's clear that the brute put up a fight. I suppose the first three shots I heard was when the hunter flushed his quarry [6] and wounded it. The last shot was when he trailed it here and finished it."

He examined the ground closely and found what he had hoped to find—the print of hunting boots. They pointed along the cliff in the direction he had been going. Eagerly he hurried along, now slipping on a rotten log or a loose stone, but making headway; night was beginning to settle down on the island.

Bleak darkness was blacking out the sea and jungle when Rainsford sighted the lights. He came upon them as he turned a crook in the coast line, and his first thought was that he had come upon a village, for there were many lights. But as he forged along he saw to his great astonishment that all the lights were in one enormous building —a lofty structure with pointed towers plunging upward into the gloom. His eyes made out the shadowy outlines of a palatial château; [7] it was set on a high bluff, and on three sides of it cliffs dived down to where the sea licked greedy lips in the shadows.

"Mirage," thought Rainsford. But it was no mirage, he found, when he opened the tall, spiked iron gate. The stone steps were real enough; the massive door with a leering gargoyle [8] for a knocker was real enough; yet above it all hung an air of unreality.

He lifted the knocker, and it creaked up stiffly, as if it had never before been used. He let it fall, and it startled him with its booming loudness. He thought he heard steps within; the door remained closed. Again Rainsford lifted the heavy knocker and let it fall. The door opened then, opened as suddenly as if it were on a spring, and Rainsford stood blinking in the river of glaring gold light that poured out. The first thing Rainsford's eyes discerned was the largest man he had ever seen—a gigantic creature, solidly made and black-bearded to the waist. In his hand the man held a long-barreled revolver, and he was pointing it straight at Rainsford's heart.

Out of the snarl of beard two small eyes regarded Rainsford.

"Don't be alarmed," said Rainsford, with a smile which he hoped was disarming. "I'm no robber. I fell off a yacht. My name is Sanger Rainsford of New York City."

6. **quarry** (kwôr′ē) : the object of a chase or hunt.
7. **château** (shä·tō′) : a castle-like house on a country estate, particularly one resembling a French manor house.
8. **gargoyle** (gär′goil) : a grotesquely carved animal or human head. Gargoyles originally served as rain spouts around the tops of buildings.

The menacing look in the eyes did not change. The revolver pointed as rigidly as if the giant were a statue. He gave no sign that he understood Rainsford's words, or that he had even heard them. He was dressed in a uniform, a black uniform trimmed with gray astrakhan.[9]

"I'm Sanger Rainsford of New York," Rainsford began again. "I fell off a yacht. I am hungry."

The man's only answer was to raise with his thumb the hammer of his revolver. Then Rainsford saw the man's free hand go to his forehead in a military salute, and he saw him click his heels together and stand at attention. Another man was coming down the broad marble steps, an erect, slender man in evening clothes. He advanced to Rainsford and held out his hand.

In a cultivated voice marked by a slight accent that gave it added precision and deliberateness, he said: "It is a very great pleasure and honor to welcome Mr. Sanger Rainsford, the celebrated hunter, to my home."

Automatically Rainsford shook the man's hand.

"I've read your book about hunting snow leopards in Tibet, you see," explained the man. "I am General Zaroff."

Rainsford's first impression was that the man was singularly handsome; his second was that there was an original, almost bizarre[10] quality about the general's face. He was a tall man past middle age, for his hair was a vivid white; but his thick eyebrows and pointed military mustache were as black as the night from which Rainsford had come. His eyes, too, were black and very bright. He had high cheek bones, a sharp-cut nose, a spare, dark face, the face of a man used to giving orders, the face of an aristocrat. Turning to the giant in uniform, the general made a sign. The giant put away his pistol, saluted, withdrew.

"Ivan is an incredibly strong fellow," remarked the general, "but he has the misfortune to be deaf and dumb. A simple fellow, but, I'm afraid, like all his race a bit of a savage."

"Is he Russian?"

"He is a Cossack,"[11] said the general, and his smile showed red lips and pointed teeth. "So am I."

9. **astrakhan** (as′trə·kan): a black or gray loosely curled fur made from the pelt of lambs raised in the region near Astrakhan, a city in southeastern Russia.
10. **bizarre** (bi·zär′): strangely out of the ordinary; odd, grotesque.
11. **Cossack** (kos′ak): a cavalryman of southern Russia in the days of the czars. Until the Revolution of 1917, Cossacks held certain privileges in return for rendering military service. They were famous for their daring and skilled horsemanship.

"Come," he said, "we shouldn't be chatting here. We can talk later. Now you want clothes, food, rest. You shall have them. This is a most restful spot."

Ivan had reappeared, and the general spoke to him with lips that moved but gave forth no sound.

"Follow Ivan, if you please, Mr. Rainsford," said the general. "I was about to have my dinner when you came. I'll wait for you. You'll find that my clothes will fit you, I think."

It was to a huge, beam-ceilinged bedroom with a canopied bed big enough for six men that Rainsford followed the silent giant. Ivan laid out an evening suit, and Rainsford, as he put it on, noticed that it came from a London tailor who ordinarily cut and sewed for none below the rank of duke.

The dining room to which Ivan conducted him was in many ways remarkable. There was a medieval magnificence about it; it suggested a baronial hall of feudal times with its oaken panels, its high ceiling, its vast refectory [12] tables where twoscore men could sit down to eat. About the hall were the mounted heads of many animals—lions, tigers, elephants, moose, bears; larger or more perfect specimens Rainsford had never seen. At the great table the general was sitting alone.

"You'll have a cocktail, Mr. Rainsford," he suggested. The cocktail was surpassingly good; and, Rainsford noted, the table appointments were of the finest—the linen, the crystal, the silver, the china.

They were eating borsch, the rich, red soup with sour cream so dear to Russian palates.[13] Half apologetically General Zaroff said: "We do our best to preserve the amenities of civilization here. Please forgive any lapses. We are well off the beaten track, you know. Do you think the champagne has suffered from its long ocean trip?"

"Not in the least," declared Rainsford. He was finding the general a most thoughtful and affable host, a true cosmopolite.[14] But there was one small trait of the general's that made Rainsford uncomfortable. Whenever he looked up from his plate, he found the general studying him, appraising him narrowly.

"Perhaps," said General Zaroff, "you were surprised that I recognized your name. You see, I read all books on hunting published in

12. **refectory** (ri·fek′tər·ē): a dining hall, especially in a religious house or college.
13. **palate** (pal′it): the roof of the mouth. Here it means a sense of taste or relish, so called because the palate was originally thought to be the organ of taste.
14. **cosmopolite** (koz·mop′ə·līt): a person of worldwide experience and taste.

English, French, and Russian. I have but one passion in my life, Mr. Rainsford, and it is the hunt."

"You have some wonderful heads here," said Rainsford as he ate a particularly well-cooked filet mignon.[15] "That Cape buffalo is the largest I ever saw."

"Oh, that fellow. Yes, he was a monster."

"Did he charge you?"

"Hurled me against a tree," said the general. "Fractured my skull. But I got the brute."

"I've always thought," said Rainsford, "that the Cape buffalo is the most dangerous of all big game."

For a moment the general did not reply; he was smiling his curious, red-lipped smile. Then he said slowly: "No. You are wrong, sir. The Cape buffalo is not the most dangerous big game." He sipped his wine. "Here in my preserve on this island," he said in the same slow tone, "I hunt more dangerous game."

Rainsford expressed his surprise. "Is there big game on this island?"

The general nodded. "The biggest."

"Really?"

"Oh, it isn't here naturally, of course. I have to stock the island."

"What have you imported, general?" Rainsford asked. "Tigers?"

The general smiled. "No," he said. "Hunting tigers ceased to interest me some years ago. I exhausted their possibilities, you see. No thrill left in tigers, no real danger. I live for danger, Mr. Rainsford."

The general took from his pocket a gold cigarette case and offered his guest a long black cigarette with a silver tip; it was perfumed and gave off a smell like incense.

"We will have some capital hunting, you and I," said the general. "I shall be most glad to have your society."

"But what game—" began Rainsford.

"I'll tell you," said the general. "You will be amused, I know. I think I may say, in all modesty, that I have done a rare thing. I have invented a new sensation. May I pour you another glass of port?"

"Thank you, general."

The general filled both glasses and said: "God makes some men poets. Some he makes kings, some beggars. Me he made a hunter. My hand was made for the trigger, my father said. He was a very rich man with a quarter of a million acres in the Crimea,[16] and he

15. **filet mignon** (fi·lā′ min·yon′): a choice cut of beef.
16. **Crimea** (krī·mē′ə): a peninsula in southern Russia.

was an ardent sportsman. When I was only five years old he gave me
a little gun, specially made in Moscow for me, to shoot sparrows with.
When I shot some of his prize turkeys with it, he did not punish me;
he complimented me on my marksmanship. I killed my first bear in
the Caucasus [17] when I was ten. My whole life has been one prolonged hunt. I went into the army—it was expected of noblemen's
sons—and for a time commanded a division of Cossack cavalry, but
my real interest was always the hunt. I have hunted every kind of
game in every land. It would be impossible for me to tell you how
many animals I have killed."

The general puffed at his cigarette.

"After the debacle [18] in Russia I left the country, for it was im-
prudent for an officer of the Czar to stay there. Many noble Russians
lost everything. I, luckily, had invested heavily in American securities,
so I shall never have to open a tearoom in Monte Carlo or drive a
taxi in Paris. Naturally, I continued to hunt—grizzlies in your
Rockies, crocodile in the Ganges,[19] rhinoceros in East Africa. It was
in Africa that the Cape buffalo hit me and laid me up for six months.
As soon as I recovered I started for the Amazon to hunt jaguars, for
I had heard they were unusually cunning. They weren't." The Cossack sighed. "They were no match at all for a hunter with his wits
about him, and a high-powered rifle. I was bitterly disappointed. I
was lying in my tent with a splitting headache one night when a
terrible thought pushed its way into my mind. Hunting was beginning to bore me! And hunting, remember, had been my life. I have
heard that in America businessmen often go to pieces when they give
up the business that has been their life."

"Yes, that's so," said Rainsford.

The general smiled. "I had no wish to go to pieces," he said. "I
must do something. Now, mine is an analytical mind, Mr. Rainsford.
Doubtless that is why I enjoy the problems of the chase."

"No doubt, General Zaroff."

"So," continued the general, "I asked myself why the hunt no
longer fascinated me. You are much younger than I am, Mr. Rainsford, and have not hunted as much, but you perhaps can guess the
answer."

17. **Caucasus** (kô′kə·səs): the region between the Black and Caspian seas in
Russia.
18. **debacle** (dā·bäk′əl): a sudden and disastrous defeat; a large-scale breakdown
or collapse; here, the reference is to the overthrow of the czarist Russian government by the Bolshevik Revolution in 1917.
19. **Ganges** (gan′jēz): a river in India.

"What was it?"

"Simply this: hunting had ceased to be what you call 'a sporting proposition.' It had become too easy. I always got my quarry. Always. There is no greater bore than perfection."

The general lit a fresh cigarette.

"No animal had a chance with me any more. That is no boast; it is a mathematical certainty. The animal had nothing but his legs and his instinct. Instinct is no match for reason. When I thought of this, it was a tragic moment for me, I can tell you."

Rainsford leaned across the table, absorbed in what his host was saying.

"It came to me as an inspiration what I must do," the general went on.

"And that was?"

The general smiled the quiet smile of one who has faced an obstacle and surmounted it with success. "I had to invent a new animal to hunt," he said.

"A new animal? You're joking."

"Not at all," said the general. "I never joke about hunting. I needed a new animal. I found one. So I bought this island, built this house, and here I do my hunting. The island is perfect for my purposes—there are jungles with a maze of trails in them, hills, swamps—"

"But the animal, General Zaroff?"

"Oh," said the general, "it supplies me with the most exciting hunting in the world. No other hunting compares with it for an instant. Every day I hunt, and I never grow bored now, for I have a quarry with which I can match my wits."

Rainsford's bewilderment showed in his face.

"I wanted the ideal animal to hunt," explained the general. "So I said: 'What are the attributes of an ideal quarry?' And the answer was, of course: 'It must have courage, cunning, and, above all, it must be able to reason.'"

"But no animal can reason," objected Rainsford.

"My dear fellow," said the general, "there is one that can."

"But you can't mean—" gasped Rainsford.

"And why not?"

"I can't believe you are serious, General Zaroff. This is a grisly joke."

"Why should I not be serious? I am speaking of hunting."

"Hunting? Hunting? General Zaroff, what you speak of is murder."

The general laughed with entire good nature. He regarded Rainsford quizzically.[20] "I refuse to believe that so modern and civilized a young man as you seem to be harbors romantic ideas about the value of human life. Surely your experiences in the war—"

"Did not make me condone cold-blooded murder," finished Rainsford stiffly.

Laughter shook the general. "How extraordinarily droll [21] you are!" he said. "One does not expect nowadays to find a young man of the educated class, even in America, with such a naive,[22] and, if I may say so, mid-Victorian point of view. It's like finding a snuffbox in a limousine. Ah, well, doubtless you had Puritan ancestors. So many Americans appear to have had. I'll wager you'll forget your notions when you go hunting with me. You've a genuine new thrill in store for you, Mr. Rainsford."

"Thank you, I'm a hunter, not a murderer."

"Dear me," said the general, quite unruffled, "again that unpleasant word. But I think I can show you that your scruples are quite ill-founded."

"Yes?"

"Life is for the strong, to be lived by the strong, and, if need be, taken by the strong. The weak of the world were put here to give the strong pleasure. I am strong. Why should I not use my gift? If I wish to hunt, why should I not? I hunt the scum of the earth—sailors from tramp ships—lascars,[23] blacks, Chinese, whites, mongrels—a thoroughbred horse or hound is worth more than a score of them."

"But they are men," said Rainsford hotly.

"Precisely," said the general. "That is why I use them. It gives me pleasure. They can reason, after a fashion. So they are dangerous."

"But where do you get them?"

The general's left eyelid fluttered down in a wink. "This island is called Ship Trap," he answered. "Sometimes an angry god of the high seas sends them to me. Sometimes, when Providence is not so kind, I help Providence a bit. Come to the window with me."

Rainsford went to the window and looked out toward the sea.

"Watch! Out there!" exclaimed the general, pointing into the night. Rainsford's eyes saw only blackness, and then, as the general pressed a button, far out to sea Rainsford saw the flash of lights.

The general chuckled. "They indicate a channel," he said, "where

20. **quizzically** (kwiz′i·kəl·lē) : in a questioning manner.
21. **droll** (drōl) : humorously odd.
22. **naive** (nä·ēv′) : simple; unworldly.
23. **lascars** (las′kərz) : East Indian sailors.

there's none; giant rocks with razor edges crouch like a sea monster with wide-open jaws. They can crush a ship as easily as I crush this nut." He dropped a walnut on the hardwood floor and brought his heel grinding down on it. "Oh, yes," he said, casually, as if in answer to a question, "I have electricity. We try to be civilized here."

"Civilized? And you shoot down men?"

A trace of anger was in the general's black eyes, but it was there for but a second, and he said in his most pleasant manner: "Dear me, what a righteous young man you are! I assure you I do not do the thing you suggest. That would be barbarous. I treat these visitors with every consideration. They get plenty of good food and exercise. They get into splendid physical condition. You shall see for yourself tomorrow."

"What do you mean?"

"We'll visit my training school," smiled the general. "It's in the cellar. I have about a dozen pupils down there now. They're from the Spanish bark *San Lucar* that had the bad luck to go on the rocks out there. A very inferior lot, I regret to say. Poor specimens and more accustomed to the deck than to the jungle."

He raised his hand, and Ivan, who served as waiter, brought thick Turkish coffee. Rainsford, with an effort, held his tongue in check.

"It's a game, you see," pursued the general blandly. "I suggest to one of them that we go hunting. I give him a supply of food and an excellent hunting knife. I give him three hours' start. I am to follow, armed only with a pistol of the smallest caliber and range. If my quarry eludes me for three whole days, he wins the game. If I find him—" the general smiled— "he loses."

"Suppose he refuses to be hunted?"

"Oh," said the general, "I give him his option, of course. He need not play that game if he doesn't wish to. If he does not wish to hunt, I turn him over to Ivan. Ivan once had the honor of serving as official knouter [24] to the Great White Czar, and he has his own ideas of sport. Invariably, Mr. Rainsford, invariably they choose the hunt."

"And if they win?"

The smile on the general's face widened. "To date I have not lost," he said. Then he added hastily: "I don't wish you to think me a braggart, Mr. Rainsford. Many of them afford only the most elementary sort of problem. Occasionally I strike a tartar. [25] One almost did win. I eventually had to use the dogs."

24. **knouter** (nout'ər): someone who flogs others with a knotted whip.
25. **tartar** (tär'tər): an unexpectedly strong and difficult opponent.

"The dogs?"

"This way, please. I'll show you."

The general steered Rainsford to a window. The lights from the windows sent a flickering illumination that made grotesque patterns on the courtyard below, and Rainsford could see moving about there a dozen or so huge black shapes; as they turned toward him, their eyes glittered greenly.

"A rather good lot, I think," observed the general. "They are let out at seven every night. If anyone should try to get into my house —or out of it—something extremely regrettable would occur to him." He hummed a snatch of song from the *Folies Bergères*.[26]

"And now," said the general, "I want to show you my new collection of heads. Will you come with me to the library?"

"I hope," said Rainsford, "that you will excuse me tonight, General Zaroff. I'm really not feeling well."

"Ah, indeed?" the general inquired solicitously. "Well, I suppose that's only natural, after your long swim. You need a good, restful night's sleep. Tomorrow you'll feel like a new man, I'll wager. Then we'll hunt, eh? I've one rather promising prospect—" Rainsford was hurrying from the room.

"Sorry you can't go with me tonight," called the general. "I expect rather fair sport—a big, strong black. He looks resourceful—Well, good night, Mr. Rainsford; I hope you have a good night's rest."

The bed was good, and the pajamas of the softest silk, and he was tired in every fiber of his being, but nevertheless Rainsford could not quiet his brain with the opiate of sleep. He lay, eyes wide open. Once he thought he heard stealthy steps in the corridor outside his room. He sought to throw open the door; it would not open. He went to the window and looked out. His room was high up in one of the towers. The lights of the château were out now, and it was dark and silent, but there was a fragment of sallow moon, and by its wan light he could see, dimly, the courtyard; there, weaving in and out in the pattern of shadow, were black, noiseless forms; the hounds heard him at the window and looked up, expectantly, with their green eyes. Rainsford went back to the bed and lay down. By many methods he tried to put himself to sleep. He had achieved a doze when, just as morning began to come, he heard, far off in the jungle, the faint report of a pistol.

General Zaroff did not appear until luncheon. He was dressed faultlessly in the tweeds of a country squire. He was solicitous about the state of Rainsford's health.

26. **Folies Bergères** (fō·lē ber·zher´): a famous Parisian theatrical revue.

"As for me," sighed the general, "I do not feel so well. I am worried, Mr. Rainsford. Last night I detected traces of my old complaint."

To Rainsford's questioning glance the general said: "Ennui.[27] Boredom."

Then, taking a second helping of crepes suzette,[28] the general explained: "The hunting was not good last night. The fellow lost his head. He made a straight trail that offered no problems at all. That's the trouble with these sailors; they have dull brains to begin with, and they do not know how to get about in the woods. They do excessively stupid and obvious things. It's most annoying. Will you have another glass of Chablis,[29] Mr. Rainsford?"

"General," said Rainsford firmly, "I wish to leave this island at once."

The general raised his thickets of eyebrows; he seemed hurt. "But, my dear fellow," the general protested, "you've only just come. You've had no hunting—"

"I wish to go today," said Rainsford. He saw the dead black eyes of the general on him, studying him. General Zaroff's face suddenly brightened.

He filled Rainsford's glass with venerable Chablis from a dusty bottle.

"Tonight," said the general, "we will hunt—you and I."

Rainsford shook his head. "No, general," he said. "I will not hunt."

The general shrugged his shoulders and delicately ate a hothouse grape. "As you wish, my friend," he said. "The choice rests entirely with you. But may I not venture to suggest that you will find my idea of sport more diverting than Ivan's?"

He nodded toward the corner to where the giant stood, scowling, his thick arms crossed on his hogshead of a chest.

"You don't mean—" cried Rainsford.

"My dear fellow," said the general, "have I not told you I always mean what I say about hunting? This is really an inspiration. I drink to a foeman worthy of my steel [30]—at last." The general raised his glass, but Rainsford sat staring at him.

"You'll find this game worth playing," the general said enthusiastically. "Your brain against mine. Your woodcraft against mine.

27. **Ennui** (än'wē).
28. **crepes suzette** (krep' soo·zet') : thin French pancakes served with a hot, orange-flavored sauce.
29. **Chablis** (shà·blē') : a dry white Burgundy wine.
30. **steel**: a sword. What figurative meaning is implied here?

Your strength and stamina against mine. Outdoor chess! And the stake is not without value, eh?"

"And if I win—" began Rainsford huskily.

"I'll cheerfully acknowledge myself defeated if I do not find you by midnight of the third day," said General Zaroff. "My sloop [31] will place you on the mainland near a town." The general read what Rainsford was thinking.

"Oh, you can trust me," said the Cossack. "I will give you my word as a gentleman and a sportsman. Of course you, in turn, must agree to say nothing of your visit here."

"I'll agree to nothing of the kind," said Rainsford.

"Oh," said the general, "in that case—But why discuss that now? Three days hence we can discuss it over a bottle of Veuve Cliquot,[32] unless—"

The general sipped his wine.

Then a businesslike air animated him. "Ivan," he said to Rainsford, "will supply you with hunting clothes, food, a knife. I suggest you wear moccasins; they leave a poorer trail. I suggest, too, that you avoid the big swamp in the southeast corner of the island. We call it Death Swamp. There's quicksand there. One foolish fellow tried it. The deplorable part of it was that Lazarus followed him. You can imagine my feelings, Mr. Rainsford. I loved Lazarus; he was the finest hound in my pack. Well, I must beg you to excuse me now. I always take a siesta after lunch. You'll hardly have time for a nap, I fear. You'll want to start, no doubt. I shall not follow till dusk. Hunting at night is so much more exciting than by day, don't you think? Au revoir,[33] Mr. Rainsford, au revoir." General Zaroff, with a deep, courtly bow, strolled from the room.

From another door came Ivan. Under one arm he carried khaki hunting clothes, a haversack [34] of food, a leather sheath containing a long-bladed hunting knife; his right hand rested on a cocked revolver thrust in the crimson sash about his waist.

Rainsford had fought his way through the bush for two hours. "I must keep my nerve. I must keep my nerve," he said through tight teeth.

31. **sloop** (slo͞op): a single masted boat with a triangular sail set in the direction of the boat's length.
32. **Veuve Cliquot** (vûv′ klē·kō′): a famous French champagne.
33. **Au revoir** (ō rə·vwär′): *French*, good-by, till we meet again.
34. **haversack** (hav′ər·sak): a bag, worn over one shoulder, used for carrying rations on a march or hike.

He had not been entirely clearheaded when the château gates snapped shut behind him. His whole idea at first was to put distance between himself and General Zaroff, and to this end he had plunged along, spurred on by the sharp rowels [35] of something very like panic. Now he had got a grip on himself, had stopped, and was taking stock of himself and the situation. He saw that straight flight was futile; inevitably it would bring him face to face with the sea. He was in a picture with a frame of water, and his operations, clearly, must take place within that frame.

"I'll give him a trail to follow," muttered Rainsford, and he struck off from the rude path he had been following into the trackless wilderness. He executed a series of intricate loops; he doubled on his trail again and again, recalling all the lore of the fox hunt, and all the dodges of the fox. Night found him leg-weary, with hands and face lashed by the branches, on a thickly wooded ridge. He knew it would be insane to blunder on through the dark, even if he had the strength. His need for rest was imperative and he thought: "I have played the fox, now I must play the cat of the fable." [36] A big tree with a thick trunk and outspread branches was nearby, and, taking care to leave not the slightest mark, he climbed up into the crotch, and stretching out on one of the broad limbs, after a fashion, rested. Rest brought him new confidence and almost a feeling of security. Even so zealous a hunter as General Zaroff could not trace him there, he told himself; only the devil himself could follow that complicated trail through the jungle after dark. But, perhaps the general was a devil—

An apprehensive night crawled slowly by like a wounded snake, and sleep did not visit Rainsford, although the silence of a dead world was on the jungle. Toward morning when a dingy gray was varnishing the sky, the cry of some startled bird focused Rainsford's attention in that direction. Something was coming through the bush, coming slowly, carefully, coming by the same winding way Rainsford had come. He flattened himself down on the limb, and through a screen of leaves almost as thick as tapestry, he watched. . . . That which was approaching was a man.

It was General Zaroff. He made his way along with his eyes fixed

35. rowels (rou'əls): the spiked wheels on spurs.
36. the fox . . . the cat of the fable: The fable alluded to is "The Fox and the Cat" by Aesop. In spite of all his clever plans of escape, the boastful fox is caught by the hunting dogs; the cat simply climbs a tree to find safety. Rainsford, like the fox, first tries all kinds of intricate maneuvers; now, tired, he realizes it is time to rest and wait.

in utmost concentration on the ground before him. He paused, almost beneath the tree, dropped to his knees and studied the ground. Rainsford's impulse was to hurl himself down like a panther, but he saw that the general's right hand held something metallic—a small automatic pistol.

The hunter shook his head several times, as if he were puzzled. Then he straightened up and took from his case one of his black cigarettes; its pungent incenselike smoke floated up to Rainsford's nostrils.

Rainsford held his breath. The general's eyes had left the ground and were traveling inch by inch up the tree. Rainsford froze there, every muscle tensed for a spring. But the sharp eyes of the hunter stopped before they reached the limb where Rainsford lay; a smile spread over his brown face. Very deliberately he blew a smoke ring into the air; then he turned his back on the tree and walked carelessly away, back along the trail he had come. The swish of the underbrush against his hunting boots grew fainter and fainter.

The pent-up air burst hotly from Rainsford's lungs. His first thought made him feel sick and numb. The general could follow a trail through the woods at night; he could follow an extremely difficult trail; he must have uncanny powers; only by the merest chance had the Cossack failed to see his quarry.

Rainsford's second thought was even more terrible. It sent a shudder of cold horror through his whole being. Why had the general smiled? Why had he turned back?

Rainsford did not want to believe what his reason told him was true, but the truth was as evident as the sun that had by now pushed through the morning mists. The general was playing with him! The general was saving him for another day's sport! The Cossack was the cat; he was the mouse. Then it was that Rainsford knew the full meaning of terror.

"I will not lose my nerve. I will not."

He slid down from the tree, and struck off again into the woods. His face was set and he forced the machinery of his mind to function. Three hundred yards from his hiding place he stopped where a huge dead tree leaned precariously on a smaller, living one. Throwing off his sack of food, Rainsford took his knife from its sheath and began to work with all his energy.

The job was finished at last, and he threw himself down behind a fallen log a hundred feet away. He did not have to wait long. The cat was coming again to play with the mouse.

Following the trail with the sureness of a bloodhound came General Zaroff. Nothing escaped those searching black eyes, no crushed blade of grass, no bent twig, no mark, no matter how faint, in the moss. So intent was the Cossack on his stalking that he was upon the thing Rainsford had made before he saw it. His foot touched the protruding bough that was the trigger. Even as he touched it, the general sensed his danger and leaped back with the agility of an ape. But he was not quite quick enough; the dead tree, delicately adjusted to rest on the cut living one, crashed down and struck the general a glancing blow on the shoulder as it fell; but for his alertness, he must have been smashed beneath it. He staggered, but he did not fall; nor did he drop his revolver. He stood there, rubbing his injured shoulder, and Rainsford, with fear again gripping at his heart, heard the general's mocking laugh ring through the jungle.

"Rainsford," called the general, "if you are within sound of my voice, as I suppose you are, let me congratulate you. Not many men know how to make a Malay man-catcher. Luckily for me, I too have hunted in Malacca. You are proving interesting, Mr. Rainsford. I am going now to have my wound dressed; it's only a slight one. But I shall be back. I shall be back."

When the general, nursing his bruised shoulder, had gone, Rainsford took up his flight again. It was flight now, a desperate, hopeless flight, that carried him on for some hours. Dusk came, then darkness, and still he pressed on. The ground grew softer under his moccasins; the vegetation grew ranker, denser; insects bit him savagely. Then, as he stepped forward, his foot sank into the ooze. He tried to wrench it back, but the muck sucked viciously at his foot as if it were a giant leech. With a violent effort, he tore his foot loose. He knew where he was now. Death Swamp and its quicksand.

His hands were tight closed as if his nerve were something tangible that someone in the darkness was trying to tear from his grip. The softness of the earth had given him an idea. He stepped back from the quicksand a dozen feet or so and, like some huge prehistoric beaver, he began to dig.

Rainsford had dug himself in in France when a second's delay meant death. That had been a placid pastime compared to his digging now. The pit grew deeper; when it was above his shoulders, he climbed out and from some hard saplings cut stakes and sharpened them to a fine point. These stakes he planted in the bottom of the pit with the points sticking up. With flying fingers he wove a rough carpet of weeds and branches and with it he covered the mouth of the pit. Then, wet with sweat and aching with tiredness, he crouched behind the stump of a lightning-charred tree.

He knew his pursuer was coming; he heard the padding sound of feet on the soft earth, and the night breeze brought him the perfume of the general's cigarette. It seemed to Rainsford that the general was coming with unusual swiftness; he was not feeling his way along, foot by foot. Rainsford, crouching there, could not see the general, nor could he see the pit. He lived a year in a minute. Then he felt an impulse to cry aloud with joy, for he heard the sharp crackle of the breaking branches as the cover of the pit gave way; he heard the sharp scream of pain as the pointed stakes found their mark. He leaped up from his place of concealment. Then he cowered back. Three feet from the pit a man was standing, with an electric torch in his hand.

"You've done well, Rainsford," the voice of the general called. "Your Burmese tiger pit has claimed one of my best dogs. Again you score. I think, Mr. Rainsford, I'll see what you can do against my whole pack. I'm going home for a rest now. Thank you for a most amusing evening."

At daybreak Rainsford, lying near the swamp, was awakened by a sound that made him know that he had new things to learn about fear. It was a distant sound, faint and wavering, but he knew it. It was the baying of a pack of hounds.

Rainsford knew he could do one of two things. He could stay where he was and wait. That was suicide. He could flee. That was postponing the inevitable. For a moment he stood there, thinking. An idea that held a wild chance came to him, and, tightening his belt, he headed away from the swamp.

The baying of the hounds drew nearer, then still nearer, nearer, ever nearer. On a ridge Rainsford climbed a tree. Down a watercourse, not a quarter of a mile away, he could see the bush moving. Straining his eyes, he saw the lean figure of General Zaroff; just ahead of him Rainsford made out another figure whose wide shoulders surged through the tall jungle weeds; it was the giant Ivan, and he seemed pulled forward by some unseen force; Rainsford knew that Ivan must be holding the pack in leash.

They would be on him any minute now. His mind worked frantically. He thought of a native trick he had learned in Uganda. He slid down the tree. He caught hold of a springy young sapling and to it he fastened his hunting knife, with the blade pointing down the trail; with a bit of wild grapevine he tied back the sapling. Then he ran for his life. The hounds raised their voices as they hit the fresh scent. Rainsford knew now how an animal at bay feels.

He had to stop to get his breath. The baying of the hounds stopped abruptly, and Rainsford's heart stopped too. They must have reached the knife.

He shinned excitedly up a tree and looked back. His pursuers had stopped. But the hope that was in Rainsford's brain when he climbed died, for he saw in the shallow valley that General Zaroff was still on his feet. But Ivan was not. The knife, driven by the recoil of the springing tree, had not wholly failed.

Rainsford had hardly tumbled to the ground when the pack took up the cry again.

"Nerve, nerve, nerve!" he panted, as he dashed along. A blue gap showed between the trees dead ahead. Ever nearer drew the hounds. Rainsford forced himself on toward that gap. He reached it. It was the shore of the sea. Across a cove he could see the gloomy gray stone of the château. Twenty feet below him the sea rumbled and hissed. Rainsford hesitated. He heard the hounds. Then he leaped far out into the sea. . . .

When the general and his pack reached the place by the sea, the Cossack stopped. For some minutes he stood regarding the blue-green expanse of water. He shrugged his shoulders. Then he sat down, took a drink of brandy from a silver flask, lit a cigarette, and hummed a bit from *Madame Butterfly*.[37]

General Zaroff had an exceedingly good dinner in his great paneled dining hall that evening. With it he had a bottle of Pol Roger[38] and half a bottle of Chambertin.[39] Two slight annoyances kept him from perfect enjoyment. One was the thought that it would be difficult to replace Ivan; the other was that his quarry had escaped him; of course the American hadn't played the game—so thought the general as he tasted his after-dinner liqueur. In his library he read, to soothe himself, from the works of Marcus Aurelius.[40] At ten he went up to his bedroom. He was deliciously tired, he said to himself, as he locked himself in. There was a little moonlight, so, before turning on his light, he went to the window

37. *Madame Butterfly:* an opera by the Italian composer Giacomo Puccini in which the heroine commits suicide.
38. **Pol Roger** (pul rō·zhā′) : a French champagne.
39. **Chambertin** (sham·ber·tən′) : a red Burgundy wine.
40. **Marcus Aurelius** (mär′kəs ô·rē′lē·əs) : a Roman emperor and philosopher who ruled fairly and humanely. He expressed his philosophy in his book, *Meditations*.

and looked down at the courtyard. He could see the great hounds, and he called, "Better luck another time," to them. Then he switched on the light.

A man, who had been hiding in the curtains of the bed, was standing there.

"Rainsford!" screamed the general. "How in God's name did you get here?"

"Swam," said Rainsford. "I found it quicker than walking through the jungle."

The general sucked in his breath and smiled. "I congratulate you," he said. "You have won the game."

Rainsford did not smile. "I am still a beast at bay," he said, in a low, hoarse voice. "Get ready, General Zaroff."

The general made one of his deepest bows. "I see," he said. "Splendid! One of us is to furnish a repast for the hounds. The other will sleep in this very excellent bed. On guard, Rainsford."

He had never slept in a better bed, Rainsford decided.

Meaning

1. At the beginning of this story, in answer to Whitney's statement that hunted animals understand "the fear of pain and the fear of death," Rainsford replies "the world is made up of two classes—the hunters and the hunted." Explain what this philosophy means. Do you think he would hold the same opinion at the end of his experience with General Zaroff? Why or why not?

2. How does General Zaroff carry this philosophy to extremes? When do you realize what his "game" is? When Rainsford calls Zaroff's game hunts "murder," how does Zaroff justify himself?

3. *Conflict* in a short story may be (a) man against man, (b) man against society, (c) man against nature, or (d) man against himself. Which of these conflicts occur in this story? Justify your answer with specific textual references.

4. Moments of decision often reveal what kind of person a man is. Note Rainsford's reactions in the crucial moments when he is thrown from the ship and when he is being pursued by Zaroff. What are his strongest characteristics? Are you prepared to believe that he would act as he does during the chase? Why?

Method

1. What purpose does the first section of the story—everything up to Rainsford's arrival on the island—serve in the story?

2. How does the author use Rainsford's past to create a sense of probability for the "game" part of the story?
3. How does the author gradually increase the tension and suspense?
4. How do the following events serve as foreshadowings?
   (a) Whitney informs Rainsford that the mysterious island off to the right of the ship is called "Ship-Trap Island."
   (b) Rainsford says in a discussion about hunting: "Who cares how a jaguar feels?"
   (c) Rainsford is sure he has heard someone off in the blackness fire a gun three times.
   (d) Rainsford hears a high screaming sound and is unable to recognize the animal that makes it.
5. The *climax* is the highest point of interest or suspense in a story. It usually marks the turning point at which the reader can foresee the way the struggle will end. What point in this story would you consider the climax? How did the author build toward it?
6. How does the setting of this story become an integral part of the plot? What does it add to the story?
7. Characterization may be achieved by (a) physical description of a character by the author, (b) a description by another character, (c) the use of dialogue or conversation, (d) an explanation of the character's inner thoughts, (e) the behavior or actions of the character, (f) the reactions of the character to another character or to a situation. Which of these methods does Connell use? Illustrate your choices with examples from the text.

Language: Meaning from Context

In your reading you will come across words that are either completely new to you or that you have not noticed before. There are several ways to unlock the meanings of these words. You can consult a dictionary, ask another person, try to relate these words to words you already know, or attack the meaning through context.

Context comes from the Latin prefix *com* (together with) and the Latin verb *texere* (to weave). Applied here, context means the parts of a sentence, paragraph, or speech occurring just before and after a specified word. These words form a setting (context) which determines the meaning of a particular word when it is used in their company.

For example, look at the following sentences:
1. She flew into a *rage* when she saw her broken vase.
2. Hoop skirts were the *rage* in my grandmother's day.

In the first example, *rage* means violent anger; in the second, it means fashion or fad.

However, it is not unusual for an author to want to suggest ambiguity by using a word with more than one meaning. How might this be true of the title "The Most Dangerous Game"?

When you study a word in context, ask yourself to identify the place, time, situation, and speaker or writer associated with each problem word.

Try to define the italicized words in the following sentences, using contextual clues. Then check your definitions with a dictionary.

1. "Sometimes I think evil is a *tangible* thing—with wave lengths, just as sound and light have."
2. "We do our best to preserve the *amenities* of civilization here."
3. [My war experiences] "did not make me *condone* cold-blooded murder," finished Rainsford stiffly.
4. "Once he [Rainsford] thought he heard *stealthy* steps in the corridor outside his room."

Composition

1. Good prose writers often use similes and metaphors to appeal to our senses and emotions. A simile is a comparison using *like* or *as*. For example, Connell describes Rainsford as ready "to hurl himself down like a panther" when he sees Zaroff approaching him in the jungle. A metaphor is a comparison without *like* or *as*. For example, "My whole life has been one prolonged hunt." Remember that a metaphor may be indicated by a verb or participle, as in "a dingy gray was *varnishing* the sky."

Write a composition in which you explain several of the similes and metaphors that Connell uses in this story. Begin with the following topic sentence: "In 'The Most Dangerous Game' the author, Richard Connell, uses a great many imaginative comparisons to make the scenes vivid to us." Develop this topic sentence by naming the similes and metaphors and explaining what each one means.

2. Write a character sketch of General Zaroff so that the reader has a complete picture of the man, physically and intellectually. Use as a guide the methods an author may use for characterization.

Jack London
[1876–1916]

Jack London's life history reads like the combined adventures of the heroes in his novels and short stories. He could tell of running away to sea, traveling as a tramp across the United States, seeking gold in Alaska, building a schooner, the *Snark*, making and spending a million dollars, and—of writing fifty books.

Although today he is not considered to be among the greatest of American writers, at the height of his career he enjoyed wide popularity and great wealth from his writing, the major part of which is in the short-story form. Moreover, his method of using realistic details to relate his adventures influenced many American writers.

His days in the Yukon provided him with firsthand material for his novel *The Call of the Wild*, in which he showed the effects of an animal's association with man. "To Build a Fire" is also about the Yukon, and here London depicts the splendor and terror of nature. The story also exemplifies his attitude toward man and animal.

To Build a Fire

Day had broken cold and gray, exceedingly cold and gray, when the man turned aside from the main Yukon trail and climbed the high earth bank, where a dim and little-traveled trail led eastward through the fat spruce timberland. It was a steep bank, and he paused for breath at the top, excusing the act to himself by looking at his watch. It was nine o'clock. There was no sun or hint of sun, though there was not a cloud in the sky. It was a clear day, and yet there seemed an intangible pall [1] over the face of things, a subtle gloom that made the day dark, and that was due to the absence of sun. This fact did not worry the man. He was used to the lack of sun. It had been days since he had seen the sun, and he knew that a few more days must pass before that cheerful orb, due south, would just peep above the skyline and dip immediately from view.

The man flung a look back along the way he had come. The Yukon

1. **pall** (pôl): a dark covering, usually a cloth draped over a coffin. Here it refers to the gloomy atmosphere.

"To Build a Fire" from *Lost Faces* by Jack London. Reprinted by permission of Irving Shepard.

lay a mile wide and hidden under three feet of ice. On top of this ice were as many feet of snow. It was all pure white, rolling in gentle undulations [2] where the ice jams of the freeze-up had formed. North and south, as far as his eye could see, it was unbroken white, save for a dark hairline that curved and twisted from around the spruce-covered island to the south, and that curved and twisted away into the north, where it disappeared behind another spruce-covered island. This dark hairline was the trail—the main trail—that led south five hundred miles to the Chilkoot Pass, Dyea,[3] and salt water; and that led north seventy miles to Dawson, and still on to the north a thousand miles to Nulato, and finally to St. Michael on the Bering Sea, a thousand miles and half a thousand more.

But all this—the mysterious, far-reaching hairline trail, the absence of sun from the sky, the tremendous cold, and the strangeness and weirdness of it all—made no impression on the man. It was not because he was long used to it. He was a newcomer in the land, a cheechako,[4] and this was his first winter. The trouble with him was that he was without imagination. He was quick and alert in the things of life, but only in the things, and not in the significances. Fifty degrees below zero meant eighty-odd degrees of frost. Such fact impressed him as being cold and uncomfortable, and that was all. It did not lead him to meditate upon his frailty as a creature of temperature, and upon man's frailty in general, able only to live within certain narrow limits of heat and cold, and from there on it did not lead him to the conjectural [5] field of immortality and man's place in the universe. Fifty degrees below zero stood for a bite of frost that hurt and that must be guarded against by the use of mittens, ear flaps, warm moccasins, and thick socks. Fifty degrees below zero was to him just precisely fifty degrees below zero. That there should be anything more to it than that was a thought that never entered his head.

As he turned to go on, he spat speculatively. There was a sharp, explosive crackle that startled him. He spat again. And again, in the air, before it could fall to the snow, the spittle crackled. He knew that at fifty below, spittle crackled on the snow, but this spittle had

---

2. **undulations** (un'dyə·lā'shəns): waves. The snow had a rolling appearance.
3. **Dyea** (dī'ā): a former village in southeast Alaska. When gold was discovered in 1896 in the Klondike region, Dyea became the supply center and starting point for the trail over the Chilkoot Pass to the northern mining fields and towns such as Dawson and Nulato.
4. **cheechako** (chē·chä'kō): in Alaska and the Yukon, a newcomer; a tenderfoot.
5. **conjectural** (kən·jek'chər·əl): based on surmise or guesswork. To conjecture is to come to conclusions using incomplete or merely probable evidence.

crackled in the air. Undoubtedly it was colder than fifty below—how much colder he did not know. But the temperature did not matter. He was bound for the old claim on the left fork of Henderson Creek, where the boys were already. They had come over across the divide from the Indian Creek country, while he had come the roundabout way to take a look at the possibilities of getting out logs in the spring from the islands in the Yukon. He would be into camp by six o'clock; a bit after dark, it was true, but the boys would be there, a fire would be going, and a hot supper would be ready. As for lunch, he pressed his hand against the protruding bundle under his jacket. It was also under his shirt, wrapped up in a handkerchief and lying against the naked skin. It was the only way to keep the biscuits from freezing. He smiled agreeably to himself as he thought of those biscuits, each cut open and sopped in bacon grease, and each enclosing a generous slice of fried bacon.

He plunged in among the big spruce trees. The trail was faint. A foot of snow had fallen since the last sled had passed over, and he was glad he was without a sled, traveling light. In fact, he carried nothing but the lunch wrapped in the handkerchief. He was surprised, however, at the cold. It certainly was cold, he concluded, as he rubbed his numb nose and cheekbones with his mittened hand. He was a warm-whiskered man, but the hair on his face did not protect the high cheekbones and the eager nose that thrust itself aggressively into the frosty air.

At the man's heels trotted a dog, a big native husky, the proper wolf dog, gray-coated and without any visible or temperamental difference from its brother, the wild wolf. The animal was depressed by the tremendous cold. It knew that it was no time for traveling. Its instinct told it a truer tale than was told to the man by the man's judgment. In reality, it was not merely colder than fifty below zero; it was colder than sixty below, than seventy below. It was seventy-five below zero. Since the freezing point is thirty-two above zero, it meant that one hundred and seven degrees of frost obtained. The dog did not know anything about thermometers. Possibly in its brain there was no sharp consciousness of a condition of very cold such as was in the man's brain. But the brute had its instinct. It experienced a vague but menacing apprehension that subdued it and made it slink along at the man's heels and that made it question eagerly every unwonted [6] movement of the man, as if expecting him to go into camp or to seek shelter somewhere and build a fire. The dog had

6. **unwonted** (un·wun'tid): unusual, unfamiliar.

learned fire, and it wanted fire, or else to burrow under the snow and cuddle its warmth away from the air.

The frozen moisture of its breathing had settled on its fur in a fine powder of frost, and especially were its jowls, muzzle, and eyelashes whitened by its crystaled breath. The man's red beard and mustache were likewise frosted, but more solidly, the deposit taking the form of ice and increasing with every warm, moist breath he exhaled. Also, the man was chewing tobacco, and the muzzle of ice held his lips so rigidly that he was unable to clear his chin when he expelled the juice. The result was that a crystal beard of the color and solidity of amber [7] was increasing its length on his chin. If he fell down it would shatter itself, like glass, into brittle fragments. But he did not mind the appendage. It was the penalty all tobacco chewers paid in that country, and he had been out before in two cold snaps. They had not been so cold as this, he knew, but by the spirit thermometer [8] at Sixty Mile he knew they had been registered at fifty below and at fifty-five.

He held on through the level stretch of woods for several miles, crossed a wide flat, and dropped down a bank to the frozen bed of a small stream. This was Henderson Creek, and he knew he was ten miles from the forks. He looked at his watch. It was ten o'clock. He was making four miles an hour, and he calculated that he would arrive at the forks at half-past twelve. He decided to celebrate that event by eating his lunch there.

The dog dropped in again at his heels, with a tail drooping discouragement, as the man swung along the creek bed. The furrow of the old sled trail was plainly visible, but a dozen inches of snow covered the marks of the last runners. In a month no man had come up or down that silent creek. The man held steadily on. He was not much given to thinking, and just then particularly he had nothing to think about save that he would eat lunch at the forks and that at six o'clock he would be in camp with the boys. There was nobody to talk to, and had there been, speech would have been impossible because of the ice muzzle on his mouth. So he continued monotonously to chew tobacco and to increase the length of his amber beard.

Once in a while the thought reiterated itself that it was very cold and that he had never experienced such cold. As he walked along he rubbed his cheekbones and nose with the back of his mittened hand. He did this automatically, now and again changing hands. But rub

7. **amber:** a reddish- or brownish-yellow vegetable resin used in making beads.
8. **spirit thermometer:** an alcohol thermometer used particularly in severe cold.

as he would, the instant he stopped his cheekbones went numb, and the following instant the end of his nose went numb. He was sure to frost his cheeks; he knew that, and experienced a pang of regret that he had not devised a nose strap of the sort Bud wore in cold snaps. Such a strap passed across the cheeks, as well, and saved them. But it didn't matter much, after all. What were frosted cheeks? A bit painful, that was all; they were never serious.

Empty as the man's mind was of thought, he was keenly observant, and he noticed the changes in the creek, the curves and bends and timber jams, and always he sharply noted where he placed his feet. Once, coming around a bend, he shied abruptly, like a startled horse, curved away from the place where he had been walking, and retreated several paces back along the trail. The creek, he knew, was frozen clear to the bottom—no creek could contain water in that arctic winter—but he knew also that there were springs that bubbled out from the hillsides and ran along under the snow and on top of the ice of the creek. He knew that the coldest snaps never froze these springs, and he knew likewise their danger. They were traps. They hid pools of water under the snow that might be three inches deep, or three feet. Sometimes a skin of ice half an inch thick covered them, and in turn was covered by the snow. Sometimes there were alternate layers of water and ice skin, so that when one broke through he kept on breaking through for a while, sometimes wetting himself to the waist.

That was why he had shied in such panic. He had felt the give under his feet and heard the crackle of a snow-hidden ice skin. And to get his feet wet in such a temperature meant trouble and danger. At the very least it meant delay, for he would be forced to stop and build a fire, and under its protection to bare his feet while he dried his socks and moccasins. He stood and studied the creek bed and its banks, and decided that the flow of water came from the right. He reflected a while, rubbing his nose and cheeks, then skirted to the left, stepping gingerly and testing the footing for each step. Once clear of the danger, he took a fresh chew of tobacco and swung along at his four-mile gait.

In the course of the next two hours he came upon several similar traps. Usually the snow above the hidden pools had a sunken, candied appearance that advertised the danger. Once again, however, he had a close call; and once, suspecting danger, he compelled the dog to go on in front. The dog did not want to go. It hung back until the man shoved it forward, and then it went quickly across the white, unbroken surface. Suddenly it broke through, floundered to one side, and got away to firmer footing. It had wet its forefeet and legs, and almost immediately the water that clung to it turned to ice. It made quick efforts to lick the ice off its legs, then dropped down in the snow and began to bite out the ice that had formed between the toes. This was a matter of instinct. To permit the ice to remain would mean sore feet. It did not know this. It merely obeyed the mysterious prompting that arose from the deep crypts [9] of its being. But the man knew, having achieved a judgment on the subject, and he removed the mitten from his right hand and helped tear out the ice particles. He did not expose his fingers more than a minute, and was astonished at the swift numbness that smote [10] them. It certainly was cold. He pulled on the mitten hastily, and beat the hand savagely across his chest.

At twelve o'clock the day was at its brightest. Yet the sun was too far south on its winter journey to clear the horizon. The bulge of the earth intervened between it and Henderson Creek, where the man walked under a clear sky at noon and cast no shadow. At half-past twelve, to the minute, he arrived at the forks of the creek. He was pleased at the speed he had made. If he kept it up, he would certainly be with the boys by six. He unbuttoned his jacket and shirt and drew forth his lunch. The action consumed no more than a quarter of a minute, yet in that brief moment the numbness laid hold of the exposed fingers. He did not put the mitten on, but instead struck the fingers a dozen sharp smashes against his leg. Then he sat down on a snow-covered log to eat. The sting that followed upon the striking of his fingers against his leg ceased so quickly that he was startled. He had had no chance to take a bite of biscuit. He struck the fingers repeatedly and returned them to the mitten, baring the other hand for the purpose of eating. He tried to take a mouthful, but the ice muzzle prevented. He had forgotten to build a fire and thaw out. He chuckled at his foolishness, and as he chuckled he noted the numbness creeping into the exposed fingers. Also, he noted that the stinging which had first come to his toes when he sat down was already passing away. He wondered whether the toes were warm or numb. He moved them inside the moccasins and decided that they were numb.

9. **crypts** (kripts): usually chambers or vaults wholly or partly underground, used for burial. As used here, the word refers to something deep and unknown in an animal's nature that causes it to act instinctively to protect itself.
10. **smote** (smōt): past tense of the verb *smite*, which means to strike, often suddenly and with great force.

He pulled the mitten on hurriedly and stood up. He was a bit frightened. He stamped up and down until the stinging returned into the feet. It certainly was cold, was his thought. That man from Sulfur Creek had spoken the truth when telling how cold it sometimes got in the country. And he had laughed at him at the time! That showed one must not be too sure of things. There was no mistake about it, it *was* cold. He strode up and down, stamping his feet and threshing his arms, until reassured by the returning warmth. Then he got out matches and proceeded to make a fire. From the undergrowth, where high water of the previous spring had lodged a supply of seasoned twigs, he got his firewood. Working carefully from a small beginning, he soon had a roaring fire, over which he thawed the ice from his face and in the protection of which he ate his biscuits. For the moment the cold of space was outwitted. The dog took satisfaction in the fire, stretching out close enough for warmth and far enough away to escape being singed.

When the man had finished, he filled his pipe and took his comfortable time over a smoke. Then he pulled on his mittens, settled the ear flaps of his cap firmly about his ears, and took the creek trail up the left fork. The dog was disappointed and yearned back toward the fire. This man did not know cold. Possibly all the generations of his ancestry had been ignorant of cold, of real cold, of cold one hundred and seven degrees below freezing point. But the dog knew; all its ancestry knew, and it had inherited the knowledge. And it knew that it was not good to walk abroad in such fearful cold. It was the time to lie snug in a hole in the snow and wait for a curtain of cloud to be drawn across the face of outer space whence this cold came. On the other hand, there was no keen intimacy between the dog and the man. The one was the toil-slave of the other, and the only caresses it had ever received were the caresses of the whiplash and of harsh and menacing throat sounds that threatened the whiplash. So the dog made no effort to communicate its apprehension to the man. It was not concerned in the welfare of the man; it was for its own sake that it yearned back toward the fire. But the man whistled, and spoke to it with the sound of whiplashes, and the dog swung in at the man's heels and followed after.

The man took a chew of tobacco and proceeded to start a new amber beard. Also, his moist breath quickly powdered with white his mustache, eyebrows, and lashes. There did not seem to be so many springs on the left fork of the Henderson, and for half an hour the man saw no signs of any. And then it happened. At a place where there were no signs, where the soft, unbroken snow seemed to advertise solidity beneath, the man broke through. It was not deep. He wet himself halfway to the knees before he floundered out to the firm crust.

He was angry, and cursed his luck aloud. He had hoped to get into camp with the boys at six o'clock, and this would delay him an hour, for he would have to build a fire and dry out his footgear. This was imperative at that low temperature—he knew that much; and he turned aside to the bank, which he climbed. On top, tangled in the underbrush about the trunks of several small spruce trees, was a highwater deposit of dry firewood—sticks and twigs, principally, but also larger portions of seasoned branches and fine, dry, last year's grasses. He threw down several large pieces on top of the snow. This served for a foundation and prevented the young flame from drowning itself in the snow it otherwise would melt. The flame he got by touching a match to a small shred of birch bark that he took from his pocket. This burned even more readily than paper. Placing it on the foundation, he fed the young flame with wisps of dry grass and with the tiniest dry twigs.

He worked slowly and carefully, keenly aware of his danger. Gradually, as the flame grew stronger, he increased the size of the twigs with which he fed it. He squatted in the snow, pulling the twigs out from their entanglement in the brush and feeding directly to the flame. He knew there must be no failure. When it is seventy-five below zero, a man must not fail in his first attempt to build a fire—that is, if his feet are wet. If his feet are dry, and he fails, he can run along the trail for a half a mile and restore his circulation. But the circulation of wet and freezing feet cannot be restored by running when it is seventy-five below. No matter how fast he runs, the wet feet will freeze the harder.

All this the man knew. The old-timer on Sulfur Creek had told him about it the previous fall, and now he was appreciating the advice. Already all sensation had gone out of his feet. To build the fire, he had been forced to remove his mittens, and the fingers had quickly gone numb. His pace of four miles an hour had kept his heart pumping blood to the surface of his body and to all the extremities. But the instant he stopped, the action of the pump eased down. The cold of space smote the unprotected tip of the planet, and he, being on that unprotected tip, received the full force of the blow. The blood of his body recoiled before it. The blood was alive, like the dog, and like the dog it wanted to hide away and cover itself up from the fearful cold. So long as he walked four miles an hour, he pumped that blood, willy-nilly, to the surface; but now it ebbed away and sank down into the recesses of his body. The extremities were the first to feel its absence. His wet feet froze the faster, and his exposed fingers numbed the faster, though they had not yet begun to freeze. Nose and cheeks were already freezing, while the skin of all his body chilled as it lost its blood.

But he was safe. Toes and nose and cheeks would be only touched by the frost, for the fire was beginning to burn with strength. He was feeding it with twigs the size of his finger. In another minute he would be able to feed it with branches the size of his wrist, and then he could remove his wet footgear, and, while it dried, he could keep his naked feet warm by the fire, rubbing them at first, of course, with snow. The fire was a success. He was safe. He remembered the advice of the old-timer on Sulfur Creek, and smiled. The old-timer had been very serious in laying down the law that no man must travel alone in the Klondike after fifty below. Well, here he was; he had had the accident; he was alone; and he had saved himself. Those old-timers were rather womanish, some of them, he thought. All a man had to do was to keep his head and he was all right. Any man who was a man could travel alone. But it was surprising, the rapidity with which his cheeks and nose were freezing. And he had not thought his fingers could go lifeless in so short a time. Lifeless they were, for he could scarcely make them move together to grip a twig, and they seemed remote from his body and from him. When he touched a twig he had to look and see whether or not he had hold of it. The wires were pretty well down between him and his finger ends.

All of which counted for little. There was the fire, snapping and crackling and promising life with every dancing flame. He started to untie his moccasins. They were coated with ice; the thick German socks were like sheaths of iron halfway to the knees; and the moccasin strings were like rods of steel all twisted and knotted as by some conflagration.[11] For a moment he tugged with his numb fingers, then, realizing the folly of it, he drew his sheath knife.

But before he could cut the strings it happened. It was his own fault, or, rather, his mistake. He should not have built the fire under the spruce tree. He should have built it in the open. But it had been easier to pull the twigs from the bush and drop them directly on the fire. Now the tree under which he had done this carried a weight of snow on its boughs. No wind had blown for weeks, and each bough

11. conflagration (kon'fla·grā'shən): a large, disastrous fire.

was fully freighted. Each time he had pulled a twig he had communicated a slight agitation to the tree—an imperceptible agitation, so far as he was concerned, but an agitation sufficient to bring about the disaster. High up in the tree one bough capsized its load of snow. This fell on the boughs beneath, capsizing them. This process continued, spreading out and involving the whole tree. It grew like an avalanche, and it descended without warning upon the man and the fire, and the fire was blotted out! Where it had burned was a mantle of fresh and disordered snow.

The man was shocked. It was as though he had just heard his own sentence of death. For a moment he sat and stared at the spot where the fire had been. Then he grew very calm. Perhaps the old-timer on Sulfur Creek was right. If he had only had a trailmate, he would have been in no danger now. The trailmate could have built the fire. Well, it was up to him to build the fire over again, and this second time there must be no failure. Even if he succeeded, he would most likely lose some toes. His feet must be badly frozen by now, and there would be some time before the second fire was ready.

Such were his thoughts, but he did not sit and think them. He was busy all the time they were passing through his mind. He made a new foundation for a fire, this time in the open, where no treacherous tree could blot it out. Next he gathered dry grasses and tiny twigs from the high-water flotsam.[12] He could not bring his fingers together to pull them out, but he was able to gather them by the handful. In this way he got many rotten twigs and bits of green moss that were undesirable, but it was the best he could do. He worked methodically, even collecting an armful of the larger branches to be used later when the fire gathered strength. And all the while the dog sat and watched him, a certain yearning wistfulness in its eyes, for it looked upon him as the fire provider, and the fire was slow in coming.

When all was ready, the man reached in his pocket for a second piece of birch bark. He knew the bark was there, and, though he could not feel it with his fingers, he could hear its crisp rustling as he fumbled for it. Try as he would, he could not clutch hold of it. And all the time, in his consciousness, was the knowledge that each instant his feet were freezing. This thought tended to put him in a panic, but he fought against it and kept calm. He pulled on his mittens with his teeth, and threshed his arms back and forth, beating his hands with all his might against his sides. He did this sitting down,

12. flotsam (flot′səm): the floating wreckage of a ship or its cargo; hence, anything drifting about on a body of water. The word is derived from the Old English verb *flotian*, to float.

and he stood up to do it; and all the while the dog sat in the snow, its wolf brush of a tail curled around warmly over its forefeet, its sharp wolf ears pricked forward intently as it watched the man. And the man, as he beat and threshed with his arms and hands, felt a great surge of envy as he regarded the creature that was warm and secure in its natural covering.

After a time he was aware of the first faraway signals of sensation in his beaten fingers. The faint tingling grew stronger till it evolved into a stinging ache that was excruciating,[13] but which the man hailed with satisfaction. He stripped the mitten from his right hand and fetched forth the birch bark. The exposed fingers were quickly going numb again. Next he brought out his bunch of sulfur matches. But the tremendous cold had already driven the life out of his fingers. In his effort to separate one match from the others, the whole bunch fell in the snow. He tried to pick it out of the snow, but failed. The dead fingers could neither touch nor clutch. He was very careful. He drove the thought of his freezing feet, and nose, and cheeks, out of his mind, devoting his whole soul to the matches. He watched, using the sense of vision in place of that of touch, and when he saw his fingers on each side of the bunch, he closed them—that is, he willed to close them, for the wires were down, and the fingers did not obey. He pulled the mitten on the right hand, and beat it fiercely against his knee. Then, with both mittened hands, he scooped the bunch of matches, along with much snow, into his lap. Yet he was no better off.

After some manipulation he managed to get the bunch between the heels of his mittened hands. In this fashion he carried it to his mouth. The ice crackled and snapped when by a violent effort he opened his mouth. He drew the lower jaw in, curled the upper lip out of the way, and scraped the bunch with his upper teeth in order to separate a match. He succeeded in getting one, which he dropped on his lap. He was no better off. He could not pick it up. Then he devised a way. He picked it up in his teeth and scratched it on his leg. Twenty times he scratched before he succeeded in lighting it. As it flamed he held it with his teeth to the birch bark. But the burning brimstone[14] went up his nostrils and into his lungs, causing him to cough spasmodically.[15] The match fell into the snow and went out.

The old-timer on Sulfur Creek was right, he thought in the moment of controlled despair that ensued: after fifty below, a man should

13. **excruciating** (ĭks·krōō′shē·ā′tĭng) : causing great pain.
14. **brimstone**: sulfur.
15. **spasmodically** (spăz·mŏd′ĭ·kə·lē) : suddenly and violently.

travel with a partner. He beat his hands, but failed in exciting any sensation. Suddenly he bared both hands, removing the mittens with his teeth. He caught the whole bunch between the heels of his hands. His arm muscles, not being frozen, enabled him to press the hand heels tightly against the matches. Then he scratched the bunch along his leg. It flared into flame, seventy sulfur matches at once! There was no wind to blow them out. He kept his head to one side to escape the strangling fumes, and held the blazing bunch to the birch bark. As he so held it, he became aware of sensation in his hand. His flesh was burning. He could smell it. Deep down below the surface he could feel it. The sensation developed into pain that grew acute. And still he endured it, holding the flame of the matches clumsily to the bark that would not light readily because his own burning hands were in the way, absorbing most of the flame.

At last, when he could endure no more, he jerked his hands apart. The blazing matches fell sizzling into the snow, but the birch bark was alight. He began laying dry grass and the tiniest twigs on the flame. He could not pick and choose, for he had to lift the fuel between the heels of his hands. Small pieces of rotten wood and green moss clung to the twigs, and he bit them off as well as he could with his teeth. He cherished the flame carefully and awkwardly. It meant life, and it must not perish. The withdrawal of blood from the surface of his body now made him begin to shiver, and he grew more awkward. A large piece of green moss fell squarely on the little fire. He tried to poke it out with his fingers, but his shivering frame made him poke too far, and he disrupted the nucleus of the little fire, the burning grasses and tiny twigs separating and scattering. He tried to poke them together again, but in spite of the tenseness of the effort, his shivering got away with him, and the twigs were hopelessly scattered. Each twig gushed a puff of smoke and went out. The fire provider had failed. As he looked apathetically [16] about him, his eyes chanced on the dog, sitting across the ruins of the fire from him, in the snow, making restless, hunching movements, slightly lifting one forefoot and then the other, shifting its weight back and forth on them with wistful eagerness.

The sight of the dog put a wild idea into his head. He remembered the tale of the man, caught in a blizzard, who killed a steer and crawled inside the carcass, and so was saved. He would kill the dog and bury his hands in the warm body until the numbness went out of them. Then he could build another fire. He spoke to the dog,

16. **apathetically** (ap'ə·thet'i·kə·lē): without interest or emotion.

calling it to him; but in his voice was a strange note of fear that frightened the animal, who had never known the man to speak in such a way before. Something was the matter, and its suspicious nature sensed danger—it knew not what danger, but somewhere, somehow, in its brain arose an apprehension of the man. It flattened its ears down at the sound of the man's voice, and its restless, hunching movements and the liftings and shiftings of its forefeet became more pronounced; but it would not come to the man. He got on his hands and knees and crawled toward the dog. This unusual posture again excited suspicion, and the animal sidled [17] mincingly [18] away.

The man sat up in the snow for a moment and struggled for calmness. Then he pulled on his mittens, by means of his teeth, and got up on his feet. He glanced down at first in order to assure himself that he was really standing up, for the absence of sensation in his feet left him unrelated to the earth. His erect position in itself started to drive the webs of suspicion from the dog's mind; and when he spoke peremptorily [19] with the sound of whiplashes in his voice, the dog rendered its customary allegiance and came to him. As it came within reaching distance, the man lost his control. His arms flashed out to the dog, and he experienced genuine surprise when he discovered that his hands could not clutch, that there was neither bend nor feeling in the fingers. He had forgotten for the moment that they were frozen and that they were freezing more and more. All this happened quickly, and before the animal could get away, he encircled its body with his arms. He sat down in the snow, and in this fashion held the dog, while it snarled and whined and struggled.

But it was all he could do, hold its body encircled in his arms and sit there. He realized that he could not kill the dog. There was no way to do it. With his helpless hands he could neither draw nor hold his sheath knife nor throttle [20] the animal. He released it, and it plunged wildly away, its tail between its legs and still snarling. It halted forty feet away and surveyed him curiously, with ears sharply pricked forward. The man looked down at his hands in order to locate them, and found them hanging on the ends of his arms. It struck him as curious that one should have to use his eyes in order to find out where his hands were. He began threshing his arms back and forth, beating the mittened hands against his sides. He did this

17. **sidled** (sīd′əld): moved sideways in a cautious manner.
18. **mincingly** (min′sing·lē): with short steps in a dainty, affected manner.
19. **peremptorily** (pə·remp′tə·rə·lē): in a commanding manner.
20. **throttle** (throt′l): choke or strangle. What is the mechanical meaning of this word?

for five minutes, violently, and his heart pumped enough blood up to the surface to put a stop to his shivering. But no sensation was aroused in his hands. He had an impression that they hung like weights on the ends of his arms, but when he tried to run the impression down, he could not find it.

A certain fear of death, dull and oppressive, came to him. This fear quickly became poignant [21] as he realized that it was no longer a mere matter of freezing his fingers and toes, or of losing his hands and feet, but that it was a matter of life and death, with the chances against him. This threw him into a panic, and he turned and ran up the creek bed along the old, dim trail. The dog joined in behind and kept up with him. He ran blindly, without intention, in fear such as he had never known in his life. Slowly, as he plowed and floundered through the snow, he began to see things again—the banks of the creek, the old timber jams, the leafless aspens, and the sky. The running made him feel better. He did not shiver. Maybe, if he ran on, his feet would thaw out; and, anyway, if he ran far enough, he would reach the camp and the boys. Without doubt he would lose some fingers and toes and some of his face; but the boys would take care of him, and save the rest of him when he got there. And at the same time there was another thought in his mind that said he would never get to the camp and the boys; that it was too many miles away, that the freezing had too great a start on him, and that he would soon be stiff and dead. This thought he kept in the background and refused to consider. Sometimes it pushed itself forward and demanded to be heard, but he thrust it back and strove to think of other things.

It struck him as curious that he could run at all on feet so frozen that he could not feel them when they struck the earth and took the weight of his body. He seemed to himself to skim along above the surface, and to have no connection with the earth. Somewhere he had once seen a winged Mercury,[22] and he wondered if Mercury felt as he felt when skimming over the earth.

His theory of running until he reached camp and the boys had one flaw in it: he lacked the endurance. Several times he stumbled, and finally he tottered, crumpled up, and fell. When he tried to rise, he failed. He must sit and rest, he decided, and next time he would merely walk and keep on going. As he sat and regained his breath, he noted that he was feeling quite warm and comfortable. He was not shivering, and it even seemed that a warm glow had come to his chest

21. **poignant** (poin'yənt): painfully affecting the feelings; piercing.
22. **Mercury**: in Roman mythology, the herald and messenger of the gods. He is depicted as having winged feet.

and trunk. And yet, when he touched his nose or cheeks, there was no sensation. Running would not thaw them out. Nor would it thaw out his hands and feet. Then the thought came to him that the frozen portions of his body must be extending. He tried to keep this thought down, to forget it, to think of something else; he was aware of the panicky feeling that he caused, and he was afraid of the panic. But the thought asserted itself, and persisted, until it produced a vision of his body totally frozen. This was too much, and he made another wild run along the trail. Once he slowed down to a walk, but the thought of the freezing extending itself made him run again.

And all the time the dog ran with him, at his heels. When he fell down a second time, it curled its tail over its forefeet and sat in front of him, facing him, curiously eager and intent. The warmth and security of the animal angered him, and he cursed it till it flattened down its ears appeasingly.[23] This time the shivering came more quickly upon the man. He was losing in his battle with the frost. It was creeping into his body from all sides. The thought of it drove him on, but he ran no more than a hundred feet when he staggered and pitched headlong. It was his last panic. When he had recovered his breath and control, he sat up and entertained in his mind the conception of meeting death with dignity. However, the conception did not come to him in such terms. His idea of it was that he had been making a fool of himself, running around like a chicken with its head cut off—such was the simile that occurred to him. Well, he was bound to freeze anyway, and he might as well take it decently. With this new-found peace of mind came the first glimmerings of drowsiness. A good idea, he thought, to sleep off to death. It was like taking an anesthetic.[24] Freezing was not so bad as people thought. There were lots worse ways to die.

He pictured the boys finding his body next day. Suddenly he found himself with them, coming along the trail and looking for himself. And, still with them, he came around a turn in the trail and found himself lying in the snow. He did not belong with himself any more, for even then he was out of himself, standing with the boys and looking at himself in the snow. It certainly was cold, was his thought. When he got back to the States, he could tell the folks what real cold was. He drifted on from this to a vision of the old-timer on Sulfur Creek. He could see him quite clearly, warm and comfortable, and smoking a pipe.

23. **appeasingly:** trying to make peace.
24. **anesthetic** (an'is·thet'ik): a drug or gas that causes loss of physical sensation or pain.

"You were right, old hoss; you were right," the man mumbled to the old-timer of Sulfur Creek.

Then the man drowsed off into what seemed to him the most comfortable and satisfying sleep he had ever known. The dog sat facing him and waiting. The brief day drew to a close in a long, slow twilight. There were no signs of a fire to be made, and, besides, never in the dog's experience had it known a man to sit like that in the snow and make no fire. As the twilight drew on, its eager yearning for the fire mastered it, and with a great lifting and shifting of fore-feet, it whined softly, then flattened its ears down in anticipation of being chidden [25] by the man. But the man remained silent. Later, the dog whined loudly. And still later it crept close to the man and caught the scent of death. This made the animal bristle [26] and back away. A little longer it delayed, howling under the stars that leaped and danced and shone brightly in the cold sky. Then it turned and trotted up the trail in the direction of the camp it knew, where were the other food providers and fire providers.

25. **chidden** (chid'n) : scolded.
26. **bristle**: become agitated; take on an aggressive appearance.

Meaning

1. Before setting out alone on a long journey in the frozen Yukon, what specific details should the man have noted about the day and the trail? Why does his first survey make no impression on him? What element is the dog acutely aware of?

2. "Its [the dog's] instinct told it a truer tale than was told to the man by the man's judgment." Cite incidents in the story that indicate the dog's instinct to be more effective for survival than the man's judgment. How does this view of the superiority of the animal's instinct conflict with the view of instinct presented in "The Most Dangerous Game?"

3. Describe the man's last two efforts to build a fire. What force defeats these attempts? To what extent did the man defeat himself?

4. What advice did the old-timer of Sulfur Creek give the man? When did the man finally realize that the old-timer was right? Using the entire story as a guide, summarize those things that would have made the man victorious in his struggle with the elements.

Method

1. Identify the protagonist and the antagonist in this story. List some incidents that will support your answer.

2. What point in the story do you consider the *climax?* What descriptive details help to heighten the climax?

3. Why do you think the author left his character unnamed?

4. Look back at the first paragraph and see if you can find any foreshadowing of the final outcome of the story. How does this paragraph also create suspense?

5. *Comparing* means discussing things that are alike; *contrasting* means discussing things that are different. Compare and contrast the use of setting in "To Build a Fire" with the use of setting in "The Most Dangerous Game." What part does setting play in each story? Could the setting of either story be changed without affecting the story? If so, what other setting would you suggest?

6. What feeling or mood does London arouse by his repetition of the words "cold and gray" in his opening sentence? How is a strong mood of hopelessness built up in the story? Give specific examples.

7. Would the story have been less realistic and less interesting if London had chosen to have the man survive his ordeal in the Yukon? Why or why not?

Composition

1. In this adventure story, the main character, unlike Rainsford in "The Most Dangerous Game," is defeated by his opposing force. Write a composition in which you compare and contrast Rainsford and the man in "To Build a Fire." Discuss the problems they face and how they go about solving them. Compare the last thoughts of each character and explain the irony in the thoughts of each. (When the implied meaning is quite different from the surface meaning, a statement is said to be ironic.)

2. In an essay, describe the conflict in "To Build a Fire" and, considering the nature of the two opposing forces, show how the man's defeat and death is the most satisfactory ending to this story.

James Thurber

[1894—1961]

This was the man who left the world "a magnificent legacy of laughter" in his writing and cartoons. His drawings of flop-eared dogs, dominant-looking females, and discontented males he did rapidly and with much personal enjoyment. However, in composing his short stories and essays, for which he is primarily known, he worked slowly and carefully, doing much revising and rewriting. Thurber was happiest when working, and despite almost complete blindness by the time he was fifty, he continued to write. He sometimes wrote with heavy black pencil on large yellow sheets; more often he dictated his stories to a secretary.

In 1926 Thurber joined the staff of *The New Yorker*, for which he wrote throughout the rest of his life, providing it with stories, essays, and cartoons, and helping to set its tone. His experiences on the magazine and with its editor and founder, Harold Ross, are recounted in *The Years with Ross* (1959).

Thurber's writings appeal to people of many ages and tastes. He wrote children's books such as *The Thirteen Clocks* and *The White Deer*, and for grownups fairy tales such as *Fables for Our Times*. *My Life and Hard Times* (1933) contains amusing sketches about his early boyhood and his difficulties as a student at Ohio State University. He collaborated with the actor Elliott Nugent in writing a Broadway comedy, *The Male Animal*. Selections from his writings and cartoons were dramatized in A *Thurber Carnival*, a successful musical revue which appeared in 1960.

"The Secret Life of Walter Mitty" illustrates Thurber's method of using a surface humor to satirize, or make fun of, something else. Here the world of daydreams is dramatized in a unique and inimitable manner.

The Secret Life of Walter Mitty

"We're going through!" The Commander's voice was like thin ice breaking. He wore his full-dress uniform, with the heavily braided white cap pulled down rakishly over one cold gray eye. "We can't make it, sir. It's spoiling for a hurricane, if you ask me." "I'm not asking you, Lieutenant Berg," said the Commander. "Throw on the power light! Rev her up to 8,500! We're going through!" The pounding of the cylinders increased: ta-pocketa-pocketa-pocketa-*pocketa-pocketa.* The Commander stared at the ice forming on the pilot window. He walked over and twisted a row of complicated dials. "Switch on No. 8 auxiliary!" he shouted. "Switch on No. 8 auxiliary!" repeated Lieutenant Berg. "Full strength in No. 3 turret!" [1] shouted the Commander. "Full strength in No. 3 turret!" The crew, bending to their various tasks in the huge, hurtling [2] eight-engined navy hydroplane,[3] looked at each other and grinned. "The Old Man'll get us through," they said to one another. "The Old Man ain't afraid of Hell! . . ."

"Not so fast! You're driving too fast!" said Mrs. Mitty. "What are you driving so fast for?"

"Hmm?" said Walter Mitty. He looked at his wife, in the seat beside him, with shocked astonishment. She seemed grossly unfamiliar, like a strange woman who had yelled at him in a crowd. "You were up to fifty-five," she said. "You know I don't like to go more than forty. You were up to fifty-five." Walter Mitty drove on toward Waterbury in silence, the roaring of the SN202 through the worst storm in twenty years of Navy flying fading in the remote, intimate airways of his mind. "You're tensed up again," said Mrs. Mitty. "It's one of your days. I wish you'd let Dr. Renshaw look you over."

Walter Mitty stopped the car in front of the building where his wife went to have her hair done. "Remember to get those overshoes while I'm having my hair done," she said. "I don't need overshoes," said Mitty. She put her mirror back into her bag. "We've been all through that," she said, getting out of the car. "You're not a young man any longer." He raced the engine a little. "Why don't you wear your gloves? Have you lost your gloves?" Walter Mitty reached into a pocket and brought out the gloves. He put them on, but after she had turned and gone into the building and he had driven on to a red light, he took them off again. "Pick it up, brother!" snapped a cop as the light changed, and Mitty hastily pulled on his gloves and lurched ahead. He drove around the streets aimlessly for a time, and then he drove past the hospital on his way to the parking lot.

. . . "It's the millionaire banker, Wellington McMillan," said the

---

1. **turret:** the enclosure in an airplane for the gun and/or gunners.
2. **hurtling** (hûrt′ling): moving with a rushing or crashing sound.
3. **hydroplane** (hī′drə·plān′): an airplane that can land or take off from the water; it moves at great speed on the water.

pretty nurse. "Yes?" said Walter Mitty, removing his gloves slowly. "Who has the case?" "Dr. Renshaw and Dr. Benbow, but there are two specialists here, Dr. Remington from New York and Dr. Pritchard-Mitford from London. He flew over." A door opened down a long, cool corridor and Dr. Renshaw came out. He looked distraught [4] and haggard. "Hello, Mitty," he said. "We're having the devil's own time with McMillan, the millionaire banker and close personal friend of Roosevelt. Obstreosis [5] of the ductal tract. Tertiary. Wish you'd take a look at him." "Glad to," said Mitty.

In the operating room there were whispered introductions: "Dr. Remington, Dr. Mitty. Dr. Pritchard-Mitford, Dr. Mitty." "I've read your book on streptothricosis," said Pritchard-Mitford, shaking hands. "A brilliant performance, sir." "Thank you," said Walter Mitty. "Didn't know you were in the States, Mitty," grumbled Remington. "Coals to Newcastle, [6] bringing Mitford and me up here for a tertiary." "You are very kind," said Mitty. A huge, complicated machine, connected to the operating table, with many tubes and wires, began at this moment to go pocketa-pocketa-pocketa. "The new anesthetizer [7] is giving away!" shouted an intern. "There is no one in the East who knows how to fix it!" "Quiet, man!" said Mitty, in a low, cool voice. He sprang to the machine, which was now going pocketa-pocketa-queep-pocketa-queep. He began fingering delicately a row of glistening dials. "Give me a fountain pen!" he snapped. Someone handed him a fountain pen. He pulled a faulty piston out of the machine and inserted the pen in its place. "That will hold for ten minutes," he said. "Get on with the operation." A nurse hurried over and whispered to Renshaw, and Mitty saw the man turn pale. "Coreopsis has set in," said Renshaw nervously. "If you would take over, Mitty?" Mitty looked at him and at the craven [8] figure of Benbow, who drank, and at the grave, uncertain faces of the two great specialists. "If you wish," he said. They slipped a white gown on him; he adjusted a mask and drew on thin gloves; nurses handed him shining . . . .

"Back it up, Mac! Look out for that Buick!" Walter Mitty jammed

---

4. distraught (dis·trôt′): worried and tense.

5. obstreosis (əb·strē·ō′sis): Some of these medical terms are legitimate; others are not.

6. Coals to Newcastle: Newcastle is a city in England noted for its production of coal. "To carry coals to Newcastle" means to take things to a place where they are already in abundant supply; to waste labor.

7. anesthetizer (a·nes′thə·tīz′ər): from the verb *anesthetize*, to make insensitive to pain, especially by the use of an **anesthetic** (an′is·thet′ik), a drug or gas that deadens sensation.

8. craven (krā′vən): noticeably lacking in courage; afraid.

on the brakes. "Wrong lane, Mac," said the parking-lot attendant, looking at Mitty closely. "Gee. Yeh," muttered Mitty. He began cautiously to back out of the lane marked "Exit Only." "Leave her sit there," said the attendant. "I'll put her away." Mitty got out of the car. "Hey, better leave the key." "Oh," said Mitty, handing the man the ignition key. The attendant vaulted into the car, backed it up with insolent skill, and put it where it belonged.

They're so darn cocky, thought Walter Mitty, walking along Main Street; they think they know everything. Once he had tried to take his chains off, outside New Milford, and he had got them wound around the axles. A man had had to come out in a wrecking car and unwind them, a young, grinning garageman. Since then Mrs. Mitty always made him drive to a garage to have the chains taken off. The next time, he thought, I'll wear my right arm in a sling; they won't grin at me then. I'll have my right arm in a sling and they'll see I couldn't possibly take the chains off myself. He kicked at the slush on the sidewalk. "Overshoes," he said to himself, and he began looking for a shoe store.

When he came out into the street again, with the overshoes in a box under his arm, Walter Mitty began to wonder what the other thing was his wife had told him to get. She had told him twice before they set out from their house for Waterbury. In a way he hated these weekly trips to town—he was always getting something wrong. Kleenex, he thought, Squibb's, razor blades? No. Toothpaste, toothbrush, bicarbonate, carborundum,[9] initiative,[10] and referendum?[11] He gave it up. But she would remember it. "Where's the what's-its-name?" she would ask. "Don't tell me you forgot the what's-its-name." A newsboy went by shouting something about the Waterbury trial.

. . . "Perhaps this will refresh your memory." The District Attorney suddenly thrust a heavy automatic at the quiet figure on the witness stand. "Have you ever seen this before?" Walter Mitty took the gun and examined it expertly. "This is my Webley-Vickers 50.80,"[12] he said calmly. An excited buzz ran around the courtroom. The Judge rapped for order. "You are a crack shot with any sort of

---

9. **carborundum** (kär′bə·run′dəm): a technical trade name for an abrasive used to wear or grind down something.
10. **initiative** (in·ish′ē·ə·tiv): in government, the right of the voters to propose legislative matters by getting together a petition and submitting it to popular vote or to the legislature for approval.
11. **referendum** (ref′ə·ren′dəm): in government, the practice of submitting a measure passed upon by a legislative body or by popular initiative to a vote of the people for ratification or rejection.
12. **Webley-Vickers 50.80**: Mitty invents an impressive name and unlikely caliber for his obviously exceptional weapon.

firearms, I believe?" said the District Attorney, insinuatingly.[13] "Objection!" shouted Mitty's attorney. "We have shown that the defendant could not have fired the shot. We have shown that he wore his right arm in a sling on the night of the fourteenth of July." Walter Mitty raised his hand briefly, and the bickering attorneys were stilled. "With any known make of gun," he said evenly, "I could have killed Gregory Fitzhurst at three hundred feet *with my left hand*." Pandemonium broke loose in the courtroom. A woman's scream rose above the bedlam, and suddenly a lovely, dark-haired girl was in Walter Mitty's arms. The District Attorney struck at her savagely. Without rising from his chair, Mitty let the man have it on the point of the chin. "You miserable cur!" [14] . . .

"Puppy biscuit," said Walter Mitty. He stopped walking, and the buildings of Waterbury rose up out of the misty courtroom and surrounded him again. A woman who was passing laughed. "He said 'Puppy biscuit,' " she said to her companion. "That man said 'Puppy biscuit' to himself." Walter Mitty hurried on. He went into an A & P, not the first one he came to but a smaller one farther up the street. "I want some biscuit for small, young dogs," he said to the clerk. "Any special brand, sir?" The greatest pistol shot in the world thought a moment. "It says 'Puppies Bark for It' on the box," said Walter Mitty.

His wife would be through at the hairdresser's in fifteen minutes, Mitty saw in looking at his watch, unless they had trouble drying it; sometimes they had trouble drying it. She didn't like to get to the hotel first; she would want him to be there waiting for her as usual. He found a big leather chair in the lobby, facing the window, and he put the overshoes and the puppy biscuit on the floor beside it. He picked up an old copy of *Liberty* and sank down into the chair. "Can Germany Conquer the World Through the Air?" Walter Mitty looked at the pictures of bombing planes and of ruined streets.

. . . "The cannonading has got the wind up in young Raleigh, sir," said the sergeant. Captain Mitty looked at him through tousled hair. "Get him to bed," he said wearily, "with the others. I'll fly alone." "But you can't, sir," said the sergeant anxiously. "It takes two men to handle that bomber, and the Archies [15] are pounding hell out of the air. Von Richtman's circus is between here and Saulier." "Somebody's got to get that ammunition dump," said Mitty. "I'm

---

13. **insinuatingly** (in·sin'yŏŏ·āt'ing·lē) : in a sly or indirect manner.
14. **cur**: a mongrel dog; a contemptible person.
15. **Archies**: a term used by the Allied troops in World War I for antiaircraft guns.

going over. Spot of brandy?" He poured a drink for the sergeant and one for himself. War thundered and whined around the dugout and battered at the door. There was a rending of wood, and splinters flew through the room. "A bit of a near thing," said Captain Mitty carelessly. "The box barrage is closing in," said the sergeant. "We only live once, Sergeant," said Mitty, with his faint, fleeting smile. "Or do we?" He poured another brandy and tossed it off. "I never see a man could hold his brandy like you, sir," said the sergeant. "Begging your pardon, sir." Captain Mitty stood up and strapped on his huge Webley-Vickers automatic. "It's forty kilometers through hell, sir," said the sergeant. Mitty finished one last brandy. "After all," he said softly, "what isn't?" The pounding of the cannon increased; there was the rat-tat-tatting of machine guns, and from somewhere came the menacing pocketa-pocketa-pocketa of the new flame throwers. Walter Mitty walked to the door of the dugout humming "Auprès de ma Blonde." [16] He turned and waved to the sergeant. "Cheerio!" he said. . . .

Something struck his shoulder. "I've been looking all over this hotel for you," said Mrs. Mitty. "Why do you have to hide in this old chair? How did you expect me to find you?" "Things close in," said Walter Mitty vaguely. "What?" Mrs. Mitty said. "Did you get the what's-its-name? The puppy biscuit? What's in that box?" "Overshoes," said Mitty. "Couldn't you have put them on in the store?" "I was thinking," said Walter Mitty. "Does it ever occur to you that I am sometimes thinking?" She looked at him. "I'm going to take your temperature when I get you home," she said.

They went out through the revolving doors that made a faintly derisive [17] whistling sound when you pushed them. It was two blocks to the parking lot. At the drugstore on the corner she said, "Wait here for me. I forgot something. I won't be a minute." She was more than a minute. Walter Mitty lighted a cigarette. It began to rain, rain with sleet in it. He stood up against the wall of the drugstore, smoking. . . . He put his shoulders back and his heels together. "To hell with the handkerchief," said Walter Mitty scornfully. He took one last drag on his cigarette and snapped it away. Then, with that faint, fleeting smile playing about his lips, he faced the firing squad; erect and motionless, proud and disdainful, Walter Mitty the Undefeated, inscrutable [18] to the last.

16. **"Auprès de ma Blonde"** (o·prē·də·mə·blonde′): a French World War I song, "Close to My Blonde."
17. **derisive** (di·rī′siv): expressing ridicule or scorn.
18. **inscrutable** (in·skrōo′tə·bəl): mysterious; not easily understood.

Meaning

1. Make a list of the settings Mitty sees himself in and the characters he becomes. In what general type of role does he see himself in his dreams?
2. What impression do you have of the parking-lot attendant? Mention details to show that your knowledge of him is limited to what Mitty tells you.
3. Remember that a writer can make a serious comment about life while entertaining his readers with his humor. What serious comment might Thurber be making in this story?
4. Mitty's last daydream concerns a firing squad, which he faces "erect and motionless, proud and disdainful, Walter Mitty the Undefeated, inscrutable to the last."

   Are the words *undefeated* and *inscrutable* ironic, or could they really be applicable to Mitty?

Method

1. Mitty's daydreams are the result of a process of association; they are related to the everyday world. For example, as he passes the hospital he imagines himself a surgeon. List some of the things and places in Mitty's life that start him daydreaming. How, in each dream, is he led back to reality? How does this process aid in the development of the plot?
2. What is the author's purpose in beginning the story with a daydream rather than an actual event? Why is so large a proportion of the story devoted to the daydreams?
3. Why is there no description of Mitty except as he seems himself in his secret life?
4. Mitty is characterized mainly through his actions. How would you describe him? Is he tall, short, strong, weak, assertive, mild? How would you describe Mrs. Mitty? Is she dominant, assured, indifferent to her husband's welfare? Give specific references in the text to substantiate your statements.
5. Second-rate movie and television stories often have stock characters who always have the same traits and whose actions are quite predictable: at a crucial moment the beautiful young girl will be rescued by the dashing hero. By presenting Mitty's daydreams as stereotyped adventure situations, with clichés, hackneyed dialogue, and stock characters, Thurber makes fun of such stories. What effect does this have on the reader's reaction to the "virtue" being illustrated by each daydream? How does this add to your characterization or description of Mitty?
6. There are various ways in which a writer can create humor. One is to present something that is *incongruous*, or not in keeping with what is

suitable, reasonable, or proper. Such an incongruity, or inconsistency occurs in *The Pickwick Papers* when Charles Dickens has Mrs. Leo Hunter read at her garden party a poem entitled "Ode to an Expiring Frog." An ode is meant to be a dignified, serious poem. And you know what an expiring frog is.

Another way to create humor is to use amusing sounding names and to exaggerate physical description, as Washington Irving, an early American writer, did when describing Wouter Van Twiller as ". . . exactly five feet, six inches in height, and six feet, five inches in circumference."

Dialogue can also be humorous. And so can visual-oral contrast, as in the life-insurance advertisement which showed a little girl patting a big collie and saying, "Hello, pussycat." Still another method is to create nonsense words or unexpected sounds, as did the child who described his reactions to a horror story as "the cold scringes."

How has Thurber used incongruity, nonsense words, exaggeration, dialogue, and names to create humor in this story?

Language: Onomatopoeia, A Word from a Sound

Several times in the story Thurber uses the word "pocketa." It is impossible to find this word in a dictionary, even a very large one, since it exists and has meaning only in the context of this story. Where did the author get the word? He made it up by writing an imitation of a sound. What sound? A pounding cylinder in a hydroplane, and later the failing equipment in a hospital operating room. When spoken very rapidly, "pocketa-pocketa" sounds like the sputtering of a motor. What other machines can it be used to describe?

Words which sound like the things they describe are called onomatopoetic (on'ə·mat'ə·pō·et'ik) words. *Pop, zip, buzz, bow-wow,* and *splash* are examples of well known onomatopoeias (on'ə·mat'ə·pē'əs). Name five other words that are onomatopoetic.

Composition

1. Using Thurber's "Walter Mitty" as a guide, write a short story about a daydream in which someone becomes a hero or heroine, only to be brought back to earth again. Don't forget the "person, place, or thing" association to get the hero or heroine from the daydream back to reality. Be specific about the setting of the dream, and be sure to describe the clothing, manners, and actions of the daydreamer. Use dialogue to bring your characters to life.

2. Write an account of a humorous incident you have seen or been a part of in which the presence of dissimilar persons or things led to the comic situation.

O. Henry

Could a prison term explain the name O. Henry? William Sydney Porter, convicted of embezzlement and working as a prison drug clerk, may have seen the name of Etienne-Ossian Henry, a French pharmacist, in the publication *U.S. Dispensary*, shortened it to O. Henry, and adopted it as his pen name. Another theory is that he took the name of a prison guard, Orrin Henry.

William Sydney Porter was born in Greensboro, North Carolina in 1862. Despite the fact that his father was a physician, Porter had little formal education, but he did read widely.

He worked for about five years in his uncle's drugstore, and then, at the age of twenty, left to work on a ranch in Texas. He subsequently held a number of jobs, including one in a bank, the manage-ment of which accused him of embezzlement. He was thirty-four and married at the time.

There is some doubt as to Porter's actual intent to steal, but instead of waiting for a trial, he fled to Honduras. He subsequently returned because he learned that his wife was dying of tuberculosis. He was arrested and tried on the charge of embezzlement, convicted, and sentenced to three years in prison.

He came to New York in 1902 and worked for *The New York World*, for which he wrote a number of stories. His stay there was brief, for he died of tuberculosis in 1910, at the age of forty-eight.

His writings may be divided into stories of the Southwest, of Latin America, and of New York, which he referred to as "Baghdad-on-the-Subway." *The Four Million*, his best-known New York collection, contains his observations on the lives of everyday New Yorkers, the "four million" of the title. Other collections are *The Trimmed Lamp*, *The Voice of the City*, *Roads of Destiny*, and *Rolling Stones*.

O. Henry was greatly influential in creating and setting a pattern for a type of short story today called the commercial or craft story, as opposed to the quality story. There is an excess of sentimentality or emotion in his stories, and the plots are contrived and filled with coincidences. At times the surprise or trick ending (at which he excelled) seems a bit forced. Nevertheless, his popularity is deserved, for he was essentially a storyteller—and a very good one.

The Gift of the Magi *

One dollar and eighty-seven cents. That was all. And sixty cents of it was in pennies. Pennies saved one and two at a time by bulldozing the grocer and the vegetable man and the butcher until one's cheeks burned with silent imputation of parsimony [1] that such close dealing implied. Three times Della counted it. One dollar and eighty-seven cents. And the next day would be Christmas.

There was clearly nothing to do but flop down on the shabby little couch and howl. So Della did it. Which instigates the moral reflection that life is made up of sobs, sniffles, and smiles, with sniffles predominating.

While the mistress of the home is gradually subsiding from the first stage to the second,[2] take a look at the home. A furnished flat at eight dollars per week. It did not exactly beggar description,[3] but it certainly had that word on the lookout for the mendicancy squad.[4]

In the vestibule [5] below was a letter box into which no letter would go, and an electric button from which no mortal finger could coax a ring. Also appertaining thereunto [6] was a card bearing the name "Mr. James Dillingham Young."

The "Dillingham" had been flung to the breeze during a former period of prosperity when its possessor was being paid thirty dollars per week. Now, when the income was shrunk to twenty dollars, the letters of "Dillingham" looked blurred, as though they were thinking seriously of contracting to a modest and unassuming D. But whenever Mr. James Dillingham Young came home and reached his flat above he was called "Jim" and greatly hugged by Mrs. James Dillingham Young, already introduced to you as Della. Which is all very good.

* Magi (mā′jī): the three wise men from the East who gave gifts of gold, frankincense, and myrrh to the infant Jesus as a sign of their love, respect, and honor.
1. imputation (im′pyŏŏ·tā′shən) of parsimony (pär′sə·mō′nē): accusation of stinginess.
2. first stage . . . second: that is, from sobs to sniffles.
3. beggar description: exceed the powers of. (The implication is that the apartment was almost beyond description.)
4. mendicancy (men′də·kən·sē) squad: a police squad that picked up beggars or mendicants.
5. vestibule (ves′tə·byōol): a hallway or small room between the outer door and the interior of a building.
6. appertaining thereunto: belonging to, or associated with.

"The Gift of the Magi" from *The Four Million* by O. Henry. Published by Doubleday & Company, Inc.

Della finished her cry and attended to her cheeks with the powder rag. She stood by the window and looked out dully at a gray cat walking a gray fence in a gray backyard. Tomorrow would be Christmas Day, and she had only one dollar and eighty-seven cents with which to buy Jim a present. She had been saving every penny she could for months, with this result. Twenty dollars a week doesn't go far. Expenses had been greater than she had calculated. They always are. Only one dollar and eighty-seven cents to buy a present for Jim. Her Jim. Many a happy hour she had spent planning for something nice for him. Something fine and rare and sterling—something just a little bit near to being worthy of the honor of being owned by Jim.

There was a pier glass [7] between the windows of the room. Perhaps you have seen a pier glass in an eight-dollar flat. A very thin and very agile person may, by observing his reflection in a rapid sequence of longitudinal [8] strips, obtain a fairly accurate conception of his looks. Della, being slender, had mastered the art.

Suddenly she whirled from the window and stood before the glass. Her eyes were shining brilliantly, but her face had lost its color within twenty seconds. Rapidly she pulled down her hair and let it fall to its full length.

Now there were two possessions of the James Dillingham Youngs in which they both took a mighty pride. One was Jim's gold watch that had been his father's and his grandfather's. The other was Della's hair. Had the Queen of Sheba [9] lived in the flat across the air shaft, Della would have let her hair hang out the window someday to dry, just to depreciate [10] Her Majesty's jewels and gifts. Had King Solomon been the janitor, with all his treasures piled up in the basement, Jim would have pulled out his watch every time he passed, just to see him pluck at his beard from envy.

So now Della's beautiful hair fell about her, rippling and shining like a cascade of brown waters. It reached below her knee and made itself almost a garment for her. And then she did it up again nervously and quickly. Once she faltered for a minute and stood still while a tear or two splashed on the worn red carpet.

7. **pier** (pir) **glass**: a tall mirror designed to occupy the space between two windows.
8. **longitudinal** (lon'jə·tōō'də·nəl): lengthwise.
9. **Queen of Sheba**: a biblical allusion (1 Kings 10:1–3), to the encounter between the Queen of Sheba (Sheba is generally considered to have been located in southwestern Arabia) and King Solomon of Israel. The queen, who had come to test Solomon's great wisdom, was so impressed with his knowledge that she bestowed rich gifts upon him.
10. **depreciate** (di·prē'shē·āt): lessen the value of.

On went her old brown jacket; on went her old brown hat. With a whirl of skirts and with the brilliant sparkle still in her eyes, she fluttered out the door and down the stairs to the street.

Where she stopped the sign read: "Mme Sofronie. Hair Goods of All Kinds." One flight up Della ran—and collected herself, panting. Madame, large, too white, chilly, hardly looked the "Sofronie."

"Will you buy my hair?" asked Della.

"I buy hair," said Madame. "Take yer hat off and let's have a sight at the looks of it."

Down rippled the brown cascade.

"Twenty dollars," said Madame, lifting the mass with a practiced hand.

"Give it to me quick," said Della.

Oh, and the next two hours tripped by on rosy wings. Forget the hashed metaphor. She was ransacking the stores for Jim's present.

She found it at last. It surely had been made for Jim and no one else. There was no other like it in any of the stores, and she had turned all of them inside out. It was a platinum fob chain [11] simple and chaste in design, properly proclaiming its value by substance alone and not by meretricious [12] ornamentation—as all good things should do. It was even worthy of The Watch. As soon as she saw it she knew that it must be Jim's. It was like him. Quietness and value —the description applied to both. Twenty-one dollars they took from her for it, and she hurried home with the eighty-seven cents. With that chain on his watch Jim might be properly anxious about the time in any company. Grand as the watch was, he sometimes looked at it on the sly on account of the old leather strap that he used in place of a chain.

When Della reached home her intoxication gave way a little to prudence and reason. She got out her curling irons and lighted the gas and went to work repairing the ravages made by generosity added to love. Which is always a tremendous task, dear friends—a mammoth task.

Within forty minutes her head was covered with tiny, close-lying curls that made her look wonderfully like a truant schoolboy. She looked at her reflection in the mirror long, carefully, and critically.

"If Jim doesn't kill me," she said to herself, "before he takes a second look at me, he'll say I look like a Coney Island chorus girl. But what could I do—oh! what could I do with a dollar and eighty-seven cents?"

11. **fob chain**: a short chain meant to be attached to a pocket watch.
12. **meretricious** (mer′ə·trish′əs): gaudy; deceitfully showy.

At seven o'clock the coffee was made and the frying pan was on the back of the stove hot and ready to cook the chops.

Jim was never late. Della doubled the fob chain in her hand and sat on the corner of the table near the door that he always entered. Then she heard his step on the stair away down on the first flight, and she turned white for just a moment. She had a habit of saying little silent prayers about the simplest everyday things, and now she whispered, "Please, God, make him think I am still pretty."

The door opened and Jim stepped in and closed it. He looked thin and very serious. Poor fellow, he was only twenty-two—and to be burdened with a family! He needed a new overcoat and he was without gloves.

Jim stopped inside the door, as immovable as a setter at the scent of quail. His eyes were fixed upon Della, and there was an expression in them that she could not read, and it terrified her. It was not anger, nor surprise, nor disapproval, nor horror, nor any of the sentiments that she had been prepared for. He simply stared at her fixedly with that peculiar expression on his face.

Della wriggled off the table and went to him.

"Jim, darling," she cried, "don't look at me that way. I had my hair cut off and sold it because I couldn't have lived through Christmas without giving you a present. It'll grow out again—you won't mind, will you? I just had to do it. My hair grows awfully fast. Say 'Merry Christmas!' Jim, and let's be happy. You don't know what a nice—what a beautiful, nice gift I've got for you."

"You've cut off your hair?" asked Jim, laboriously, as if he had not arrived at that patent fact yet even after the hardest mental labor.

"Cut it off and sold it," said Della. "Don't you like me just as well, anyhow? I'm me without my hair, ain't I?"

Jim looked about the room curiously.

"You say your hair is gone?" he said, with an air almost of idiocy.

"You needn't look for it," said Della. "It's sold, I tell you—sold and gone, too. It's Christmas Eve, boy. Be good to me, for it went for you. Maybe the hairs of my head were numbered," she went on with a sudden serious sweetness, "but nobody could ever count my love for you. Shall I put the chops on, Jim?"

Out of his trance Jim seemed quickly to wake. He enfolded his Della. For ten seconds let us regard with discreet scrutiny some inconsequential object in the other direction. Eight dollars a week or a million a year—what is the difference? A mathematician or a wit would give you the wrong answer. The Magi brought valuable gifts, but that was not among them. This dark assertion will be illuminated later on.

Jim drew a package from his overcoat pocket and threw it upon the table.

"Don't make any mistake, Dell," he said, "about me. I don't think there's anything in the way of a haircut or a shave or a shampoo that could make me like my girl any less. But if you'll unwrap that package you may see why you had me going awhile at first."

White fingers and nimble tore at the string and paper. And then an ecstatic scream of joy; and then, alas! a quick feminine change to hysterical tears and wails, necessitating the immediate employment of all the comforting powers of the lord of the flat.

For there lay The Combs—the set of combs, side and back, that Della had worshiped for long in a Broadway window. Beautiful combs, pure tortoise shell, with jeweled rims—just the shade to wear in the beautiful vanished hair. They were expensive combs, she knew, and her heart had simply craved and yearned over them without the least hope of possession. And now they were hers, but the tresses that should have adorned the coveted adornments were gone.

But she hugged them to her bosom, and at length she was able to look up with dim eyes and a smile and say: "My hair grows so fast, Jim!"

And then Della leaped up like a little singed [13] cat and cried, "Oh, oh!"

Jim had not yet seen his beautiful present. She held it out to him eagerly upon her open palm. The dull precious metal seemed to flash with a reflection of her bright and ardent spirit.

"Isn't it a dandy, Jim? I hunted all over town to find it. You'll have to look at the time a hundred times a day now. Give me your watch. I want to see how it looks on it."

Instead of obeying, Jim tumbled down on the couch and put his hands under the back of his head and smiled.

"Dell," said he, "let's put our Christmas presents away and keep 'em awhile. They're too nice to use just at present. I sold the watch to get the money to buy your combs. And now suppose you put the chops on."

The Magi, as you know, were wise men—wonderfully wise men—who brought gifts to the Babe in the manger. They invented the art of giving Christmas presents. Being wise, their gifts were no doubt wise ones, possibly bearing the privilege of exchange in case of dupli-

13. **singed** (sinj'd): burned slightly.

cation. And here I have lamely related to you the uneventful chronicle of two foolish children in a flat who most unwisely sacrificed for each other the greatest treasures of their house. But in a last word to the wise of these days let it be said that of all who give gifts these two were the wisest. Of all who give and receive gifts, such as they are wisest. Everywhere they are wisest. They are the Magi.

Meaning

1. What is the real source of Jim's shock when he first sees Della?
2. What kind of characters are Della and Jim? Do they seem to have real individuality and depth?
3. *Sentimental* means having an excess of sentiment or emotion. Would you consider this story sentimental? Why or why not?
4. The *theme* of a short story is simply the total meaning of the story—some observation that the writer wanted to make about life or human nature. Whether the theme is stated or implied, you should be able to state it in a single sentence.

    What is the theme of this "chronicle of two foolish children?" How does the reference to the Magi provide a clue to the meaning? Notice that the wise men brought *gifts* and that Della and Jim exchanged *gifts*, yet the title is singular. Why?
5. A situation or event that turns out to be in strange contrast to what was intended or expected is said to be *ironic*. What ironies does the plot of this story contain?

Method

1. O. Henry as the narrator often introduces his own opinions into the story. Find some examples of this. Do you enjoy his advice and comments, or do they interfere with the action of the story?
2. Which element of the story will you probably remember the longest: setting, character, or plot? Why?
3. To be effective, a "surprise ending" should be carefully foreshadowed. Point out passages in which O. Henry prepares us for the final turn of events.
4. What is incongruous, unsuitable, or inconsistent about the names James *Dillingham* Young and Mme Sofronie?
5. "Oh, and the next two hours tripped by on rosy wings. Forget the hashed metaphor. She was ransacking the stores for Jim's present." O. Henry's hashed metaphor is usually referred to as a mixed metaphor. Why is his metaphor hashed or mixed?
6. At one point in the story, in order to symbolize or heighten Della's mood, O. Henry says: "She stood by the window and looked out

dully at a gray cat walking a gray fence in a gray backyard." How effective is this symbolism?

7. Read the explanation of the commercial short story on pages 6–7. How does "The Gift of the Magi" typify the characteristics of this type of short story? Give specific examples.

Language: Colloquial Usage

O. Henry's language varies from an elaborate, overworked diction (he speaks of "imputation of parsimony" instead of the simpler "charge of stinginess") to very colloquial or informal usage when he pictures Della "bulldozing" the grocer, has her "flop" on the couch, or lets her give Jim a "dandy" of a watch chain. Colloquial language is used in people's everyday conversations and gives a flavor to informal talking or writing. It would not be appropriate for formal writing or speaking.

Change the following expressions from "The Gift of the Magi" into colloquial or less formal language:

1. mistress of the home
2. some inconsequential object
3. uneventful chronicle
4. privilege of exchange

Composition

Write a composition on "Gift-giving" or "Christmastime" from any aspect—personal or general; serious, humorous, or ironic; personal essay or narrative.

Pearl S. Buck

Life itself richly equipped Pearl Sydenstricker Buck with material for her novels, short stories, and nonfiction works. She was born in West Virginia in 1892, and when she was very young she was taken by her missionary parents to China. There she spent her childhood, in the city of Chinkiang on the Yangtse River.

At seventeen she left China to attend Randolph-Macon College in Virginia. After graduation she returned to China, married an American agricultural missionary, Dr. John Lossing Buck, and went with him to north China. For years she was busy with missionary work, the care of her home and children, and teaching English literature in various Chinese universities. It wasn't until she was thirty that she began her writing career—with a magazine article on Chinese life which was accepted by the *Atlantic Monthly*.

With the publication of *The Good Earth* in 1931, she achieved fame as a writer. This novel, which won the Pulitzer prize for fiction in 1932, has been translated into more than thirty languages. Its success encouraged her to write other novels, as well as short stories, about China and other Asian countries, and eventually about the United States. She has also adapted plays for television and written her autobiography, *My Several Worlds*. In 1938 Pearl Buck became the first and only American woman to be honored with the Nobel prize for literature.

"My chief pleasure and interest," Pearl Buck says, "has always been people." This, more than any other factor, has been the basis for her life's work. Her interest in people has been expressed in other ways besides her writings. In 1941 she founded the East and West Association "devoted to mutual understanding between peoples." In 1949 she organized Welcome House, an adoption agency for Asian-American children.

Her best writing is distinguished for its sincere and comprehensive study of Chinese peasant life. "The Angel" mirrors on a small scale the world with which the name Pearl Buck is spontaneously associated.

The Angel

The old Chinese night watchman, standing at dawn by the gate of the mission compound in the midst of the crowd about him, said he had seen an angel in the starry night. He had not, he said gravely, been able to sleep for a long time afterward. True, it was his business to stay awake all night and walk slowly about the brick walls of the school and about Miss Barry's little house, clacking his bamboo sticks together to warn away thieves who might be loitering there. This he had done very faithfully when he was young, but as he grew old he slept once or twice in the night, waking to clack the more assiduously,[1] and then more and more often he slept. Now, since last summer, he frequently curled in a dark corner of Miss Barry's garden, in her fern bed, and slept very hard, only waking at dawn to clack tremendously and dutifully.

As for Miss Barry, she had wondered often what dog lay in her ferns and was regularly irritated that her ferns were being spoiled, so often irritated, in fact, that the old man, fearing her discovery of him, slept sometimes under a tree or elsewhere. But always he liked the soft ferns best, and he could not forbear [2] creeping back there sometimes in the night when his bones ached, although always the next morning, when he heard Miss Barry's clear quick voice cry, once more discouraged, "Oh, who has let that dog in again?" he shook his head, smitten with secret guilt, but pretended ignorance lest he be discharged.

For Miss Barry was not to be counted upon. She might be endlessly patient, as she was, for instance, when cholera got into the compound and sixteen girls died in the school, and he nearly died as well and would have except that she came herself and injected the foreign medicine into his blood and saved him. Then as suddenly, quite without reason, she would lose all her patience over some small thing, a flower dried up for want of water, or dust upon her veranda steps. At these times he had even seen her lips tremble and tears come into her eyes, to his astonishment, and it seemed as though she suffered somehow a loss to herself.

Now on this day, he was wakened out of the fern bed by the cry everywhere that Miss Barry had suddenly disappeared; and, rising

1. **assiduously** (ə·sij′o͞o·əs·lē): diligently; thoroughly.
2. **forbear**: keep oneself from doing something.

dazedly, his spiky hair full of fern leaves, he was questioned as to whether or not he had seen her. But he had not, he said earnestly. He had only seen an angel. He had, he repeated over and over, seen it just before dawn on this moonless night just passed. But, as he told them all as they stood about him in the early sunlight, the men and women teachers of the school and the girl students, and even the two foreigners, Mr. and Mrs. Jones, the stars had been very bright, since it was autumn and beyond the time of the rains. Therefore he had been able to see the angel clearly. It had approached him noiselessly over the grass, its long hair floating and white, and it wore long loose robes and on its shoulders were misty tips of wings, almost hidden by the hair—fluffy tips like the wooly white shawl Miss Barry sometimes wore. . . .

How did he know it was an angel? When Mr. Jones, the missionary, asked this, the old night watchman stared at him indignantly. Had he not been an immersed Baptist for many years? He had gone clear under the water in the pool beneath the pulpit in the compound church on a very cold day fifteen years ago, when the water was supposed to be warmed and was not because the pastor preached too long a sermon and let the water get cold, and afterward two out of the three of them who were immersed had caught cold and Miss Barry had said "they couldn't even baptize right." Naturally, the night watchman now said, "I know an angel when I see one, being so good a Christian as I am." Besides, he added in argument to Mr. Jones, had he not seen photographs of angels on the cards the Americans sent when they did not want them any more, and was there not an image of an angel set on top of the school Christmas tree every year? Of course he knew an angel when he saw it.

"And then," Mr. Jones asked abruptly, "what became of the angel?"

The old watchman rubbed his rough head thoughtfully and tried to remember. He had been waked out of a sound sleep, he remembered, by a cry.

"The angel screamed," he said.

"What did it scream?" asked Mr. Jones.

The old watchman tried to remember again. He was somewhat nervous under this direct questioning and afraid of making a mistake, which might be very disastrous, since Mr. Jones paid him his monthly salary of six dollars. He considered awhile and then decided that an angel would not only scream. It would scream something—some words. He decided to guess, piecing together his memories of mission Christmases.

"The angel said, 'Hallelujah, peace on earth,' " he replied bravely, his brown and wrinkled face apprehensive.

Mr. and Mrs. Jones looked at each other.

"How strange!" breathed Mrs. Jones. It was early in the morning and she had not combed her hair, and now in the sunshine she felt uneasy and tousled, the more because she was a large woman of fifty and her hair was scanty and wiry gray, and was always a trial to her, and because Mr. Jones noticed it so often and was critical of her about it. Now she endeavored to look at him as though she were not conscious of her appearance in the present exigency.[3] She had come as she was because the alarm had been given to Mrs. Jones first when Miss Barry's amah[4] went to her room with early tea according to her habit, and found Miss Barry gone and the bed tossed in utter confusion. This in itself was strange, because Miss Barry was by nature the neatest of creatures; she rose every morning and laid her covers so exactly back that the bed looked scarcely slept in at all and was never any trouble to make, although even so the amah had to be careful, since Miss Barry was very particular. But this morning the amah had run straight to rouse Mrs. Jones, and two hours had passed and Miss Barry had not been found, nor had Mrs. Jones combed her hair.

Now Mrs. Jones turned to her husband. "I really think, my dear," she suggested, for hers was a nature which never did more, "that we had better go home and get things together and think over what we have heard and what the night watchman says, and I will just tidy myself a bit." These last words she added since she caught Mr. Jones's eye even now fixed in distaste upon her hair and there was no use in pretending.

But Mr. Jones would not at first take her suggestion. He never did, preferring to ignore it until it seemed to be the thing he would have done in any case.

"What did the angel do then?" he demanded of the watchman sternly. He was a small, precise man, a little younger than his wife, but seeming older because of his dictatorial look and manner. Now he fixed his dead gray eyes upon the old Chinese, profoundly distrusting this declaration of what the angel had said, distrusting, indeed, all this tale of an angel. After all, one believed in them, of course, as an orthodox[5] Christian, but still. . . .

---

3. **exigency** (ek′sə·jən·sē): emergency; a situation requiring immediate attention.
4. **amah** (ä′mə): a female Chinese servant.
5. **orthodox** (or′thə·doks): believing in the established faith and following its traditional practices or beliefs.

The old man's face now cleared in relief. He knew quite well what had become of the angel. He had sat up in his ferny bed and stared after the white figure which had moved with great swiftness over the lawn to the gate. He considered an instant. He would like, for the sake of his dramatic soul, to have said it spread white wings and flew over the gate into the eastern sky above. But he regarded with terror Mr. Jones's eyes, impenetrably disbelieving and gray as a fish's eyes. He decided hastily upon the truth.

"The angel went across the grass as though without walking, and then opened the gate, but without noise, and then went away," he said. And, suddenly realizing he was hungry and that the sun was high, he added firmly, "That is all I saw and all I know of the affair."

Mr. Jones, seeing this was true, was ready now to take his wife's suggestion. Together they went out of Miss Barry's exquisite little garden, blooming in this early autumn with chrysanthemums and late roses, into the bare schoolyard and then into their own rather barren court. Mrs. Jones found flowers a trial to care for, what with the long drought [6] and equally long rains of the China climate, and Mr. Jones did not think of flowers or notice them. Occasionally Miss Barry had brought over a handful of tea roses or a stalk of lilies. Especially when she was invited to supper, she came bringing flowers in her hand, and watched a little anxiously while Mrs. Jones arranged them tightly in a glass.

"Oh, let me," she often cried out, and under Mrs. Jones's surprised eyes she pulled and loosened and arranged the flowers. "There!" she would say at last. "They hate being crowded."

"Well, I never," Mrs. Jones had said helplessly the other day. "Really, Miss Barry, one would think they were creatures!"

"So they are," Miss Barry had replied sharply—her temper grew on her, poor thing, as she got older. Then she added fearlessly in her somewhat downright way, "Besides, I like seeing a thing done *right*."

Mrs. Jones now thought of this remark as in a large, vague melancholy she followed her little husband up their steps. It was what Miss Barry said more and more often as she grew older—she was always wanting things done right. She would tidy a schoolgirl's black hair, loosing the braid to plait it again swiftly and strongly and tie it firmly at the end with a bit of cord.

"Learn to do your hair right," she admonished. Or she would summon a servant sharply and point out dust in a corner. "If you sweep the room at all, do it *right*," she said sternly.

6. **drought** (drout): a long period without rain.

Scarcely a day passed, Mrs. Jones reflected, when she had not heard the phrase upon Miss Barry's lips. It had come to be almost an unconscious thing with her, a constant hovering upon the lips of her inner determined spirit. And last summer, when she was having the masons and carpenters repair the school, the phrase became really a mania with her. Mrs. Jones remembered meeting her one hot August morning, very damp heat it was, so that one felt dead and inert with it, and yet Miss Barry had looked as carefully dressed as ever in her white linen; and although her thin oval face was flushed a dark red, her white heavy hair was smooth and coiled neatly on top of her head. She was hurrying down the brick path from the school and talking to herself strangely and loudly when she met Mrs. Jones. Indeed she had not seemed to see Mrs. Jones at all, looking full at her but with completely blank eyes, while she cried out passionately, "I simply will not have it slipshod—it's got to be done right—done *right*, done *right*."

Then, suddenly perceiving Mrs. Jones, she controlled herself, forcing a smile to her rather thin, delicate lips. "Oh, it's you, Mrs. Jones. I—I—do forgive me! I am afraid I have lost patience. These Chinese workmen—still, I try not to be unjust—Mrs. Jones, will you be so kind as to come and see what they have done even in the little while I was eating my breakfast? I can't leave them an instant without something going wrong."

And although Mrs. Jones had not wanted to go at all, she was unable to refuse the passionate demand of Miss Barry's dark and tragic eyes, and so she had lumbered after Miss Barry's thin, quick figure, sighing a little because what she had to see was on the third floor of the school dormitory. They had picked their way among the bits of fallen plaster, and the gaping masons had stopped to stare and comment upon the white women and guffaw after they had passed. Miss Barry, hearing the coarse laughter, held her white head higher, and pressed her lips together more firmly, ignoring them. But her eyes glittered. "Look at that, if you please," she said at last, pointing at a wall. She had a delicate hand, fleshless, and always trembling a little now, but with beautiful, shapely bones. Mrs. Jones followed its direction. At first she could perceive nothing but a lathed, plasterless wall.

"Look at these laths,[7] Mrs. Jones," said Miss Barry. Why, actually there were tears in the woman's eyes! "Year after year the plaster

7. **laths:** thin, narrow strips of wood nailed to a building frame to support a coat of plaster.

falls from these laths because they are so closely and carelessly placed that the plaster can't get between. Have I not begged and besought and showed these masons what to do, and offered to pay double— anything, anything, to get it done *right*. This year I paid a carpenter to tear it all down. Look at them—he has torn the laths off and nailed them back just as they were! It's impossible for anybody in this whole race to do anything *right*. Until they learn, all the Christianity in the world won't save them!"

Mrs. Jones had been genuinely shocked at this. She suggested gently, "My *dear* Miss Barry! Really, such talk is very near to blasphemy."

"It is true," replied Miss Barry, her spare face setting into its habitual lines of tragic, repressed impatience.

That day, Mrs. Jones now remembered, Miss Barry had first mentioned the dog in the fern bed, although afterward she spoke of it often, always with increasing agitation. They had walked back to Miss Barry's home together, and on the way Miss Barry's darting glance had sprung about her garden. She spied a faded rose or two on the bushes and twisted them off swiftly and dexterously and tucked them into the loose earth underneath.

Then irritation had lit her face again. She was looking at the fern bed, and quickly she walked to it. "I declare, that dog has been in here again," she said. "Look at these little new fronds all broken!" The irritation was gone. A tender sorrow had its place. Kneeling on the grass, she slipped her daintily pointed old fingers under the silvery curls of the broken fronds. "The poor little struggling things," she whispered, under her breath, forgetting Mrs. Jones. "As soon as they have courage and come up again, so lovely and so fragile, that beast gets in—" She rose to her feet energetically, "I *must* get hold of that watchman," she said. "He sleeps at night and doesn't remember to look for the dog—I know he sleeps—he's like them all—lazy and careless. You have to be after every one of them to get anything done *right*. . . ."

This morning in her own somewhat untidy sitting room Mrs. Jones sank into an old wicker chair and breathed awhile and remembered these things about Miss Barry. She must go upstairs and do her hair, but just a minute's rest. . . . Well, of course Miss Barry had never known that it was the old watchman himself who slept in her ferns. Poor soul, it would probably have finished her if she had known *that!*

Later, at breakfast, seeing her slipshod Chinese manservant as he shuffled about the table, his bare feet thrust into the toes of his shoes, she was reminded again of Miss Barry. Only three nights ago she and Mr. Jones had been over there to supper. Miss Barry always had everything so nice. There were lace mats on the dark, shining table and a bowl of pink roses in the middle of it. The servant was neat and white-robed and well trained. Miss Barry had expended endless effort on him. And now, although he knew perfectly what he was to do, her glance followed him as he served the cream soup, the chicken jelly, the lettuce, the smooth cylinder of vanilla ice cream.

"She always wanted things too perfect," said Mrs. Jones suddenly, aware comfortably of the value of her own carelessness.

"Who?" said Mr. Jones.

"Miss Barry," replied Mrs. Jones.

"I wish I knew what to do next," said Mr. Jones, perturbed. He had been eating rapidly and in silence, thinking hard. "It's perfectly evident she got up out of her bed and wandered about in the garden and out of the gate. But she was such a rational creature—and had she anything to disturb her recently that you know about, Nellie?"

"No, nothing especially," said Mrs. Jones, reflecting. "You saw her at supper the other day—I haven't seen her since."

"I've sent runners out on the streets to inquire if anybody saw a foreign lady," said Mr. Jones. "And I've sent word to the magistrate's office. It's very embarrassing, I'm sure. I've never heard of such a thing happening before in the mission. If you are finished, let's go to her room. We may find a family letter or something which will explain. You are sure she has confided nothing of a personal nature to you recently or at any time?"

Mrs. Jones looked surprisedly at her husband. "Why, no, Elmer," she answered mildly. "You know she was the sort who never tells anybody anything. We've lived here next to her all these years and still I don't even know what family she has. I didn't talk with her easily. If we did talk, she was always full of something she was trying to do. She never rested. I think there is an older sister somewhere in Vermont, but I don't know. You know how she was—just putting her life into the school, and her garden the only pleasure she took. Why, she hasn't been away even in the summers for years. Last time I asked her if she didn't think she ought to go, she answered that if she did, she knew her garden would be ruined while she was away because the Chinese were so slack they'd never do a thing all summer, and she wasn't going to have all the time and energy she had put into her flowers thrown away as it was that one summer she wasn't here seven years ago. She's never been away from the mission since. She always acted about the flowers as though they were real creatures."

Mr. Jones said no more. He waited with obvious impatience while Mrs. Jones placidly finished her last slice of toast, her large face tranquilly [8] mournful. Then he rose briskly, "Now," he said, "let's go to work. If we can't find her, I'll have to notify the American Consul at the port."

But when they had arrived at Miss Barry's sparsely furnished, neat room, they found nothing. There was the tossed bed, the linen sheets strangely crumpled. "She always had to have linen sheets," said Mrs. Jones sadly. "And such a time she had getting them washed right! She used to talk about it."

Mr. Jones opened the closet gingerly. It seemed improper to do so, for Miss Barry's garments, hung up neatly and straightly within, were startlingly like herself, and she was the last person into whose room one could consider a man's venturing. . . . Yet, Mr. Jones had thought sometimes, once she must have been beautiful. The shape of her face, the very slightly arched, delicate nose, the fine lines of the head, the dark, keen eyes, the white, fine skin, and the masses of straight, smooth hair, white as long as he could remember—surely once she had been beautiful. But no one really knew her. She had lived alone here so long in the mission house, vigilant, unsparing of them all, but most of herself, somehow always an exquisite New England spinster even in the midst of this sprawling, dirty, slipshod city, summoning all the dauntlessness [9] of her forefathers to maintain herself against its overwhelming amorphous,[10] careless life. Yes, staring at these garments, Mr. Jones saw her, always shiningly neat and clean, always embattled.[11]

Then suddenly they found out everything about her. While Mr. Jones was staring at the gauntly [12] hanging dresses, silver-gray poplin, white linen, a lavender silk for best, all with the neatest little collars and cuffs, his wife cried out, "Elmer, I believe there's a letter to her sister here—I found it under the blotting pad on the desk—"

She held four carefully written sheets toward her husband. He took them and glanced at them, and then looked at his wife. "I suppose," he said nervously, "that under the circumstances we would be justified in reading it?" He could not somehow imagine reading casually Miss Barry's private letters.

8. **tranquilly** (trang′kwi·lē): calmly; peacefully.
9. **dauntlessness**: fearlessness; courage, fortitude, and endurance.
10. **amorphous** (ə·môr′fəs): shapeless.
11. **embattled**: prepared for a struggle or battle.
12. **gauntly** (gont·lē): in a thin and angular way.

"Well, how else are we going to know anything?" said Mrs. Jones, wondering at him.

So they sat down on the gray wicker couch and silently began to read the letter, Mr. Jones holding the pages, Mrs. Jones looking over his shoulder.

"Dear Sister Elizabeth," it began, "I hope you are fully recovered from your rheumatism. The climate in Vermont is conducive to this trouble. I trust you are taking care of yourself. I sent you the usual amount by the last mail. Do not worry that I cannot spare this. I need very little for myself, and you are now all that is left me of my dear ones. I regularly give a little in charity, but find much given or given openly only works harm, as these people are naturally lazy and ready to receive indefinitely and so be spared effort, although I truly wish to be helpful to them."

Here the fine handwriting changed. It was as though Miss Barry had paused awhile and then taken up her pen again in agitation. "My dear sister Elizabeth, pray for me that I may have love in my heart toward these people for whom I have spent my life. For I am distressed to find, as I grow older, that I like them less and less. Indeed, I fear they are incorrigibly set in their idle ways. It may be, as my neighbor Mrs. Jones says, that their souls can be saved even though their bodies are unwashed and their minds and their hands idle. But to me God must be served aright, and he is better served, surely, in cleanliness and order—"

Here again there was a break, and the hue of the ink was fresh. The date was changed also.

"She wrote this last night," murmured Mrs. Jones. . . .

"I have not been able to finish this letter, my dear sister. The repairs on the school have been interminably slow due to slipshod, careless work. I have not been able to endure it with patience, I fear. I have exhausted myself in repeated demands that paint be repainted because dirty fingermarks were left on it, bricks reset that were carelessly placed, and a thousand like things, which, seeming small, yet render life intolerable to a cultivated and sensitive person. I think tonight with an agony of loneliness of our dear childhood home in New England. I think there never was paint so white as on our house and fence. How did it keep so white? I remember the garden. Here in my tiny poor garden my life is a struggle against weeds, against dirty footsteps, even against incessant [13] spittle upon my walks, for this is the distressing habit of casual persons here. Indeed, my life,

13. **incessant:** continual; unceasing.

which once I planned so nobly, has, now that I look back upon it, resolved itself into nothing but a battle against filth and laziness—and I have lost. I might as well have tried to stop the dirty muddy Yangtze River as it flows past this heathen city. Yet I have only a few more years left me and am too old at the battle now to give up. I shall go on trying—trying to get even a few small things done *right*."

Here there was the last break, here were the last few lines: "I must pause now, while it occurs to me, although I am undressed and ready for bed, to go and see if a stray dog is sleeping in my ferns. It has done so spasmodically [14] all summer, to my great annoyance, each time crushing a dozen or more of the delicate fronds—oh, Elizabeth, I think I am not well! Something is wrong with me. I feel so often as though I would scream aloud like a child if I have once again to make one of these Chinese do a thing over *right*. I suppose I have begged the watchman hundreds of times to keep this dog out of my garden. I have struggled so long and he will not learn. Elizabeth, I will confess to you that secretly I have come to hate these people. May God forgive me—I cannot help it. They have killed me."

Here Mr. and Mrs. Jones were interrupted by the old night watchman. His face was quite distorted with weeping and he cried out, beside himself, "O sir, O mistress, Miss Barry is found! The men you sent out have returned—they say a few night vendors saw a white woman with long, streaming white hair running down the street to the river, crying out as she went some foreign words. And we all went down to the river then, where the bank rises to a cliff, and we were afraid to look down except that a servant at the gate of the temple told us that near dawn he had seen a spirit pass, screaming as it went, and it ran straightway and leaped over the cliff, and he turned his face away and dared not follow. So we went. Sir, she essayed [15] to leap into the river, but she failed. She only fell upon the rocks. There she lies, all white! Oh, she was good—we all knew she was good, though she had a temper not to be loved. It was she I saw, sir—she appeared before me as an angel—I said I saw an angel—now I have seen an angel—"

He turned and ran from the room, babbling and weeping.

Mr. and Mrs. Jones looked at each other silently. Then Mr. Jones coughed and spoke. "I must notify the consul—and I had better keep this letter and send it to the relative," he said solemnly, and taking out a little notebook, he slipped the letter into its pages. Then

14. **spasmodically** (spaz·mod′i·kə·lē): fitfully; on and off.
15. **essayed** (e·sād′): tried.

he and Mrs. Jones tiptoed from the empty room. Upon the shining, dark, immaculate floor there were now their unconscious, dusty footprints, and the dustiest of them all were the prints of the old watchman's bare feet.

Meaning

1. What were the things that Miss Barry seemed to value most in life? Considering her life's work, what is odd about her sense of values?
2. What was there about the city and the culture in which she found herself that was especially frustrating to her? Refer to specific passages in the text.
3. What kind of person was the old night watchman?
4. What kinds of conflicts did Miss Barry have to fight against? Which of these was the strongest?
5. What is ironic about Miss Barry's life, her final feelings about the Chinese, and the outcome of the story? What makes Miss Barry's admission that she had come to hate the Chinese a pathetic cry?
6. What is the theme of "The Angel"?
7. A *motif* is an element (a character, an idea, a phrase) in a story that recurs again and again. Miss Barry's irritation about the "dog" that sleeps in her ferns is the first such motif introduced in the story. The second is her growing insistence that things be done "right," and with it the nervous strain that eventually drives her out of her mind. These two motifs begin to come together when Mrs. Jones thinks, "Well, of course Miss Barry had never known that it was the old watchman himself who slept in her ferns. Poor soul, it would probably have finished her if she had known *that*!"
   How do we know that Miss Barry did learn that it was the old watchman himself who slept in her ferns?
8. Judging from what you know of Miss Barry, would you agree with her when she says, "They have killed me"?
9. Is suicide a believable way for Miss Barry to have resolved her problem? What other possible solutions might she have chosen? Would one of them fit into the story better than the resolution used?
10. Is this a story of failure, of success, or of both?
11. "Cleanliness is next to godliness" is a motto with which many Americans are familiar. Do you think Miss Barry would have agreed with this saying? Is there a point at which she goes even further, implying that cleanliness is more important than godliness? Are there individuals or groups on the American scene today who appear to be dirty? Are other Americans, like Miss Barry, irritated by what they consider their dirtiness or laziness? Are they—or Miss Barry—justified in their reactions? Why or why not? Is there any one group of national, racial, or religious origin within our nation uniquely hard-

working and clean? Or is the ability to work hard and keep clean more a matter of the kind of work a person does, the amount of money he earns, the family that has brought him up, and the sort of education he has had?

Method

1. Since Miss Barry is dead when the story begins, how does the author reveal her character?
2. How does the author use the word *right* to further the plot and to develop character?
3. A character who contrasts sharply with another character and who, through this contrast, strengthens the reader's impression of the latter, is called a *character foil*. How is Mrs. Jones a character foil for Miss Barry?
4. Whose view of the situation is the story primarily concerned with?
5. Why does the author stress the changes in ink and handwriting in Miss Barry's letter?
6. A *symbol* is an object which stands for an idea or a person. For example, the cross is a symbol of Christianity, the Star of David of Judaism, the lion of courage, Uncle Sam of the United States. An author may use one or several objects as symbols, and the reader determines their meaning from the context of the story. In this story Miss Barry's garden, particularly the fern bed, appears to represent qualities missing from her life. What are they?
7. Do the Joneses understand Miss Barry? Does the night watchman understand her? How do the footprints in the last sentence of the story vividly point out the real relationship of their owners with Miss Barry? What device makes this realization so effective in the reader's mind?
8. *Tone* refers to the writer's attitude or feelings about his subject and his characters. An author conveys his tone through his choice and arrangement of words and details.

   Read the last paragraph aloud. Does the author intend to be sympathetic, ironic, happy, humorous? What kind of language is used? What tone of voice should be used in reading this paragraph? Now take an overall view of the story. Is the tone the same?

Language: Latin Roots for English Words

In this story, Mr. Jones is referred to as being "a small, precise man, a little younger than his wife, but seeming older because of his *dictatorial* look and manner." The word *dictatorial* comes from the Latin *-dic* or *-dict* meaning "say, speak," or "word." You are familiar with this root in such words as *dictate* and *dictator*. A dictatorial person is one given to dictating, or who has a commanding, domineering manner.

Several other words are built on the Latin root *-dict*. Check your dictionary to see how "say, speak," and "word" are a part of *dictation, diction, dictum,* and *edict.*

Many English words are built on Latin roots. Name some words built on the following roots:

Root	Meaning
1. *-port*	carry
2. *-scribe*	write
3. *-mand*	order
4. *-clude*	close

Composition

Most stories can be interpreted on more than one level. The first, or basic, level is the story itself; the second, or symbolic, level is the application of the story's theme.

On the basic or literal level, "The Angel" is the story of a missionary in China who committed suicide because of frustrations in her job. On a more advanced level, Pearl Buck was saying something about missionaries in foreign lands, differences in cultures, and the necessity to adapt. And what she was saying is as applicable to missionaries and Peace Corps workers today who are serving in foreign lands and working with and teaching native populations as it was to Miss Barry.

Using the following topic sentence, write a composition on the qualifications needed by the missionary or Peace Corps worker: For the person who wants to serve in a foreign country, the need to serve is not enough. The man or woman who wants to help others needs (1) patience, (2) understanding, (3) an awareness of the values and beauties to be found in other cultures and a willingness to learn these values, and (4) a sense of proportion and balance.

Develop your composition by giving details and particulars and examples, real or imaginary, to develop these points.

MacKinlay Kantor

MacKinlay Kantor was born February 4, 1904, in Webster City, Iowa. He spent most of his youth there and obtained valuable experience helping his mother edit the town's daily newspaper for four years. Later he lived in Chicago, where he held a variety of jobs before returning to Iowa to work on the Cedar Rapids *Republican*. He gave up newspaper work in 1927 and devoted his time to writing fiction.

During World War II he became involved in aviation, an interest he still maintains. He has also had experience as a war correspondent, and as a technical consultant for the U.S. Air Force.

As a writer, Kantor believes in using whatever subject is most interesting to him at a given time. "Sometimes the subject is historical," he says, "sometimes contemporaneous, and it has even verged on the fantastic."

Andersonville, a historical novel about the horrors of life in and around the Confederate prison at Andersonville, Georgia, during the Civil War, won the Pulitzer prize in 1956. Another historical novel, *Spirit Lake* (1961), set in mid-nineteenth-century Iowa, tells about an Indian massacre of thirty white settlers. To gather background material for his novel *Signal Thirty-Two* (1950), he spent a year with the New York City Police Department, and followed the life and routine of a patrolman. *Glory for Me* (1945), a novel in verse, about the return of three American soldiers to the same hometown, was made into a motion picture, *The Best Years of Our Lives*. A book that reveals many of Kantor's varied subjects is *Author's Choice* (1944), a collection of forty of his short stories.

Valedictory *

The principal had told him to reserve the three center rows. As soon as Tyler Morley had turned on the auditorium lights, he began to fasten twine around those seats, thus holding them sacred. They were desks arranged in double rows, two and two.

* **Valedictory** (val'ə·dik'tər·ē) : a leave-taking; also the farewell address at graduating exercises, usually given by the student with the highest grades. The word *valedictory* is derived from two Latin words: *vale*, farewell, and *dicere*, to say.

"Valedictory" by MacKinlay Kantor from *The Saturday Evening Post*, May 28, 1938, copyright 1938 by The Curtis Publishing Company. Reprinted by permission of Paul R. Reynolds Inc., 599 Fifth Avenue, New York, New York, 10017.

He thought ribbon would have been better than twine, but the decoration committee had not thought to provide any ribbon. The committee was busy in the domestic science room, preparing bouquets of flowers which had been brought to the high school building shortly after supper. The graduation exercises would not begin for an hour. Still, old Ty Morley kept hearing the muffled explosion of big doors on the ground floor, where boys and girls already were arriving.

He barricaded the rear aisles with his little rope of twine, and went to rest his stiff elbows on the windowsill. This last moment of May was one of the best evenings May had offered. It wasn't very dark yet; a slice of moon shone clean and bright; and the river timber —a bank of soft maples and cottonwoods stretching along the eastern border of Shelldrake—seemed mysterious with the musk [1] of fresh foliage.

Mr. Morley breathed deeply. He wondered whether the air smelled flowery in Lexington, Nebraska. He had never been to Lexington, but he was going there soon.

The paper had said so, five nights before; it had said so in two different ways and in two different places; and now Mr. Morley brought out his old alligator-hide pocketbook and looked at the clippings again. They were fuzzy from much handling. One item had been cut from a longer article discussing the school board meeting. The paragraph said that T. A. Morley had tendered [2] his resignation as janitor in the local schools, and that Ed Jensen had been retained to fill the place left vacant by Mr. Morley.

The other item was more important, for it was clipped from the society column, and Mr. Morley had not appeared in the society column since he and his wife entertained the In-His-Name class and the Daughters of the King class of the Baptist Church, in 1911. That was just three weeks before his wife died.

> Friends of T. A. Morley will be interested to hear that he plans soon to leave for Lexington, Nebraska, where he will spend an indefinite time with his daughter, Mrs. R. F. Wackstraw. Mr. Morley paid a personal call to the *Clarion* office this morning, and stated that he regrets leaving Shelldrake and his many friends here, where he has been employed since 1901 as janitor in the local schools, having also served as constable formerly, and having worked before that for the Western Grain Elevator Company. His many friends and his comrades of the

1. **musk:** a penetrating, earthy odor.
2. **tendered:** past tense of the verb *to tender,* to present for acceptance; to offer. What are the meanings of *tender* when used as an adjective? a noun?

G.A.R.[3] will be sorry to lose him from our midst. Mr. Morley continues in good health and spirits, although he is well past the seventy mark, but says he can no longer engage in arduous physical duties. The *Clarion* wishes him a pleasant journey to Nebraska.

Miss Roache, the Senior adviser, came to the south door of the auditorium, lugging a dripping basket of snowball blooms.

She called, "Ty."

"Yes, ma'am!" said Mr. Morley, and he limped toward her, stuffing the clippings into his wallet.

"Ty, will you please bring up those other baskets? Help Gracey MacIntyre with them. She's so little and they're so big."

"My," he said, and bent down to touch the damp white blooms in the basket, "they're mighty pretty, ain't they?"

"They smell good," said Miss Roache. "Hurry up, Ty. Folks are beginning to come in. We haven't got the stage dressed."

He went down to the domestic science kitchen, and he found Gracey MacIntyre—a skinny ash-blonde of sixteen—struggling tearfully with baskets of bridal wreath and bleeding hearts. "Half the committee didn't show up," she wailed. "They just let a few of us do the work."

"Well," said Mr. Morley, "don't go plaguing yourself, Gracey. We'll get them up right away. . . . My, that's pretty, ain't it?" He pointed to a long wicker basket filled with yellow iris, and girded at the base with purple crepe paper on which the figures "1922," cut from yellow paper, had been pasted. Purple and gold were the school colors.

He thought that he should take "1922" first, because obviously it was to occupy the center of the stage. He bent over and tried to lift it, and suddenly his shoulders felt numb. That wouldn't do. He didn't know what was getting into him; maybe the Decoration Day parade was too strenuous yesterday. That stiffness in his knee didn't seem to let up at all, although he rubbed it with liniment every night.

He remembered how he had gone into No. 4 on the second floor to set a mousetrap, several days previously. Miss Kirkland had been confident that a mouse was in her cupboard. It was late in the afternoon, and cloudy and dark, and the two girls who ran into the room and then out again didn't see Mr. Morley on his knees in the corner. But one of them said, "Whoo—liniment! I guess Ty's been in here." Probably he smelled of liniment all the time.

3. **G.A.R.:** Grand Army of the Republic, an organization of Union Civil War veterans that grew politically powerful during the late nineteenth century.

The girl who talked about his liniment was Amy Galliver. He remembered the first time he saw Amy; it must have been ten or twelve years before, when she was just a little tyke, starting in Miss Plummer's first grade. That was when he was janitor of the old South Building.

He was sweeping, he remembered, or getting ready to, and sowing the reddish sweeping compound over the floor. Amy came scooting up the stairs, and she slipped on the sweeping compound and came near breaking her neck. Her face was puffy and red with sudden tears, as he picked her up and brushed off the clinging particles that covered her pink sweater and her long cotton stockings. "Now don't cry, sissy," he had told her. "You won't have no tears left for when you need them! Say," he said, "I bet I know who you are. I bet you are a Galliver; you've got Galliver written all over your face."

Now he climbed the cold steps of the composition stairway, supporting the heavy basket before him. This wasn't like the stairways in the old South Building. Those were rutty and knotted and dangerous to walk upon. He remembered how he had complained to Amos Apgar, of the school board, about those steps. But Amos said the board was retrenching,[4] and they couldn't afford to do any remodeling at that time. And the next week, Buster Waterfield fell on the stairs and broke his wrist. When Doctor Waterfield got after the school board, they fixed those stairs in a hurry.

Mr. Morley brought up more baskets, and now the girls of the decoration committee—the Junior girls who would not graduate until 1923—were twittering all over the stage.

Two parents had come early. They sat, forlorn but dignified, in the back seats of the reserved section. They were Mr. Isaac Kobitsky and his wife. Mr. Kobitsky dealt in secondhand furniture. But his son Theodore was graduating tonight, and Theodore was a star pupil.

Mr. Morley walked along the back of the auditorium making certain that all the windows were open.

"Too much draft for you, Mrs. Kobitsky?"

"No," she said. "Is a lovely night. Is beautiful."

Mr. Morley laughed. "I tell you, this is a fine night for graduation. This is one of the finest graduating nights I ever see."

Mr. Kobitsky bowed politely.

"You ought to move up front," said Mr. Morley, "where you can get a real good look at Theodore." The Kobitskys thanked him, but they did not move.

---

4. retrenching (ri·trench′ing): cutting down on expenses.

There were many more students trampling through the building now, and when Ty looked from the window again, he heard cars parking in front of the Methodist Church. Beneath the heavy elm branches he saw people coming north on Bank Street. He thought that maybe he'd better go down to the washrooms on the ground floor and see that there were plenty of paper towels. No, it was too late to go in, over on the girls' side; but he'd take a look in the boys' room, just to make sure.

He met Buster Waterfield and Cooky Keane on the first flight of stairs. Buster was getting to resemble his father, though, of course, he didn't have Doctor Waterfield's mustache. But he was a good-looking kid, and Ty stopped a moment to admire the new blue suit that Buster was wearing. "My," he said, "Buster, that's a mighty fine-looking suit."

"Graduation present," said Buster. "Like it?" Proudly, he fingered the sharp-pointed lapels.

"Why," said Ty, "you look like you were dressed up and going someplace!" And perhaps because he was tired at the end of this day, he rested his left hand for a moment on Buster's firm shoulder. "And Cooky," he said, "you're all togged out [5] too."

Cooky flushed slightly. "Well," he said, "I haven't got a new suit. Got a new tie, that's all."

Mr. Keane had just sold out his Hay, Grain & Feed Company to a man from Mason City, but people said that he had really lost it because of an overdue note.

The janitor laughed, and his right hand lay on Cooky Keane's sleeve. "Far as that goes," he said, "a new suit isn't so downright important, graduation or any other time. You just keep on playing that clarinet of yours, and you'll make your mark. You'll have more new suits than you'll know what to do with!"

The Keane boy swallowed. "I'll tell you this, Ty," he whispered. "I did have an offer to play at the Iowa State Fair this summer, with Carl King's band. You know, the big Fort Dodge one."

"What did I tell you?" said Mr. Morley, and journeyed to the washroom.

He saw smoke when he opened the vestibule door, and the next few steps he took were taken in haste, because for twenty-one years he had lived in dread of fire. But there wasn't any blaze. There were only two freshmen, and one of those was Reverend Lemley's kid, and he was still in short pants.

5. **togged out**: dressed up.

"I smell smoke in here," said Ty, sniffing until his ragged white mustache moved up and down.

The Lemley kid said, "Aw, go on! You couldn't smell anything through all that brush," and then he shrieked at his own wit and tried to dart away.

But Ty's wrinkled hand tightened on the boy's coat—took him by the scruff of the neck, as it were. "Now you listen to me, Horace Lemley," said Ty. "You give me those cigarettes you've got in your pocket!"

The boy twisted and fought. "Let go me!" he snarled. "I haven't got any cigarettes." But Ty found them, stuffed into a jacket pocket.

"Now you listen here to me," he said. "I'm going to do something about this."

"All the kids smoke," muttered Horace, looking at the floor. His companion in crime shuffled his feet and kept making faces, trying to laugh it off.

"No, they don't," said Ty. "I guess I know who smokes around here and who doesn't. You get to be fifteen or sixteen or seventeen, like Buster or Cooky or somebody, and I wouldn't make no kick. A boy that age doesn't get a chance to smoke enough to hurt him, ordinarily. He just smokes evenings, when he's out with the boys, or something like that. And Buster never touched a cigarette all through football and basketball and track, I'll have you know that! But you're too little. You may be bright, but you ain't more than thirteen. You tell me where you got these cigarettes."

Horace Lemley said, "Found them."

"No you never. Tell me, or I'll tell the Reverend," and so Horace told.

Ty Morley said, "Dinwiddy's Recreation Parlor! Well, Horace, I won't tell your old man. But I bet I give George Dinwiddy an earful tomorrow. He's sold these things to little kids just once too often to suit me. Now you vamoose," and he gave the boy a swat with his hand. They fled; he heard giggles beyond the door, and he shook his head and thought ill of George Dinwiddy.

There were plenty of paper towels. So Ty went to the main entrance to make certain that the doors were hooked open. Folks were coming in now, in a regular procession. Most of the graduation girls had coats wrapped around them to hide the glory of their dresses, though heaven knew it wasn't cold tonight.

Some of them had flowers in their hair, too; and Ty thought about the flowers on the stage again, and he hoped that next year there wouldn't be any drought around graduation time. A drought in late May cut down the supply of garden flowers something terrible. And then, with a shock that left him weak and empty, he realized that he wouldn't be here next time a class got ready to graduate. He'd be away out in Nebraska, with Eunice's folks.

He wondered what kind of graduations they had in Lexington, Nebraska. It wouldn't make much difference, because he wouldn't be janitor any more. He wouldn't know the kids.

And of course he knew these kids—the ones who were graduating upstairs. He had set to work with his broad dustpan and his brown-bristled broom, he had painted the little kindergarten chairs bright red, in the old South Building, before any of these kids was born. He had rung the nine o'clock gong and the one-fifteen gong and the three-thirty gong, when some of the teachers who helped these young people to graduate were only little children themselves. He guessed that he had talked to each of these kids a million times, and that wasn't counting the occasions when he'd been called in to tell them about the war.

Miss Stark, for instance, would send some youngster traipsing down the basement stairs after Ty Morley, and then he'd mutter and say, "Well, I don't look very good," and then he'd wash his hands and lumber up to No. 2.

Miss Stark would have a big picture of Lincoln on her desk. All those little tads [6] would be sitting there, giggling and squeezing one another because of this break in their routine. Miss Stark would say in a polite voice, "Mr. Morley, we have been learning about Abraham Lincoln today, because it is his birthday, and I was wondering if you had ever seen Abraham Lincoln. . . . Children, Mr. Morley is a member of the Grand Army of the Republic. Those were the men who helped Mr. Lincoln to free all the poor slaves in the South."

She'd say, "How many children have grandfathers or other relatives who helped Mr. Morley and Mr. Lincoln to free the slaves?" and naturally most of the hands in the room would be waving violently. Looking them over, Mr. Morley could recognize the transmitted physical characteristics—infantile and unformed, perhaps, but still ready to be identified—of his friends. That was Bob White's grandson over there by the window, and those were the Neel girls over there— George Neel's granddaughters, those would be—and this little dark girl down in front looked like a Wedding.

6. tads: *informal,* little children. The word *tad* is probably a shortened form of *tadpole.*

So he'd stand there and tell them, "Well, it wasn't slavery so much as States' rights. You pay attention to what your teacher says, children, and you'll learn a lot of interesting things. She'll tell you all about Abraham Lincoln. Now me, of course I never saw Lincoln. I was a way, way down South—" He drew out the "way, way" extravagantly, so that the children laughed. "I was with the Seventeenth Corpse.[7] The Seventeenth Corpse was part of the Army of the Tennessee, but that's something you'll learn all about some day."

Miss Stark would say, "Questions?" and there'd be a lot of questions. Did Mr. Morley ever see any slaves? Sure, he saw a lot of slaves. Did Mr. Morley shoot any Rebels? "Well," he'd say, jingling with laughter, "I shot at a lot of them, and by jiminy, a lot of them shot at me!"

They would applaud, and he'd go back downstairs shaking his head and chuckling.

It was the same after the superintendent suggested that he and Charley Weidlein change places. The North Building had an extra flight of stairs, and Charley's heart was getting bad, and he couldn't climb stairs very well. So Mr. Morley went over to the old North Building just temporarily, but he stayed there four years. The change was confirmed by the board later on, and he got ten dollars more a month than he'd been getting. He was janitor of the old North Building all the time this class of 1922 went to school there. Upper Fifth, both Sixth Grades, both Seventh Grades, and Boys' Eighth and Girls' Eighth. Then old Deak Snyder died, and Ty took his place in the high school.

Miss Bidlack used to call him into the Boys' Eighth. "Mr. Morley, the boys are now studying the Civil War. I wondered if you'd tell them a few of your experiences."

He'd stand contentedly beside her desk and say, "Well, I didn't have more than the usual share, I guess. But I was with Sherman on the big advance through the South. I can tell you the dates, if you are interested in dates, and I remember all the places. In the spring of sixty-four we started over toward North Alabama and Georgia— I mean my brigade. I was in the Fifteenth Iowa Volunteer Infantry. We joined up with McPherson; and our corpse, the Seventeenth, was on the extreme left of his line. We had fighting all the way toward Atlanta. Big Shanty, Kenesaw Mountain, Noonday Creek, Brushy Mountain, Nickajack, and Turner's Ferry. There was constant fighting all the way—skirmish here and skirmish there, and sometimes a

7. **Corpse:** The author is showing Ty's mispronunciation of the word *corps*, meaning a military unit, and pronounced *kôr*.

regular battle. . . . Nope, I never got hit. They saved me for the fool-killer, I guess!"

The boys would shout and stamp their feet on the floor until the old heating pipes rattled beneath the windows, and Miss Bidlack would say patiently, when the roar had subsided, "How many of Mr. Morley's battles can you name?" And he'd hear them naming his battles as he went away through the cloakroom.

Yes, he knew the boys mighty well. The girls too. Sometimes he thought he liked boys best—maybe that was because he never had any sons of his own. He always liked Rowena Snow; her face looked so peaked [8] and kind of trusting—it made him feel sorry for her.

He first ran into Rowena in the basement of the old South Building, when she was in Miss Dundon's room. Second or Third Grade, that was. A lot of the kids brought their lunch in the winter, when the walking was bad and the weather too cold for them to go home at noon. The kids were supposed to eat together in their home rooms, but Rowena had a trick of sneaking off to an unfinished part of the basement, and she'd hide behind the big timbers and eat her lunch.

Rowena lived with her aunt out on the west end of town, and they were pretty poor; Mr. Morley didn't realize just how poor, until he came upon her unexpectedly, and found the child with her lunch. Old baking-powder biscuits—that was all. Damp and soggy and tasteless. Mr. Morley wouldn't have fed a cat with those things.

He didn't eat any lunch himself that day. But Rowena had two egg sandwiches and two jelly ones, a deviled egg, pickles, a banana and some cupcakes Mr. Morley's wife had baked. On Sunday Mr. Morley wanted to take a walk, and they happened to go past old Miss Snow's property, and they happened to stop in. Miss Snow cried by the quart; actually, there wasn't enough in that house to feed a flea. Miss Snow said she couldn't bear to face the charity people herself, so Mr. Morley went down there and talked with them. The Associated Charity folks saw to it that there was food in Miss Snow's pantry that winter, and then next spring her grown-up nephew came home and got a job in the tile factory, so things were better.

Rowena was smart. She was one of the smartest kids that ever went raring through the Shelldrake schools. She got a hundred all the time, or ninety-eight or ninety-six; she used to show her papers to Mr. Morley, and he'd be delighted. She was valedictorian of her class tonight, and that was a great honor. He knew she'd make a good speech. He'd heard some of the teachers talking, and they said Rowena would get a scholarship to go to Iowa University.

8. **peaked** (pē'kid): pale; sickly.

Yes, she was mighty smart. But she wasn't much smarter than Porter Fosselman. Porter was crippled. He used to be one of the most active kids in school, but then they had that big paralysis epidemic when Porter was in the sixth or seventh grade, and his leg was all twisted up after that.

He came fumbling back to school, with blue hollows under his eyes and a queer flame living in them. It was the same blank, hungry flame seen in the eyes of Miss Margy Gillis, as she propelled herself through the streets of Shelldrake in her little chain-driven chair. Crippled people always had that look in their eyes, it seemed to Mr. Morley. But it didn't hurt their brains. Sometimes it appeared as if they could use their brains better than most people.

Hard on them, though, after they got into high school. The other kids were always having parties and playing games, and in some of the more modern homes they had dancing, although you couldn't dance at a school party. There was that late winter afternoon, a couple of years before, when Ty Morley heard Porter Fosselman crutching his way down to the locker room, and then he heard him sniffling. All the kids were talking about the big Christmas-week party that Joanna Severance was going to give. You couldn't come within a mile of the high school and hear anything but party, party, party. They were going to dance, too.

Mr. Morley remembered that he'd seen the Fosselman boy talking to Eleanor Coughlan before the bell rang at eleven. Eleanor was a pretty girl, and you couldn't blame any boy for wanting to take her to a party. But, on the other hand, Mr. Morley thought, it was sort of hard on a girl to accept a crippled boy as her escort, especially when she was gay and wanted to dance all the time. If a girl were just a little bit selfish, she'd be apt to tell the crippled boy that she didn't want to go with him.

So Ty Morley blundered out of the boiler room and said, "Hi there, Porter Fosselman. You know about steam pipes and such; you've learned things like that down at your father's shop, and I heard Mr. Mitchell say you were the best science scholar he had. Well, you come in here and tell me what's wrong with this valve."

So Porter hobbled inside, and at first he was poky and sullen, because he didn't want anybody to see him with his eyes red. But then he got interested in the valve, and he got to explaining about it to Mr. Morley, and Mr. Morley said, "Well, well," and "Now, I never thought of that; maybe there's some kind of a deposit in that elbow, just like you say."

Of course, he wasn't very good at comforting people—not so good as a preacher would have been. He couldn't put his arm around Porter Fosselman and say, "Don't you worry. The thing for you to do is to make yourself so good-natured and good-looking and so clever that you'd please any girl. One thing; you've got a car to drive, and some of the other boys haven't got any cars. You could take a girl auto riding on Sunday afternoon. And if you don't ever act sullen or gloomy, you'll have a real good time when you go to college down at Ames. When girls get a little older and have a little more sense, you'd be surprised how little a man's legs matter."

No, you couldn't talk quite so direct, but you could tell a kind of story. Ty Morley got to telling Porter about a friend of his, who used to be a regular wizard at steam valves and such. He lost his leg in the Civil War—got it shot off at Atlanta when he wasn't much older than—well, just about the age of a high school boy. That fellow felt downhearted about it, at first; but then he got to studying and perfecting himself, kind of, in the subjects he was interested in, and after a while he had a fine job with the Chicago, Milwaukee & St. Paul.

Mr. Morley couldn't remember the name of the girl that his friend married, but she was one of the prettiest girls in town. She was kind of blonde, had big blue eyes, and so on; she got so she was crazy over Mr. Morley's friend, because he was so much smarter and more interesting than a lot of the young bucks around town, and he was certainly on the road to success. Well, they were happily married—they'd been living up in Milwaukee, Wisconsin, for at least forty years. Mr. Morley wasn't sure, but he thought his friend had been made a chief consulting engineer for the C.M. & St. P.

No, you couldn't exactly talk like a parent or a teacher or a minister, because you were just a janitor, and nobody cared much for your advice or encouragement. But there wasn't any law against your making up mild lies of this kind, and there wasn't any rule that said you couldn't pretend there was something the matter with a heating-pipe valve, even though there really wasn't anything the matter with it.

It made Mr. Morley feel warm inside to hear Porter saying, "My gosh, I'm late! Pa will be needing me down at the shop," and to hear him bounding toward the outer door on his rubber-tipped crutches, and to hear him start singing, suddenly, "Toreador, Toreador, don't spit on the floor!" [9]

9. Toreador (tôr′ē·ə·dôr′): The melody is that of "The Toreador Song" from Bizet's opera *Carmen*. The lyrics, of course, are not.

Mr. Morley was dressed up for the occasion. He had on his suit—that was the way he always spoke of it, because his other clothes were pants and coats and vests that didn't match. But this suit was a good one. He bought it for his wife's funeral, and had worn it only on great occasions since then. He kept his bronze G.A.R. button fastened in the lapel, and recently he had been alarmed to find that the cloth around the buttonhole had mildewed almost all the way through. He had a stiff, clean celluloid collar that was too wide for his neck, and a necktie of gray and black stripes. His black shoes were wearing out, but they still looked good when he shined them up. And little loops of gold and blue ribbon hung like decorations from the back of each shoe.

Still self-conscious and uncomfortable in his finery, he tiptoed up the stairs, as fewer and fewer people hurried toward the auditorium and as the first strains of the processional smote the air. The processional was "Day Is Dying in the West." Ty thought that sounded kind of gloomy for a graduation, although the high school orchestra did play it well. Silently, he closed the doors on the north side of the auditorium, and then he sneaked around the rear to close the doors at the south side.

There was a big crowd; both balconies filled, and a few people standing at the back. The American flag, which hung down in front near the stage, had come loose at one corner and dangled a bit unevenly, and Mr. Morley was chagrined [10] to see it so. He hadn't noticed. He wished that Miss Roache or the principal had told him. He took up his station in a far corner of the room, in the shadow by the dictionary table, and the last members of the graduating class were then mounting the platform steps as the orchestra sawed its way toward a finish.

My, but Rowena Snow looked pretty! She was pale, as always, but it was the pallor of excitement. Her black hair was soft and fluffy, and she had tied it with a blue ribbon. That girl would make her mark, all right, and it was certainly fine that she had won a scholarship. . . . Mr. Morley thought of cold, crushed baking-powder biscuits, and he turned up his nose at the idea.

The class sat in a double semicircle on the stage. The Reverend Mr. Chipperfield arose to pronounce the invocation. Five hundred people bowed their heads, and Mr. Morley bowed with the rest. He stole cautious glances now and then toward the doors, to see that people weren't standing in front of them. That was a fire rule.

10. **chagrined** (shə·grind′): distressed, self-reproachful.

The s sounds were washing across the silent room, just as they did in chapel. Reverend Chipperfield said: ". . . these young people of Shelldrake who stand tonight on the threshold of their lives . . ." and in that moment Ty Morley wished to blow his nose. He thought again of Lexington, Nebraska; suddenly it seemed that he would be a very great distance away from his wife's grave. He hadn't thought of that before.

Every now and then it was difficult for Mr. Morley to see those young people, sitting up on the platform with the superintendent and the principal and the president of the school board. Their faces receded and mingled in a pale mist; even the baskets of flowers seemed confused.

But he could hear well enough, though his glasses were cloudy. He listened to Lester Aiken singing a tenor solo. Yes, Lester had a fine voice—always had had. His voice was rich and mellow, firm with young manhood. And Theodore Kobitsky was the salutatorian,[11] and he was making a splendid speech. He was welcoming all the parents and friends, and saying that the class tried hard, collectively and individually, to live up to the precepts given them by the good example of their elders, and he was saying more things of the same kind.

Theodore had lived up to the precepts given him by Mr. Morley very well indeed. That was when Theodore was in Lower Fifth. Miss Black's room, that used to be—and the bigger boys were always picking on him, and even the ones his own size made life pretty uncomfortable. Because Theodore would fly into a rage, and scream and squawk, and, of course, his tormentors took pleasure in seeing him act that way. It didn't do any good for teachers to lecture or punish the other boys; they just took it out on Theodore, the first chance they got.

It was kind of difficult for a timid boy to fight back. So Mr. Morley showed Theodore a couple of tricks: he had learned those tricks from a railroad detective, long ago, when Mr. Morley served as an officer of the law. A small man could handle a bigger one that way, and thus a small boy could handle a bigger boy.

Theodore only needed a few lessons, and then one day he got his dander [12] up when the boys plagued him, and he threw Buster Water-

11. **salutatorian** (sə·lōō'tə·tôr'ē·ən): the graduating student, usually the one with the second highest grades, who delivers the opening or welcoming speech (salutatory) at commencement. The word is derived from the Latin *salus*, which means, among other things, health, safety, and greeting.
12. **dander:** anger, temper.

field down in the schoolyard gravel so hard that Buster howled. Mr. Morley reckoned that Theodore Kobitsky could hold up his head now, wherever he went. No one had ever picked on him after that.

And the Girls' Glee Club looked beautiful, clustered together up there and singing "I Would That My Love." The mist cleared from Mr. Morley's eyes; he watched the girls with pride and satisfaction, and he tried to forget that he might not see any of them again—at least not for a good while. Of course, he'd come back to Shelldrake for a visit, whenever he could afford to, but that wouldn't be very often. He had his pension, but it seemed like he ought to pay board at his daughter's place; it would make him feel more independent. Yes, he supposed that a lot of those girls would be pushing baby carriages when he came back to town.

His vision blurred again. He knew that the vague figure now standing at the front of the platform was Rowena Snow. She didn't have stage fright at all; talked as clearly and bravely as if there weren't five hundred pairs of eyes looking at her. . . . Mr. Morley began to wander mentally once more, through the dark halls of the old South Building. He swept and polished, and he fixed a leaky radiator. There was that window in Miss Dundon's room—it always stuck when she tried to open it. He worked in the North Building, too, and he smelled smoke again—the smoke that bloomed from a basement fire, back in 1915. He heard the tramp, tramp of children's feet shaking the huge stairways and parading out through the open doors; and they squealed and shouted when they got outside, because they thought a fire drill was a lot of fun; they liked to have Mr. Morley ring the fire gong. But it was no false alarm that day.

Slowly, the old man lifted his hands and clasped them together stiffly, and then unclasped them, and saw the pink, drawn scars where the fire had cooked his flesh, long, long ago.

No, of course. That wasn't long—only seven years. That was only four years after his wife died. Let's see, he was seventy-six now. There seemed to be a dream ahead of him, and beyond that dream was the age of eighty, which had always frightened him.

Take Adoniram McCoy—one of the Comrades. He was eighty now, and he seemed much older than Mr. Morley. And Captain Hathaway was eighty-six, and had to stay abed all the time.

So Tyler Morley wanted to interrupt Rowena suddenly. He wanted to say, "Now, Rowena, you better stop that talk. You'd all better go back to Number One in the old South Building, and we'll start all over again. I guess that would be pleasanter than letting ourselves grow old."

Ty opened his mouth as if he would speak, and he must have made a sound, for two women in seats nearby turned to look at him. He edged back into the shadow of the bookcase, and he felt ashamed.

". . . to the teachers who have counseled us," Rowena was saying, "and to our principal and superintendent. No one of us can forget, for a moment, the debt that he or she owes to parents or relatives who made our education possible. But it has been said that the school is the child's second home, and we feel that the faculty of the Shelldrake schools have loyally encouraged and aided us. Surely each member of the Class of 1922 will wish to return frequently to his or her dear alma mater, and give tribute to those wise friends to whom we owe so much."

Rowena said, "Our hearts are full tonight—full of the hope and ambitions which you, our parents and teachers, have cultivated so generously. But also our hearts are filled with sorrow at this parting. Whether we proceed further in our education in other classrooms, or whether we are immediately to take our places in the workaday world, there cannot but be a feeling of regret that we must leave forever the Shelldrake schools."

It was outlandish even to think of it, but Ty Morley had a confused wish that there was some place in all this ritual for mention of the janitor. Oh, that was downright crazy. Rowena might as well mention the windowpanes, or the hall doors, or the dictionary, or the bottles in the laboratory.

As far as he was concerned, there had been all too many bottles in the laboratory. He was reminded of them now, when Beatrice Churchill, the class president, came forward to present Miss Roache with a bouquet of roses. Miss Roache was the class adviser, and surely she deserved those roses, because the kids pestered the life out of her with this and that. . . . Bottles in the laboratory, yes. And one day Ty had asked Mr. Mitchell what he meant when he said that that big black flask should never be moved from its place on the shelf.

"That's a life preserver, Ty."

"What?"

"Yes! It should always be handy, in case of trouble with acid. It counteracts the effects of the acid, you see."

It was three years later, and nearly five o'clock in the afternoon, and some girls were in the laboratory, making up work they had missed during the grippe [13] epidemic, when there came that smash of breaking glass and that shuddering scream.

13. **grippe** (grip): a virus disease similar to influenza.

It seemed to Mr. Morley now, as he thought of it, that he was much spryer on his feet in those days. Yes, he was much spryer. . . . Beatrice had a few little marks on her neck, but they weren't disfiguring marks, and her face had healed perfectly. It had been awful smart of Mr. Mitchell to tell him about that remedy.

Well, maybe they didn't have either bases or acids in Lexington and if they had, it would be no concern of his. And now the world was breaking up around him, and diplomas were being presented.

There was the crisp, clean rustle of heavy paper; the Class of 1922 marched rapidly out of Mr. Morley's life. They were moving into the world, and some of them would do fine things, no doubt. No one could be happy forever, but at that moment Mr. Morley hoped that God might show special consideration to the forty-four boys and girls on the platform.

Reverend Chipperfield was pronouncing the benediction. . . . Oh, yes, that was the school song. The audience knew it, too, and stood there singing it. And maybe the orchestra had played, in between the prayer and the song, or somebody had sung a solo. . . . Mr. Morley had lost track of events.

> We're the loyal and bold, Shelldrake High,
> We're the Purple and Gold, Shelldrake High. . . .
> Amid the broad green plains that nourish our land,
> For honest effort and for learning we stand. . . .

After everyone had left the auditorium, after the flowers had been carried away, and when the principal had locked his office and gone, Mr. Morley went around turning off lights and closing windows.

He heard steps in the lower hall, and went down hastily to make sure that no loiterer had stayed behind. But it was only Ed Jensen, Mr. Morley's successor.

"Just on my way home," said Ed. "Thought I'd stop in and help you lock up."

"I never swept the auditorium," said Ty apologetically. "Seemed as if I was too blame tired tonight."

Ed Jensen said, "Pshaw, I never expected you to! I'll be on the job bright and early tomorrow. Mr. Cole told me to start in the morning. It's June first, tomorrow. Got to get started with the summer cleaning and painting."

"That's right," said Ty. "Well, Ed. I guess I might as well give you my keys and let you lock up, so's you'll feel at home."

When he reached the corner of the schoolyard, he looked back, and the whole building was dark. Ed had just switched off the last lights, and Mr. Morley could hear the jangling of Ed's keys.

He was an old fool. If Letty were alive now—of course, she had been dead eleven years—but if she were alive now, she would be sitting there on the little screen porch when he got home, and she'd say, "Ty, you're an old fool. You've got no cause to go sniveling around this way. I declare, I think you must have been actually crying, your eyes are so red!"

Of course, his eyes must be red, because they felt damp and harsh and sharp, and the starlight didn't seem to soothe them, nor the smell of flowers in everybody's yards. He heard his footsteps echoing under the dusky arch of trees, all the way out to the 1700 block on West Division Street.

He would go to bed right away, because he was so no-account. Sometimes it was hard to go right to bed when you got home at night, if you were baching it [14] the way Mr. Morley had been doing for eleven years. Sometimes you sat up and read the *Yeoman Shield* until there were no more cars traveling abroad, not even on Division Street.

Whether you lived alone or not, it was unusual for you to lock your doors in Shelldrake. . . . Mr. Morley moved across the tiny porch, feeling his way through lonely darkness and moving carefully around the sharp rockers of his little chair. His hand found the white knob of the door. He wanted to say to the door, or say to somebody, "Of course, they're just kids! They don't realize how a fellow might feel. It isn't their fault they were busy graduating, and the other folks were busy watching them; you oughtn't to expect them to pay much attention. Ed Jensen is a good man. He'll take care of things."

Standing a moment in the enclosed darkness, he became aware that the living room was not the same. There was something wrong. He could hear the mantel clock and the buzzing of a few insects outside. But now another spirit seemed to dwell there, close beside his. That wasn't as it should have been; Mr. Morley was baching it. It was hard to have Decoration Day and Graduation Day so close together—you got all stirred up, kind of. You began to imagine things.

He lighted the lamp, and he breathed more easily in the comfort of its yellowness. He set the painted china shade carefully upon its brackets, and then his hands ceased to move.

14. **baching it** (bach'ing): *slang,* living as a bachelor.

There was something on the table right beside the lamp—something that had not been there at suppertime. It was a package—a little parcel in white tissue paper. Maybe somebody had brought it there after supper. Maybe it was a mistake. Maybe they had got the wrong house. Maybe—

He held it in his hand. He knew—and yet dared not believe or recognize—what spirit it was, living there beside him. The spirit talked with a confident voice—a stalwart [15] voice, however small. Mr. Morley's hands shook violently, but somehow he got the wrappings loose, and then he had the box open.

The dial was pure and glistening, but the neat numerals buzzed and trembled when he looked at them. He turned the watch in his hands. It was a long while before he could read the inscription: To TYLER MORLEY. FROM HIS FRIENDS. CLASS OF 1922. S. H. S. "BLESSED BE THE TY." [16]

He knew that he must say something aloud, even though there were only the empty room and the happy little watch to hear him. He mumbled hoarsely, "Why, why—why, they must have put in fifty cents apiece!" He sat down in Letty's old rocker.

The watch ran on. It spoke busily, as if assuring Mr. Morley that the spirit of his children would stay close beside him, no matter whether he went to Lexington, Nebraska, or a great deal farther away.

15. stalwart (stôl′wərt): determined, steady, loyal.
16. Blessed . . . Ty: These words are probably based on the hymn, "Blest Be the Tie That Binds."

Meaning

1. In what ways can the title, the school song, and the valedictorian's address be considered applicable to Tyler Morley?
2. Through Ty Morley's character, the author is offering such comments as:
   (a) Even the humblest work when done with pride can be a source of dignity.
   (b) The occasions for charity and kindness are numerous in every life if one is aware of them.
   On what actions of Ty Morley could you base these conclusions? What other comments on life is MacKinlay Kantor making? Support your answer with textual references.
3. Ty's gift was simply left for him to discover rather than presented to him with speeches and fanfare. Considering the type of relationship he had with the students, why was this method of presenting the gift the more appropriate and meaningful?

4. Why might the students have found it easier to accept help from Mr. Morley than from some other adult in their lives? Was Ty a good psychologist? Why or why not?
5. What is the conflict?
6. What is the theme?

Method

1. Much of the story is presented in flashbacks. How does the author make the transitions from the present to the past?
2. Incidents from Ty's past are used to help characterize him. What character qualities are brought out by these incidents?
3. What is the climax of the story? How does the author build toward it?
4. "Now don't cry, sissy," Ty once told Amy Galliver. "You won't have no tears left for when you need them!" How is this dialogue in keeping with the author's characterization of Ty? Give other examples of Ty's dialogue and rewrite them in standard English. What is the effect of such rewriting?
5. This story provides an example of *stream-of-consciousness* writing— a technique by which an author attempts to reproduce the uninterrupted flow (stream) of thoughts, feelings, reflections, associations, and memories that might take place in a character's mind (consciousness) at any given moment. How does Kantor use stream of consciousness to help characterize Ty and to advance the plot? Give examples from the text.
6. Is this a commercial or a quality story? Why?

Language: Prefixes and Suffixes

The word *prefix* itself can serve as an illustration of what a prefix is. It is composed of the Latin *prae*, before, and *figere*, to fix. *Praefixus* means to set or fix before.

The following words are from "Valedictory."

	Prefix	Meaning	Word
1.	con-, com-	with, together	confused
2.	re-	back, backward, again	receded
3.	pro-	for, forward	processional
4.	dis-	away	disfiguring
5.	sub-	under	subsided
6.	ad-	to, toward	adviser

Write a sentence for each of these words. Be able to explain the root of each word.

Just as prefixes are placed before roots to change the meaning or use of the roots, so *suffixes* are added after the roots, again to change the meaning or use. Some suffixes change the roots to noun forms. Among these noun suffixes (illustrated by words from the story) are:

Suffix	Meaning	Word
1. -er, -or	doer, office, action, state	loiterer, successor
2. -ion	action, state, result	graduation
3. -ness	quality, state	stiffness
4. -ory	a place or thing for	laboratory

Give the root for each of these words. Write another word of your own to illustrate *each* of the suffixes.

Composition and Discussion

1. Are the problems of the students exaggerated or realistic? Why? Are they similar to the general problems faced by students today? What changes would have to be made to give the story a present-day setting?

2. Assume you are a reporter for the Shelldrake *Clarion*. Write an obituary-feature for Tyler Morley. Be sure to include the 5 W's and H— the *who, what, when, where, why*, and *how*. Pretend to interview some of the teachers and students who knew him at Shelldrake High School and include some quotations from them. Study an obituary-feature or the obituary page of your local newspaper for the kind of information to be included.

3. Write an essay on one of the following statements, using specific examples from your reading or personal experiences: (a) There is a quiet, tactful way to help other people; (b) Actions speak louder than words.

Elizabeth Enright
[1909–1968]

After several years of illustrating children's books for other authors, Elizabeth Enright thought it would be fun to write a book of her own for which she could do exactly the kind of pictures she wanted. In the process she decided that she liked writing better than drawing. Her book, *Kintu: A Congo Adventure*, was published in 1935 and was praised for both the story and its illustrations.

Elizabeth Enright was born in Oak Park, Illinois. Her father was a political cartoonist and her mother a magazine illustrator. In 1910 her parents moved to New York City in search of better jobs.

Miss Enright began drawing at the age of three. After high school she attended the Art Students' League in New York City and later the Parsons School of Applied Arts in Paris. At twenty she got her first job illustrating a book of fairy tales. With the success of her own book *Kintu*, she gave up illustrating as a career and devoted her energies to writing fiction. The author lived in Long Island, New York, with her husband and three sons.

Many of her short stories have appeared in such national magazines as *The New Yorker, Harper's Magazine,* and *The Ladies' Home Journal.* They have been collected in *Borrowed Summer* (1946), and *The Moment Before the Rain* (1955), in which "Nancy" appears. A reviewer in *The New York Times* wrote that some of her stories "are so relaxed and leisurely that the reader does not realize how deeply involved he has become."

Nancy

Fiona [1] Farmer was seven years old. Her mother was forty-six, her father was fifty-five, her nurse was sixty-one, and her grandmother and grandfather, with whom they were all spending the summer, had reached such altitudes of age that no one remembered what they were. From these great heights Fiona was loved and directed.

1. **Fiona**: a name which seems to have been invented by the Scottish author William Sharp (1855–1905), who wrote some of his prose and verse under the pen name "Fiona Macleod." The name is said to be derived from the Celt word *Fion* meaning fair or white.

She wore her hair as her mother had worn it in 1914, braided tight and tied back in pretzel loops with big stiff ribbons. In winter she was the only girl at school to wear a flannel petticoat and underwear with sleeves. Her mother read her all the books she had loved in her childhood: *Rebecca of Sunnybrook Farm,* and *The Five Little Peppers,* and *Under the Lilacs.*[2] Her grandmother read her the books *she* had loved as a child: *Macé's Fairy Tales,* and *Grimm's Fairy Tales,* and *The Princess and Curdie.*[3] On this mixed diet of decorum and brutality Fiona was rapidly turning into a "quaint little creature." She was a pensive child, with large attentive eyes and rather elderly manners; all her play was quiet, accompanied at times by nothing noisier than a low continuous murmuring, so it was strange that the ranks of dolls on her nursery shelves were scalped and eyeless, like the victims of a Sioux[4] massacre.

"What on earth does she do to them?" her mother said to Nana, the nurse. "Why, when I was little my dollies were really like babies to me. I took such *care* of them, I *loved* them so. . . ."

"I honestly don't know, Mrs. Farmer," Nana said. "She'll be as quiet as a mouse in here for hours at a time, and then I'll come in and find all this—this destruction! It seems so unlike her!"

Fiona's grandmother reproached her quietly. "How would you like it if your dear mother pulled all your hair out of your head and broke your arms and legs? Your dolls are your little responsibilities, your *children* in a way. . . ."

Her admonishments, though frequent, were always mild. When Fiona scratched her head, or picked her nose, she would say: "That's not very pretty, dear, is it? We don't do those things, do we?" . . . She was a lofty, dignified, conventional lady, and she smelled like an old dictionary among whose pages many flowers have been dried and pressed. She taught Fiona how to make a sachet[5] and a pomander ball[6] and to play parcheesi.[7]

Fiona liked her grandfather the best. He was a man of wonderful

---

2. *Rebecca . . . Lilacs:* written respectively by Kate Douglas Wiggin, Harriet Lothrop, and Louisa May Alcott.

3. *Macé's* (mä'sās') . . . *Curdie:* translations of books written respectively by John Macé, a French author; Jakob and Wilhelm Grimm, two scholarly German brothers; and George Macdonald, a Scottish novelist and poet.

4. *Sioux* (sōō): an Indian tribe formerly living in the Dakotas and parts of Minnesota and Nebraska.

5. *sachet* (sa·shā'): a small bag or pad filled with perfumed powder.

6. *pomander ball:* an orange or other round fruit stuck with cloves, hung in clothes closets.

7. *parcheesi* (pär·chē'zē): a game played on a board using disks and dice.

patience and politeness; deaf as a post. Every morning she followed him out to the vegetable garden where, in his old loose button-down-the-front sweater and his white canvas golf hat that sagged in a ruffle around his head, he worked along the rows of beets and cabbages with his hoe and rake. Fiona followed at his heels, speaking cease-lessly; it did not matter to her that he never heard a word she said, she told him everything. Now and then he would stop, resting on his hoe handle, and look down at her appreciatively. "Well," he would say. "You're a pleasant little companion, aren't you?" Then he would reach out his old parched hand (he was so old that he never sweated any more) and give her a brittle tap or two on the shoulder or head, and he and Fiona would smile at each other out of a mutual feeling of benevolence.

Sooner or later, though, Nana's voice would begin to caw: "Fee-ona! Fee-ona!" and she would have to go back to the house to pick up her toys or change her dress or eat a meal, or some other dull thing.

Her grandparents' house was big and cool inside. All the rooms were full of greenish light reflected from the maple trees outdoors; the floors were dark and gleaming, the carpets had been taken up for the summer, and the furniture had linen dresses on. There was no dust anywhere, not even in the corners of the empty fireplaces, for Cora and Mary, the maids who had been there for thirty years, spent their lives seeing that there was not.

Cora had arthritis, and on Sundays when Fiona had noon dinner with the whole family she marveled at the extreme slowness with which the maid moved about the table, like a running-down toy. Her face looked very still and concentrated then, relaxing only when she served Fiona, whispering: "Eat it all up now, dear, every bit, so I can tell Mary."

Oh food! People were always speaking of food to Fiona; the Sunday dinners were a trial to toil through. "Eat it all up, dear," and "Clean your plate" were phrases that were ugly in her ears.

After Sunday dinner everyone went to sleep for a while and the house droned with different pitches of snoring. Wearing nothing but a pink wrapper, Fiona would lie on the big white bed while Nana sat in an armchair by the window rattling the Sunday paper. Out-of-doors the cicadas [8] sounded hot as drills; the lazy air coming in the window brought a smell of grass, and Fiona wished that Nana would

8. cicadas (si·kā′dəs): insects known for their loud shrill sounds.

fall asleep so that she could get up and find something to play with, but Nana would not fall asleep.

But once she did.

Once on Sunday after the usual slow massive dinner, as Fiona lay in the extremity of boredom counting mosquito bites and listening to herself yawn, she heard another sound; a new one that might promise much. Quietly she raised herself to her elbows, hardly daring to believe, and saw that the impossible had happened at last. Nana lay in the armchair, abandoned,[9] with her head thrown back and her hair coming down and her mouth wide open like that of a fish; a faint guttural sound came out of it each time she breathed.

A great light seemed to flood the room, and a voice from on high addressed Fiona: "Get up and dress, but do not put on your shoes. Carry them in your hand till you get outside, and close the front door quietly behind you."

Fiona got up at once, dressed with the silence and speed of light, and departed. The upstairs hall hummed and trumpeted with the noises of sleeping; no one heard her running down the stairs.

Out-of-doors it was bright and hot; she sat on the front step and put on her sandals with her heart galloping in her chest. Though old, the members of her family were tall, their legs were long as ladders, and if they came after her they would surely catch her. Leaving the sandal straps unbuckled, Fiona ran out of the gate and down the street, terrified and exhilarated. She ran till she was giddy and breathless, but when at last she stopped and looked behind her the street on which she found herself was still and empty, steeped in Sunday.

She walked for a long time. Her heart stopped racing, and her breathing became comfortable again. Her fear, too, gave way to pleasure and pride. It was a beautiful afternoon. The street was very high with elms. The light that came through their roof of leaves was green and trembling like light through water. Fiona became a little crab crawling among the roots of seaweed. The parked cars were fishes which would eat her up, danger was everywhere. . . . She walked sideways, made claws out of her thumbs, hid behind trees, and felt that her eyes grew out on stems. But not for long. Suddenly, as sometimes happened, the fancy collapsed, betrayed her completely. There was no danger; the cars were cars only. Nothing was any better

9. **abandoned:** In addition to the usual meanings of *forsaken* and *deserted*, this word can also refer to the giving up of one's self to a natural impulse, as here, to sleep.

than real; in the end somebody would catch her and take her home
or she would return of her own accord, driven by hunger or conscience, and everything would be as it had always been.

The houses sat back from their green laps of lawn, silent and sub-
stantial, regarding her like people wearing glasses. There was a smell
of privet [10] and hot asphalt in the still air; a boring smell. . . . Intolerable boredom amounting to anguish drove Fiona to turn abruptly
and kick the iron palings of a fence that she was passing, a kick that
hurt right through her shoe.

The big street came to an end finally at a small Civil War monu-
ment and branched out beyond it in three roads. She chose the right-
hand one because there was a dog asleep on the sidewalk there, but
when she got to him she saw the flies strolling up and down his face
and he looked up at her balefully with a low ripple of sound in his
throat and she hurried on.

This street had few trees; it was broader, and the houses, while
farther apart, were shabbier. The afternoon sun was in her eyes,
drawing her along the gilded road. The wind had sprung up, too,
warm and lively, blowing from the west.

On the outskirts of the town, she came upon her destination,
though at first she did not realize it. For some time the wind had
been bringing her great blasts of radio music; and she saw now that
these had their source in a gray frame house that fairly trembled with
melody. Though not small, this was the seediest of all the houses.
It stood in the middle of a yard as full of tall grass as a field. There
were paths through the field and bald patches where people had
stamped and trampled, and many souvenirs abandoned and half
grown over: a rusted little wagon with no wheels, somebody's shoe,
an old tire. . . .

The house had a queer shape, fancy, but with everything coming
off or breaking. Some of the shutters hung by one hinge only; the
cupola [11] on top was crooked and so was the porch, from which half
the palings were gone. The fence, too, had lost many of its pickets
and stood propped against the tangle like a large comb with teeth
missing; but it had kept its gate, and hanging onto this and swinging
slowly back and forth were three little girls. Fiona walked more
slowly.

One of the girls had a bandanna tied tightly around her head, but

10. **privet:** an ornamental shrub used for hedges.
11. **cupola** (kyōo′pə·lə): a small tower built on a roof and having a dome-
shaped top.

the other two regarded her from under untrimmed dusty bangs, like animals peering out from under ferns. The gate gave a long snarl of sound as they pushed it forward.

"Where are you going?" said the tallest one.

Fiona could not be sure of the tone of this question: was it a friendly or a hostile challenge? She moved still more slowly, touching each picket with her forefinger.

"No place," she said guardedly.

"What's your name?" demanded the girl with the bandanna. She smelled of kerosene.

"Fiona Farmer," said Fiona.

"That's a funny name. My name's Darlene, and hers is Pearl, and *hers* is Merle. Nancy is a nice name."

Fiona saw that all of them were wearing red nail polish and asked a question of her own.

"Are you all three sisters?"

"Yes, and there's more of us. *Them*," said Pearl, the tallest girl, jerking her head. "In the swing."

Beyond the house Fiona now saw for the first time an old double-rocker swing full of boys.

"There's Norman and Stanley and Earl," Darlene said. "And in the house we got a baby sister named Marilyn, and down to the picture theater we got a big sister named Deanna. Come on in."

"Will they let me swing in the swing?" said Fiona.

"Sure they will. *What* did you say your name was?"

"Fiona," she admitted. "Fiona Farmer."

"Gee," said Pearl.

"We'll call her Nancy," said Darlene, who, though younger, seemed to be a leader in her way. "Come on, Nancy, you wanna swing on the gate? Get off, Merle."

Merle got off obediently, sucking her thumb.

"I would like to swing in the *swing*," Fiona said.

She came into the yard gazing up at the tipsy cupola. "Can you get up there into that kind of little tower?"

"Sure," said Darlene. "Come on up and we'll show you."

Fiona followed them through the interesting grass in which she now saw a broken doll, somebody's garter, somebody's hat, and many weathered corncobs and beer cans.

On the porch, which swayed when they walked on it, there were a tough-looking baby buggy, two sleds, a bent tricycle, a lot of chairs and boxes and bushel baskets and peck baskets, and a baby pen, and a wagon wheel, and some kindling wood. The screen door was full of holes and instead of a doorknob there was a wooden thread spool to turn.

The noise of music was stunning as they went indoors; it kept the Mason jars [12] ringing on the shelves. They walked right into it, into the thrilling heart of noise which was the kitchen, where a woman was sitting nursing a baby and shouting random conversation at an old, old woman with a beak nose.

The music ceased with a flourish and the radio announcer's tremendous tones replaced it, but this did not stop the shouted discourse of the woman with the baby. As the girls crossed the kitchen she turned for a moment to look at them, saw Fiona and said, "Who's she?"

"She's Nancy," called Darlene, against the radio.

"Who?"

"Nancy! She dropped in."

"That's Mom," Pearl said.

Fiona went over to the lady to shake her hand. She made her usual curtsy and said, "How do you do?"

Mom's hand felt limp and rather damp and startled. She was a big woman with a wide face and tired blue eyes.

"The old one's Gramma," Darlene said, so Fiona curtsied to the old lady too, and shook her hand which felt like a few twigs in a glove.

"And that's my father," Darlene added, a few seconds later when they had gone up the loud bare stairs to the next floor; Fiona peeked in the doorway of the dim, strong-smelling room but all she saw of *him* was the soles of his socks and she heard him snoring.

"Just like at home," she said. "Sunday afternoon they all sleep."

"Hell, he sleeps all *day* on Sundays," Darlene said, and Fiona felt a little humiliated for her own father.

"This is Gramma's room." Pearl threw open the door. "She likes flowers."

The room was a jungle steeped in musky twilight. A vine of some kind had crawled all over the window and parts of the wall, and on the sill, the sash, the floor below, were pots and jars and coffee tins in which stout lusty plants were growing and flowering.

"How does she open the window at night?" Fiona wondered.

12. **Mason jars:** glass jars used in home canning and preserving. They were named after John L. Mason, a nineteenth-century American inventor.

"*She* don't open no windows day or night," Darlene said. "Hell, she's *old*, she's gotta stay *warm*."

They went up another flight of stairs, narrow steep ones, crowded with magazines and articles of clothing and decayed toys. "Up here's where we sleep," Darlene said. "Us girls, all of us except Marilyn. Pearl and me and Merle sleep in the big bed and Deanna she sleeps in the cot. This is the attic like."

The big bed was made of iron with the post knobs missing. It dipped in the middle like a hammock and there, Fiona knew, the little girls would lie at night, dumped together in a tangle, quarreling or giggling in whispers.

"Look at all the comic books!" she cried, and indeed they lay everywhere in tattered profusion, a drift of stained, disordered leaves.

"We got about a hundred or a thousand of 'em, I guess," Pearl said. "You want some?"

"Could I really, Pearl? Could you spare them?"

"*Atom Annie's* a good one," Pearl said. "We got a lot about her, and here's one called *Hellray* that's real good, real scary. Take these."

Fiona looked at them longingly. "I don't know if my mother—she doesn't like for me to have comics."

"Heck, why not?"

"Well, maybe this time she won't mind," Fiona said, taking the books, determined that everything would be all right for once. "Thank you very, very much, Darlene and Pearl."

"Here's the stairs to the lookout," Darlene said. "Get out of the way, Merle, you wait till last."

They climbed the ladder steps in the middle of the room, Pearl pushed open the trap door and one by one they ascended into the tiny chamber.

It was a tipped little cubicle like a ship's cabin in stiff weather, and stiflingly hot. It seemed remote, high, cozy, and its four soiled windows showed four different views of the town faded and reduced as pictures in an old book. Flies buzzed and butted at the hot glass. Fiona felt disappointed when she saw the steeple of the church that stood across the street from her grandfather's house. She had not thought it was so near.

"Jump!" cried Darlene. They all began to jump, and the cupola jarred and trembled under the pounding.

"Won't it break?" cried Fiona, pounding with the rest. "Won't it fall off?"

"Naw, it won't break," Darlene called back. "It never did yet."

"But it might some day, though," shouted Pearl encouragingly. It was fun to jump riotously and yell, as the tiny tower rocked and resounded.

There was an interruption from below.

"Get out of there!" bawled Mom up the stairs. "How many times I told you kids to stay down out of there! You want to get your backs broke? You want to get killed? You scram down!"

"Get out of the way, Merle, let Nancy go first," Pearl said.

Mom stood at the foot of the steps wearing the baby around her neck. Anxiety had made her furious. "That place ain't safe, you know that!" she cried. "How many times have I told you?" She gave Pearl a slap on the cheek and would have given one to Darlene, too, if Darlene had not bent her neck adroitly.

"You let me catch you up there one more time and I'll get your father to lick you good!"

"Aw, climb a tree," said Darlene.

Fiona was aghast. What would happen now?

But nothing happened. Merle still quietly sucked her thumb, Darlene and Pearl seemed cool and jaunty, and as they descended through the house Mom's anger dried up like dew.

"You kids want a snack?" she said. "You didn't eat since breakfast."

"Can Nancy stay?"

"Why sure, I guess. Why not?"

"Oh, thank you very, very much. . . ."

The kitchen, like the rest of the house, had a rich, bold, musty smell. It smelled of constant usage and memories of usage. It was crowded and crusted with objects: pots, pans, kettles, boxes, jars, cans, buckets, dippers. There were two alarm clocks, one lying on its side, and both asserting a different hour, and four big Coca-Cola calendars on the wall, none for the current year. The radio was still thundering music, and close beside it, warming herself at the noise, sat Gramma, dark as a crow, chewing and chewing on her empty gums.

The stove was named Ebony Gem, and behind it in a cardboard box there was something alive; something moved. . . .

"It's kittens," said Merle, removing her thumb from her mouth and speaking for the first time. "Our cat had kittens."

"Oh, let me see!" Fiona knelt by the box. There inside it lay a bland and happy group: mother cat with her yellow eyes half closed and her paws splayed out [13] in pleasure; kittens lined up all along her, sucking.

Merle put out her little forefinger with its chipped red nail polish, stroking first one infant, then the next. "The black one's name is Blackie and the white one's name is Whitey and we call *this* one Butch because he's so. . . ."

"My father usually drowns them, all but one," Darlene interrupted. She bent her kerchiefed head close to Fiona's, so that there was a blinding smell of kerosene.[14] "Tomorrow probly," she whispered. "We don't tell Merle, it makes her feel so bad." Then she raised her voice. "She knows it's going to happen but she don't know when, huh, Merle?"

"You could take one, Nancy," Merle said, still gazing at the kittens. "You could keep it and be good to it."

"Do you mean honestly and truly?"

Fiona's joy was suffocating.

"Any one? Any one at all?"

"Except Butch," Darlene said "We're going to keep him to help with the rats."

"Could I have Blackie? Really for keeps?"

Merle plucked the dark little thing from the mother as if she were plucking off a burr and gave it to Fiona.

"I can feel its little tiny heart," Fiona said. "I'll give it milk all the time and brush its fur and it can sleep in the doll cradle. Oh look at its ears, oh Merle, oh thank you!"

Shamed by gratitude, Merle put her thumb back in her mouth and looked away.

"You kids get out from under my feet," Mom said. "Sit up to the table now, it's all ready. Come on Mama, come on *boys!*" She opened the screen door and put her head out, shouting so hard that great cords stood out on her neck.

They sat around the big table with its oilcloth cover, everything in easy reach: cereal in paper boxes, sugar, catsup. . . . They had corn-flakes and milk, Swiss cheese sandwiches with catsup, cream soda in bottles, and little cakes out of a box with pink and green beads on them. Fiona ate everything.

"Nancy eats good, don't she, Mom?" Darlene said.

13. **splayed out:** spread out.
14. **kerchiefed . . . kerosene:** probably a reference to the fact that at one time kerosene was used to remove head lice and the infected area was then protected with a scarf.

"I never had catsup before," said Fiona. "My, it certainly is delicious, isn't it?"

The table was a family battlefield. Fiona had never seen anything like it in her life. Stanley and Norman threw pieces of sandwich at each other, Earl took one of Merle's cakes and Merle cried and Mom slapped Earl; Darlene stole big swigs from Pearl's soda bottle, was loudly accused and loudly defended herself.

"You kids shut up," Mom said, eating over Marilyn's head and giving her occasional bits of cake dipped in tea. Gramma was the only quiet one; she sat bent over, all wrapped and absorbed in her old age, gazing into her cup as she drank from it with a long purring sound. Blackie was quiet too, asleep in Fiona's lap. She kept one hand on his little velvet back.

Mom pointed at Fiona with her spoon. "Looks like Margaret O'Brien [15] used to, don't she? The ribbons and all."

"Margaret who?" said Fiona.

"O'Brien, *you* know, the kid in the movies," Darlene said.

"Oh, I never go to movies," said Fiona. "I'm not allowed."

"Not allowed!" cried Darlene incredulously. "Hell, we go all the time, don't we, Mom? Even Deanna goes. We could take Nancy with us sometimes, couldn't we, Mom?"

"Maybe, if her folks say yes."

"Oh if I went with *you* it would be all right, I'm sure," cried Fiona joyously. Drunk with noise, strange flavors, gifts, and new friendship, she really believed this.

Afterward, still with catsup on their upper lips, they went outdoors to play hide-and-seek.

"You be her partner, Stanley," ordered Darlene, who was "it." "You kind of look after her, she don't know our places to hide."

Then she hid her eyes with her arm, cast herself against a tree like a girl in grief, and began to count out loud.

"The cellar," hissed Stanley, grabbing Fiona's hand. He was a big eight-year-old boy, and still clutching the kitten Fiona ran with him willingly, hesitating only for a second at sight of the dark abyss. On the steps were many cans and beer crates, but Stanley led her safely down among these and into the black deep tunnel beyond. Fiona could feel that there were solid things all around them; probably more boxes, more beer crates, but she could see nothing. Stanley's hand was warm and firm, it just fitted hers, and she liked having him lead her.

15. **Margaret O'Brien**: a popular child movie star in the latter part of the 1940's and the early 1950's.

"We can stop now," he said, "but keep quiet."

Darlene could still be heard, faintly. Her counting voice sounded deserted and defiant: "*Ninety*-five, *ninety*-six, *ninety*-seven." . . . The blackness throbbed and shimmered and the air had a dense aged smell.

"Coming, ready or not!" called the faraway defiant voice.

"We're safe here anyways," Stanley said. "She won't come down *here*, she's scared to." He laughed silently and gave Fiona's hand a squeeze. "There's rats down here."

"Oh no, oh no! Oh, Stanley, let's go up again," cried Fiona, tears of panic in her voice.

But Stanley held onto her hand. "You going to be a sissy too?" he demanded. "We got the *cat*, ain't we?"

Fiona strained the tiny kitten to her chest. Her heart was banging terribly and she wanted to cry but she would not. All around the rats were closing in, large as dogs and smiling strangely; smiling like people. She almost sobbed when Stanley said, "Now we can go, hurry up, and keep still!"

They were the first ones back.

For a long time they played and Stanley always was her partner. He knew the best places to hide: up in the boughs of a pear tree, under the porch steps, in the fearful little dark privy with its different-sized "family accommodations," and flat on their stomachs under the folded-back cellar door. Darlene was "it" till she caught Merle and Merle was "it" for hours. Fiona got spiderwebs in her mouth and gnats up her nose, tore her dress, scraped her knee, lost one hair ribbon, and gave the other to Merle, who had admired it.

When they were through with hide-and-seek they all got into the rocker swing and played gangsters. The swing leapt to and fro, to and fro, screaming wildly at the joints; surely it would break, and soon! That was the thrilling thing about this place: so many features of it—the tower, the swing, the porch—trembled at the edge of ruin, hung by a thread above the fatal plunge.

Earl and Stanley and Norman leaned over the back of one of the seats firing at the enemy. "Step on it, you guys," yelled Stanley, "they got a gat!"

"They got a rod!" yelled Norman. "They got a lotta rods!"

"What's a rod?" cried Fiona. "What's a gat?"

"Guns he means," Darlene told her. "Rods and gats is guns."

"Shoot 'em, Stanley," yelled Fiona. "With your gat, shoot the eyes out of 'em!"

Clutching the clawing kitten to her collarbone, her hair in her

open mouth, she bawled encouragement to them. The swing acceler-
ated ever more wildly: soon it would take off entirely, depart from
its hinges, fly through the air, burn a hole through the sky! . . .

"Fee-ona Farmer!"

The cry was loud enough to be heard above all sounds of war and
wind and radio music.

Beside the swing stood Nana, so tall, so highly charged with hurry
and emotion, that the children stopped their play at once.

"Who's she?" Stanley asked.

"She's my nurse," Fiona murmured.

"Your nurse! What's the matter, are you sick?"

"No . . . she just—takes care of me."

"Takes *care* of you!"

"You get out of that swing and come this in-stant!"

Having struck the bottom of disgrace, Fiona stepped down and
slowly went to Nana. From the swing the others watched as still as
children posing for a photograph.

"Put down that cat and come at once."

"Oh no!" Fiona said. "It's mine, they gave it to me."

"Put. Down. That. Cat."

Darlene came to stand beside Fiona. "But we did give it to her, we
want for her to have it."

Nana struck the kitten from Fiona's arms. "You will not take that
creature home! It's filthy, it has fleas!"

"Oh my kitty!" shrieked Fiona, diving after Blackie, but Nana
caught her wrist.

"You come!"

Fiona pulled, struggled, cast a glare of anguish at all the rapt
photograph-faces in the swing.

"You should be punished. You should be whipped. Whipped!"
Nana whistled the cruel words; Nana, who was never cruel! Her
fingers on Fiona's wrist were hard.

"Let me say good-by to them, Nana, let me say good-by to their
mother! You said I should *always* say good-by to the mother!"

"Not this time, this time it doesn't matter," Nana said. "You're
going straight home and into the tub. Heavens knows what you will
have caught!" Upon Fiona's friends she turned a single brilliant
glance like one cold flash from a lighthouse.

There was nothing to commend Fiona's departure; dragged by the
hand, whimpering, she looked back at her friends in desperation.
"Oh, Darlene!"

But it was easy to see that Darlene had detached herself. "Good-by, Nancy," she said, not without a certain pride. She did not smile or say anything else, but her attitude showed Fiona and Nana that she had no need for either of them, could not be hurt by them, and would not think of them again. As they went out the gate she turned her back and skipped away, and Fiona heard the rocker swing resume its screaming tempo.

Halfway home Nana's recriminations [16] began to modify, gradually becoming reproaches: "How could you have, Fiona, run away like that, why it's only by the grace of God I ever found you at all! And all the time I was half sick with worry I never said a word to your father and mother! I didn't want *them* to worry!"

Somewhere deep inside her Fiona understood exactly why Nana had said nothing to her parents, but she just kept on saying: "I want my kitty, I want my kitty."

Finally Nana said: "If you're a good girl maybe we'll get you another kitten."

"I don't want another, I want that one."

"Oh for pity's sakes, it had fleas; or worse. Anything belonging to the Fadgins would be bound to have—"

"Do *you* know them?"

"I know *about* them, everybody does. They're the dirtiest, the shiftlessest, the most down-at-the-heel tribe in this whole town!"

"They are not, they're nice, I love them!"

Nana relented a little. "Maybe it's hard not to be shiftless when you're that poor."

"*They* aren't poor. You should see all the things they've got! More than Grandmother's got in her whole house!"

"All right now, dearie, all right. We'll forget about it, shall we? It will be our secret and we'll never tell anyone because we don't want them to worry, do we? But you must promise me never, never to do such a thing again, hear?"

"I want my kitty," droned Fiona.

Her grandparents' house smelled cool and sweetish. There was a bowl of white and pink stock [17] on the hall table and her grandmother's green linen parasol leaned in a corner among the pearly company of her grandfather's canes.

16. **recriminations** (ri·krim'ə·nā'shəns): accusations (usually made by a person in return for an accusation made against him); countercharges.
17. **stock:** an ornamental garden plant.

In the shaded living room Fiona saw her mother knitting and her grandmother at the piano playing the same kind of music she always played, with the loose rings clicking on her fingers.

"Is that my baby?" called her mother—but Nana answered hastily, "I'm getting her right into her bath, Mrs. Farmer. She's sim-ply fil-thy."

Upstairs Nana went in to run the water in the tub. Fiona kicked off one sandal, then the other. A terrible pain took hold of her; it began in her mind and spread down to her stomach. She had never been homesick before and did not know what ailed her: she knew only that she wanted to sleep at night in a big twanging bed full of children and to eat meals at a crowded table where people threw bread at each other and drank pop. She wanted Stanley's hand to guide her and Darlene's voice to teach her and Blackie's purr to throb against her chest. . . .

Beyond the window she saw her grandfather's wilted golf hat bobbing among the cornstalks and escaped again, running on bare feet down the back stairs and out-of-doors across the billowing lawn which seemed to be colliding with the trees and sky and shadows, all flooded and dazzled with tears. Blindly she flung open the garden gate and pushed her way through the green-paper corn forest to her grandfather, who dropped his hoe and held out his arms when he saw her face.

"Come here now," he said in his gentle deaf voice. "Well, well, this won't do, no it won't, not at all. Come sit here with Grandpa, sit here in the arbor. Did you hurt yourself?"

He led her to the seat under the green grape trellis where he sometimes rested from the hot sun. He put his arm around her shoulders, offering himself as a support for grief, and Fiona howled against his waistcoat till the wet tweed chapped her check and there was not a tear left in her. He did not interrupt or ask questions but kept patting her shoulder in a sort of sympathetic accompaniment to her sobs, which he could not hear but which he felt. What's the cause of it all, he wondered. A broken toy? A scolding? Children's tragedies, he thought, children's little tragedies: there are bigger ones in store for you, Fiona, a world of them. The thought did not move him deeply, everyone must suffer, but for an instant he was not sorry to be old.

Fiona leaned against him and after a while, between the hiccups left from sobbing, she could hear the ancient heart inside his chest tick-tocking steadily, as tranquil and unhurried as he was himself. All the wild performance of her sorrow had not quickened its tempo by a single beat, and this for some reason was a comfort.

The sound of her grandmother's music, sugary and elegant, came sparkling from the house, and upstairs in the bedroom or the hall Nana began to call. "Fee-ona?" she cried. "Oh, Fee-*ona*?" There was a hint of panic in her voice now, but no response came from under the green trellis: Fiona's grandfather could not hear the calling, and Fiona, for the time being, did not choose to answer.

Meaning and Method

1. Why does the author begin the story with an account of the ages of the members of the Farmer household? What unusual words does she use to emphasize the age factor?
2. Give a physical description of Fiona. How does she react to the atmosphere and conditions in her home? What part does her imagination play in her reaction? Why does she mutilate her dolls?
3. Why does Fiona like her grandfather? How does the grandfather "escape" from the environment?
4. How do the Fadgin children react to Fiona when they first meet? Why do they change her name to Nancy? What are their feelings when Nana arrives and makes Fiona leave?
5. A *contrast* is a striking difference between two things. Its purpose is to heighten effect. An author may present contrast by showing differences between (a) ways of life, (b) environments, (c) personalities. Find examples of differences in each of these three in the story. Explain the effect of each contrast you select.
6. Why does Fiona not see the "shortcomings" in the Fadgin way of living? What does Fiona find in the Fadgin household that is missing in the Farmer household? What is the significance of the kitten? Why does Fiona not react to the kittens as she did to her dolls?
7. What is the effect of the author's writing "Put. Down. That. Cat."? Would the effect be the same had she written *Put down that cat!* Read both sentences to show how the effect differs.
8. What would you say is the theme of the story?

Language: Figures of Speech

Sometimes a writer, by comparing dissimilar objects, gives a very vivid impression of a person or thing. If the writer says that the first is *like* the second, we call this direct comparison a *simile*. In describing Fiona's grandmother, Elizabeth Enright says, ". . . she smelled like an old dictionary among whose pages many flowers had been dried and pressed."

If the writer does not use *like* or *as* in his comparison but still identifies and compares two objects, we call this implied comparison a *metaphor*. For example: "The table was a family battlefield." Sometimes a metaphor may be expressed by a verb or participle, as, ". . . the house droned with different pitches of snoring."

Another figure of speech is *personification*. This is a special type of metaphor in which nonhuman or lifeless things are given human characteristics, powers, or feelings: ". . . the lazy air coming in the window brought a smell of grass."

Simile, metaphor, and personification are among the most common figures of speech. Identify which of these devices is used in each of the following examples from "Nancy."

1. ". . . and the furniture had linen dresses on."
2. ". . . like a running-down toy."
3. "The upstairs hall hummed and trumpeted with the noises of sleeping. . . ."
4. ". . . with her heart galloping in her chest."
5. "The houses sat back from their green laps of lawn. . . ."
6. ". . . like a large comb with teeth missing. . . ."
7. ". . . Mom's anger dried up like dew."
8. "The blackness throbbed and shimmered. . . ."
9. ". . . a single brilliant glance like one cold flash from a lighthouse."

Composition and Discussion

1. Both "Nancy" and "Mitty" have "secret lives" that those supposedly close to them either do not understand or know about. Write a composition in which you compare and contrast (a) the reasons for their need to "escape" and (b) the kind of life each would like to lead. Illustrate with examples of key incidents from each story.

2. The following is a poem called "Happiness" by Carl Sandburg. Read the poem carefully and be prepared to discuss it in a panel or open-class discussion.

> I asked professors who teach the meaning of life to tell me what is happiness.
> And I went to famous executives who boss the work of thousands of men.
> They all shook their heads and gave me a smile as though I was trying to fool with them.
> And then one Sunday afternoon I wandered out along the Desplaines River
> And I saw a crowd of Hungarians under the trees with their women and children and a keg of beer and an accordion.

Consider the following questions in your discussion:
(a) What do you think the fundamental ingredients for happiness are?
(b) What essential need does Sandburg capture in his "Happiness?"
(c) What elements for happiness are missing from Fiona's life?

"Happiness," from *Chicago Poems* by Carl Sandburg, copyright 1916 by Holt, Rinehart and Winston, Inc., copyright 1944 by Carl Sandburg. Reprinted by permission of the publisher.

Morley Callaghan

Canadian-born Morley Callaghan (1903) was educated at \St. Michael's College of the University of Toronto and at Osgoode Hall Law School. During his college days, Callaghan boxed, played football, and worked as a reporter on the Toronto *Daily Star*.

There he met Ernest Hemingway, who encouraged him in his writing and offered to take some of his short-story manuscripts to Paris, where he helped get several of them accepted for publication in *The Exile*, a literary magazine of that day. Maxwell Perkins, an editor at Scribner's publishing house, was impressed by these stories and had them reprinted in *Scribner's Magazine*.

Callaghan and his wife subsequently visited Paris, in 1929. Callaghan's account of that visit and of his friendship with Hemingway and F. Scott Fitzgerald are contained in *That Summer in Paris*, published in 1963. Today Callaghan is considered one of the most distinguished of contemporary Canadian writers.

Possibly because of the journalistic background of both Hemingway and Callaghan, critics have found similarities in their styles of writing, particularly the bare speech and the objective, coldly observational tone. A recurring theme—being friendless, alone, and at odds with society—appears in many of Callaghan's works. Among his books are *They Shall Inherit the Earth, Such Is My Beloved, A Passion in Rome, The Loved and the Lost, More Joy in Heaven*, and *The Many Colored Coat*. His short stories have been collected in *Now That April's Here*.

Of "All the Years of Her Life" Callaghan said, "Once I saw a woman relaxing after she had used her fine character and her dignity to get her son out of some trouble with his employer. I remember the way her chin had trembled as she drank a cup of tea. That's all. That's why I wrote the story."

All the Years of Her Life

They were closing the drugstore, and Alfred Higgins, who had just taken off his white jacket, was putting on his coat and getting ready to go home. The little gray-haired man, Sam Carr, who owned the drugstore, was bending down behind the cash register, and when

Alfred Higgins passed him, he looked up and said softly, "Just a moment, Alfred. One moment before you go."

The soft, confident, quiet way in which Sam Carr spoke made Alfred start to button his coat nervously. He felt sure his face was white. Sam Carr usually said, "Good night," brusquely, without looking up. In the six months he had been working in the drugstore, Alfred had never heard his employer speak softly like that. His heart began to beat so loud it was hard for him to get his breath. "What is it, Mr. Carr?" he asked.

"Maybe you'd be good enough to take a few things out of your pocket and leave them here before you go," Sam Carr said.

"What things? What are you talking about?"

"You've got a compact and a lipstick and at least two tubes of toothpaste in your pocket, Alfred."

"What do you mean? Do you think I'm crazy?" Alfred blustered. His face got red and he knew he looked fierce with indignation. But Sam Carr, standing by the door with his blue eyes shining bright behind his glasses and his lips moving underneath his gray mustache, only nodded his head a few times, and then Alfred grew very frightened and he didn't know what to say. Slowly he raised his hand and dipped it into his pocket, and with his eyes never meeting Sam Carr's eyes, he took out a blue compact and two tubes of toothpaste and a lipstick, and he laid them one by one on the counter.

"Petty thieving, eh, Alfred?" Sam Carr said. "And maybe you'd be good enough to tell me how long this has been going on."

"This is the first time I ever took anything."

"So now you think you'll tell me a lie, eh? What kind of a sap do I look like, huh? I don't know what goes on in my own store, eh? I tell you you've been doing this pretty steady," Sam Carr said as he went over and stood behind the cash register.

Ever since Alfred had left school he had been getting into trouble wherever he worked. He lived at home with his mother and his father, who was a printer. His two older brothers were married and his sister had got married last year, and it would have been all right for his parents now if Alfred had only been able to keep a job.

While Sam Carr smiled and stroked the side of his face very delicately with the tips of his fingers, Alfred began to feel that familiar terror growing in him that had been in him every time he had got into such trouble.

"I liked you," Sam Carr was saying. "I liked you and would have trusted you, and now look what I got to do." While Alfred watched with his alert, frightened blue eyes, Sam Carr drummed with his fingers on the counter. "I don't like to call a cop in pointblank," he was saying as he looked very worried. "You're a fool, and maybe I should call your father and tell him you're a fool. Maybe I should let them know I'm going to have you locked up."

"My father's not at home. He's a printer. He works nights," Alfred said.

"Who's at home?"

"My mother, I guess."

"Then we'll see what she says." Sam Carr went to the phone and dialed the number. Alfred was not so much ashamed, but there was that deep fright growing in him, and he blurted out arrogantly, like a strong, full-grown man, "Just a minute. You don't need to draw anybody else in. You don't need to tell her." He wanted to sound like a swaggering, big guy who could look after himself, yet the old, childish hope was in him, the longing that someone at home would come and help him. "Yeah, that's right, he's in trouble," Mr. Carr was saying. "Yeah, your boy works for me. You'd better come down in a hurry." And when he was finished Mr. Carr went over to the door and looked out at the street and watched the people passing in the late summer night. "I'll keep my eye out for a cop" was all he said.

Alfred knew how his mother would come rushing in; she would rush in with her eyes blazing, or maybe she would be crying, and she would push him away when he tried to talk to her, and make him feel her dreadful contempt; yet he longed that she might come before Mr. Carr saw the cop on the beat passing the door.

While they waited—and it seemed a long time—they did not speak, and when at last they heard someone tapping on the closed door, Mr. Carr, turning the latch, said crisply, "Come in, Mrs. Higgins." He looked hard-faced and stern.

Mrs. Higgins must have been going to bed when he telephoned, for her hair was tucked in loosely under her hat, and her hand at her throat held her light coat tightly across her chest so her dress would not show. She came in, large and plump, with a little smile on her friendly face. Most of the store lights had been turned out and at first she did not see Alfred, who was standing in the shadow at the end of the counter. Yet as soon as she saw him she did not look as Alfred thought she would look: she smiled, her blue eyes never wavered, and with a calmness and dignity that made them forget that her clothes seemed to have been thrown on her, she put out her hand to Mr. Carr and said politely, "I'm Mrs. Higgins. I'm Alfred's mother."

Mr. Carr was a bit embarrassed by her lack of terror and her simplicity, and he hardly knew what to say to her, so she asked, "Is Alfred in trouble?"

"He is. He's been taking things from the store. I caught him redhanded. Little things like compacts and toothpaste and lipsticks. Stuff he can sell easily," the proprietor said.

As she listened, Mrs. Higgins looked at Alfred sometimes and nodded her head sadly, and when Sam Carr had finished she said gravely, "Is it so, Alfred?"

"Yes."

"Why have you been doing it?"

"I been spending money, I guess."

"On what?"

"Going around with the guys, I guess," Alfred said.

Mrs. Higgins put out her hand and touched Sam Carr's arm with an understanding gentleness, and speaking as though afraid of disturbing him, she said, "If you would only listen to me before doing anything." Her simple earnestness made her shy; her humility made her falter and look away, but in a moment she was smiling gravely again, and she said with a kind of patient dignity, "What did you intend to do, Mr. Carr?"

"I was going to get a cop. That's what I ought to do."

"Yes, I suppose so. It's not for me to say, because he's my son. Yet I sometimes think a little good advice is the best thing for a boy when he's at a certain period in his life," she said.

Alfred couldn't understand his mother's quiet composure, for if they had been at home and someone had suggested that he was going to be arrested, he knew she would be in a rage and would cry out against him. Yet now she was standing there with that gentle, pleading smile on her face, saying, "I wonder if you don't think it would be better just to let him come home with me. He looks a big fellow, doesn't he? It takes some of them a long time to get any sense," and they both stared at Alfred, who shifted away with a bit of light shining for a moment on his thin face and the tiny pimples over his cheekbone.

But even while he was turning away uneasily, Alfred was realizing that Mr. Carr had become aware that his mother was really a fine woman; he knew that Sam Carr was puzzled by his mother, as if he had expected her to come in and plead with him tearfully, and instead he was being made to feel a bit ashamed by her vast tolerance. While there was only the sound of the mother's soft, assured voice in the store, Mr. Carr began to nod his head encouragingly at her. Without being alarmed, while being just large and still and simple and hopeful, she was becoming dominant there in the dimly lit store. "Of course, I don't want to be harsh," Mr. Carr was saying. "I'll tell you what I'll do. I'll just fire him and let it go at that. How's that?" and he got up and shook hands with Mrs. Higgins, bowing low to her in deep respect.

There was such warmth and gratitude in the way she said, "I'll never forget your kindness," that Mr. Carr began to feel warm and genial himself.

"Sorry we had to meet this way," he said. "But I'm glad I got in touch with you. Just wanted to do the right thing, that's all," he said.

"It's better to meet like this than never, isn't it?" she said. Suddenly they clasped hands as if they liked each other, as if they had known each other a long time. "Good night, sir," she said.

"Good night, Mrs. Higgins. I'm truly sorry," he said.

The mother and son walked along the street together, and the mother was taking a long, firm stride as she looked ahead with her stern face full of worry. Alfred was afraid to speak to her, he was afraid of the silence that was between them, so he only looked ahead too, for the excitement and relief were still pretty strong in him; but in a little while, going along like that in silence made him terribly aware of the strength and the sternness in her; he began to wonder what she was thinking of as she stared ahead so grimly; she seemed to have forgotten that he walked beside her; so when they were passing under the Sixth Avenue elevated [1] and the rumble of the train seemed to break the silence, he said in his old, blustering way, "Thank God it turned out like that. I certainly won't get in a jam like that again."

"Be quiet. Don't speak to me. You've disgraced me again and again," she said bitterly.

"That's the last time. That's all I'm saying."

"Have the decency to be quiet," she snapped. They kept on their way, looking straight ahead.

When they were at home and his mother took off her coat, Alfred saw that she was really only half-dressed, and she made him feel afraid again when she said, without even looking at him, "You're a bad lot. God forgive you. It's one thing after another and always has been. Why do you stand there stupidly? Go to bed, why don't you?"

---

1. **elevated:** a railway running above the streets on elevated tracks.

When he was going, she said, "I'm going to make myself a cup of tea. Mind, now, not a word about tonight to your father."

While Alfred was undressing in his bedroom, he heard his mother moving around the kitchen. She filled the kettle and put it on the stove. She moved a chair. And as he listened there was no shame in him, just wonder and a kind of admiration of her strength and repose. He could still see Sam Carr nodding his head encouragingly to her; he could hear her talking simply and earnestly, and as he sat on his bed he felt a pride in her strength. "She certainly was smooth," he thought. "Gee, I'd like to tell her she sounded swell."

And at last he got up and went along to the kitchen, and when he was at the door he saw his mother pouring herself a cup of tea. He watched and he didn't move. Her face, as she sat there, was a frightened, broken face utterly unlike the face of the woman who had been so assured a little while ago in the drugstore. When she reached out and lifted the kettle to pour hot water into her cup, her hand trembled and the water splashed on the stove. Leaning back in the chair, she sighed and lifted the cup to her lips, and her lips were groping loosely as if they would never reach the cup. She swallowed the hot tea eagerly, and then she straightened up in relief, though her hand holding the cup still trembled. She looked very old.

It seemed to Alfred that this was the way it had been every time he had been in trouble before, that this trembling had really been in her as she hurried out half-dressed to the drugstore. He understood why she had sat alone in the kitchen the night his young sister had kept repeating doggedly [2] that she was getting married. Now he felt all that his mother had been thinking of as they walked along the street together a little while ago. He watched his mother, and he never spoke, but at that moment his youth seemed to be over; he knew all the years of her life by the way her hand trembled as she raised the cup to her lips. It seemed to him that this was the first time he had ever looked upon his mother.

2. **doggedly:** in a stubborn, obstinate, or determined manner.

Meaning

1. How had Mrs. Higgins previously reacted to Alfred's troubles? How does her behavior differ this time?

2. Review the discussion of conflict on pages 2–3. The most obvious conflict, of course, is the one between Mrs. Higgins and Mr. Carr, even though they seem to be in agreement. Don't forget that Mr. Carr

wanted to have Alfred arrested; Mrs. Higgins had to persuade Mr. Carr to release Alfred to her.

But there is also a conflict between mother and son, and there are conflicting emotions within the mother herself. Explain the last two conflicts.

3. What hints does the author give about the home life of the Higgins family? What is the relationship between the family life and the title of the story?

4. The reader is not told what made Mrs. Higgins behave with unexpected composure in the drugstore. What reasons can you suggest for her handling the situation as she did?

5. Near the end of the story, we find "And as he [Alfred] listened there was no shame in him, just wonder and a kind of admiration of her strength and repose." How have his feelings changed at the end of the story? Why?

6. The theme of a story is simply the total meaning—a statement the author wishes to make about life. He uses his plot, characters, conflict, etc., to present an idea that may be applicable to many people and many situations.

   Stated simply, the story is about a boy's realization of the strength of character of his mother, his finally understanding her real motivations, and his awareness of the price she has paid for the love of her family. The theme, then, may be stated as *The motivations of love are not easily or always understood*, or *Love can sometimes be a source of strength and calm in time of trouble*.

   In view of its theme, is the story complete and unified? Does it matter that so many questions are left unanswered? Does Alfred change? Does the father find out, and what does he do? Do Alfred and his mother end the "coolness" between them?

7. Whose story is this, Alfred's or the mother's?

Method

1. Are Mr. Carr, Mrs. Higgins, and Alfred clearly drawn characters? Are they stereotyped or "stock" characters? Why or why not? Identify specific techniques of characterization in the story to support your answer. Is this a quality story? Why or why not?

2. Of what four simple scenes is the story composed?

3. The author tells the story from Alfred's point of view. How does this affect the story itself?

4. Tone of voice is a powerful factor in communicating. The words with which you say something and the *way* or *manner* in which you say them may be inviting and encouraging or antagonizing and discouraging. How does this story demonstrate the importance of tone of voice in human relationships?

Language: Denotation and Connotation

The *denotation* of a word is its actual meaning, its precise dictionary definition. The *connotation* is that which it suggests in addition to its literal definition.

Both *home* and *house* denote the place or dwelling where a person lives. However, the word *home* stirs up or connotes additional meanings and associations (usually favorable ones) such as comfort, shelter, coziness, friendliness, privacy, peace, and rest.

Connotative meanings can be suggested by individual words (as *house* versus *home*), or by the context within which certain words and phrases are placed. What connotations do the words *looked upon* have when the narrator says, in the last sentence of this story, "It seemed to him [Alfred] that this was the first time he had ever looked upon his mother."

List some of the *unfavorable* connotations the following words have. First consult your dictionary to check the denotation of each word.

1. rebel	**4.** egghead	**7.** propaganda
2. rat	**5.** bureaucrat	**8.** capitalist
3. saloon	**6.** heel	**9.** tirade

Composition

1. Using one of the following topic sentences, write a composition with details and particulars and examples to support your point of view: (a) Mr. Carr should have insisted on Alfred's arrest. (b) I think [do not think] that Alfred has learned his lesson and will change.

2. Write a composition on what you think is the most important problem facing high school students today. Give reasons and examples for your choice. In the concluding paragraph, suggest ways in which parents could offer guidance on this particular problem.

Jesse Stuart

The writings of Jesse Stuart are strongly marked by his love for his native Kentucky, which provides both the subject matter and the language for his stories. Stuart was born in 1907 and grew up on a mountain farm near Riverton, Kentucky. From his earliest years he had a yearning to read, study, and write, and became the first member of his family to attend high school. By working at various times as a steel mill laborer, a quarryman, and a hired farm hand, he put himself through high school and Lincoln Memorial University in Tennessee. He has had a noteworthy career as a teacher, a lecturer, and a writer. Stuart now lives with his family on a farm in eastern Kentucky and still maintains an interest in farming, although writing is his main occupation.

His first literary success came in 1934 with the publication of *Man with a Bull-Tongue Plow*, a collection of more than seven hundred sonnets that reflect his love for the Kentucky hills. *The Thread That Runs So True* (1949) is an autobiographical account of his experiences as a schoolteacher, when he was younger than some of his pupils. Among his other prose works are *Taps for Private Tussie*, a novel about a poor southern family, and *Plowshare in Heaven*, a collection of short stories.

Simplicity of language, gentle humor, and sympathy for youth are frequently found in his stories.

Split Cherry Tree

"I don't mind staying after school," I says to Professor Herbert, "but I'd rather you'd whip me with a switch and let me go home early. Pa will whip me anyway for getting home two hours late."

"You are too big to whip," says Professor Herbert, "and I have to punish you for climbing up in that cherry tree. You boys knew better than that! The other five boys have paid their dollar each. You have been the only one who has not helped pay for the tree. Can't you borrow a dollar?"

"I can't," I says. "I'll have to take the punishment. I wish it would be quicker punishment. I wouldn't mind."

Professor Herbert stood and looked at me. He was a big man. He wore a gray suit of clothes. The suit matched his gray hair.

"You don't know my father," I says to Professor Herbert. "He might be called a little old-fashioned. He makes us mind him until we're twenty-one years old. He believes if you spare the rod you spoil the child. I'll never be able to make him understand about the cherry tree. I'm the first of my people to go to high school."

"You must take the punishment," says Professor Herbert. "You must stay two hours after school today and two hours after school tomorrow. I am allowing you twenty-five cents an hour. That is good money for a high school student. You can sweep the schoolhouse floor, wash the blackboards, and clean windows. I'll pay the dollar for you."

I couldn't ask Professor Herbert to loan me a dollar. He never offered to loan it to me. I had to stay and help the janitor and work out my fine at a quarter an hour.

I thought as I swept the floor, "What will Pa do to me? What lie can I tell him when I go home? Why did we ever climb that cherry tree and break it down for anyway? Why did we run crazy over the hills away from the crowd? Why did we do all of this? Six of us climbed up in a little cherry tree after one little lizard! Why did the tree split and fall with us? It should have been a stronger tree! Why did Eif Crabtree just happen to be below us plowing and catch us in his cherry tree? Why wasn't he a better man than to charge us six dollars for the tree?"

It was six o'clock when I left the schoolhouse. I had six miles to walk home. It would be after seven when I got home. I had all my work to do when I got home. It took Pa and me both to do the work. Seven cows to milk. Nineteen head of cattle to feed, four mules, twenty-five hogs, firewood and stovewood to cut, and water to draw from the well. He would be doing it when I got home. He would be mad and wondering what was keeping me!

I hurried home. I would run under the dark, leafless trees. I would walk fast uphill. I would run down the hill. The ground was freezing. I had to hurry. I had to run. I reached the long ridge that led to our cow pasture. I ran along this ridge. The wind dried the sweat on my face. I ran across the pasture to the house.

I threw down my books in the chipyard. I ran to the barn to spread fodder on the ground for the cattle. I didn't take time to change my clean school clothes for my old work clothes. I ran out to the barn. I saw Pa spreading fodder on the ground to the cattle. That was my job. I ran up to the fence. I says, "Leave that for me, Pa. I'll do it. I'm just a little late."

"I see you are," says Pa. He turned and looked at me. His eyes danced fire. "What in th' world has kept you so? Why ain't you been here to help me with this work? Make a gentleman out'n one boy in th' family and this is what you get! Send you to high school and you get too onery fer th' buzzards to smell!"

I never said anything. I didn't want to tell why I was late from school. Pa stopped scattering the bundles of fodder. He looked at me. He says, "Why are you gettin' in here this time o' night? You tell me or I'll take a hickory withe [1] to you right here on th' spot!"

I says, "I had to stay after school." I couldn't lie to Pa. He'd go to school and find out why I had to stay. If I lied to him it would be too bad for me.

"Why did you haf to stay atter school?" says Pa.

I says, "Our biology class went on a field trip today. Six of us boys broke down a cherry tree. We had to give a dollar apiece to pay for the tree. I didn't have the dollar. Professor Herbert is making me work out my dollar. He gives me twenty-five cents an hour. I had to stay in this afternoon. I'll have to stay in tomorrow afternoon!"

"Are you telling me th' truth?" says Pa.

"I'm telling you the truth," I says. "Go and see for yourself."

"That's jist what I'll do in th' mornin'," says Pa. "Jist whose cherry tree did you break down?"

"Eif Crabtree's cherry tree!"

"What was you doin' clear out in Eif Crabtree's place?" says Pa. "He lives four miles from th' county high school. Don't they teach you no books at that high school? Do they jist let you get out and gad over th' hillsides? If that's all they do I'll keep you at home, Dave. I've got work here fer you to do!"

"Pa," I says, "spring is just getting here. We take a subject in school where we have to have bugs, snakes, flowers, lizards, frogs, and plants. It is biology. It was a pretty day today. We went out to find a few of these. Six of us boys saw a lizard at the same time sunning on a cherry tree. We all went up the tree to get it. We broke the tree down. It split at the forks. Eif Crabtree was plowing down below us. He ran up the hill and got our names. The other boys gave their dollar apiece. I didn't have mine. Professor Herbert put mine in for me. I have to work it out at school."

"Poor man's son, huh," says Pa. "I'll attend to that myself in th'

1. withe (wīth): a slender branch.

mornin'. I'll take keer o' 'im. He ain't from this county nohow. I'll go down there in th' mornin' and see 'im. Lettin' you leave your books and gallivant all over th' hills. What kind of a school is it nohow! Didn't do that, my son, when I's a little shaver in school. All fared alike, too."

"Pa, please don't go down there," I says, "just let me have fifty cents to pay the rest of my fine! I don't want you to go down there! I don't want you to start anything with Professor Herbert!"

"Ashamed of your old Pap are you, Dave," says Pa, "atter th' way I've worked to raise you! Tryin' to send you to school so you can make a better livin' than I've made.

"I'll straighten this thing out myself! I'll take keer o' Professor Herbert myself! He ain't got no right to keep you in and let the other boys off jist because they've got th' money! I'm a poor man. A bullet will go in a professor same as it will any man. It will go in a rich man same as it will a poor man. Now you get into this work before I take one o' these withes and cut the shirt off'n your back!"

I thought once I'd run through the woods above the barn just as hard as I could go. I thought I'd leave high school and home forever! Pa could not catch me! I'd get away! I couldn't go back to school with him. He'd have a gun and maybe he'd shoot Professor Herbert. It was hard to tell what he would do. I could tell Pa that school had changed in the hills from the way it was when he was a boy, but he wouldn't understand. I could tell him we studied frogs, birds, snakes, lizards, flowers, insects. But Pa wouldn't understand. If I did run away from home it wouldn't matter to Pa. He would see Professor Herbert anyway. He would think that high school and Professor Herbert had run me away from home. There was no need to run away. I'd just have to stay, finish foddering the cattle, and go to school with Pa the next morning.

I would take a bundle of fodder, remove the hickory withe band from around it, and scatter it on rocks, clumps of green briers, and brush so the cattle wouldn't tramp it under their feet. I would lean it up against the oak trees and the rocks in the pasture just above our pigpen on the hill. The fodder was cold and frosty where it had set out in the stacks. I would carry bundles of the fodder from the stack until I had spread out a bundle for each steer. Pa went to the barn to feed the mules and throw corn in the pen to the hogs.

The moon shone bright in the cold March sky. I finished my work by moonlight. Professor Herbert really didn't know how much work I had to do at home. If he had known he would not have kept me after school. He would have loaned me a dollar to have paid my part on the cherry tree. He had never lived in the hills. He didn't know the way the hill boys had to work so that they could go to school. Now he was teaching in a county high school where all the boys who attended were from hill farms.

After I'd finished doing my work I went to the house and ate my supper. Pa and Mom had eaten. My supper was getting cold. I heard Pa and Mom talking in the front room. Pa was telling Mom about me staying in after school.

"I had to do all th' milkin' tonight, chop th' wood myself. It's too hard on me atter I've turned ground all day. I'm goin' to take a day off tomorrow and see if I can't remedy things a little. I'll go down to that high school tomorrow. I won't be a very good scholar fer Professor Herbert nohow. He won't keep me in atter school. I'll take a different kind of lesson down there and make 'im acquainted with it."

"Now, Luster," says Mom, "you jist stay away from there. Don't cause a lot o' trouble. You can be jailed fer a trick like that. You'll get th' Law atter you. You'll just go down there and show off and plague your own boy Dave to death in front o' all th' scholars!"

"Plague or no plague," says Pa, "he don't take into consideration what all I haf to do here, does he? I'll show 'im it ain't right to keep one boy in and let the rest go scot-free. My boy is good as th' rest, ain't he? A bullet will make a hole in a schoolteacher same as it will anybody else. He can't do me that way and get by with it. I'll plug 'im first. I aim to go down there bright and early in the mornin' and get all this straight! I aim to see about bug larnin' and this runnin' all over God's creation huntin' snakes, lizards, and frogs. Ransackin' th' country and goin' through cherry orchards and breakin' th' trees down atter lizards! Old Eif Crabtree ought to a-poured th' hot lead to 'em instead o' chargin' six dollars fer th' tree! He ought to a-got old Herbert th' first one!"

I ate my supper. I slipped upstairs and lit the lamp. I tried to forget the whole thing. I studied plane geometry. Then I studied my biology lesson. I could hardly study for thinking about Pa. "He'll go to school with me in the morning. He'll take a gun for Professor Herbert! What will Professor Herbert think of me! I'll tell him when Pa leaves that I couldn't help it. But Pa might shoot him. I hate to go with Pa. Maybe he'll cool off about it tonight and not go in the morning."

Pa got up at four o'clock. He built a fire in the stove. Then he built a fire in the fireplace. He got Mom up to get breakfast. Then he got me up to help feed and milk. By the time we had our work done at the barn, Mom had breakfast ready for us. We ate our breakfast. Daylight came and we could see the bare oak trees covered white with frost. The hills were white with frost. A cold wind was blowing. The sky was clear. The sun would soon come out and melt the frost. The afternoon would be warm with sunshine and the frozen ground would thaw. There would be mud on the hills again. Muddy water would then run down the little ditches on the hills.

"Now, Dave," says Pa, "let's get ready fer school. I aim to go with you this mornin' and look into bug larnin', frog larnin', lizard and snake larnin', and breakin' down cherry trees! I don't like no sicha foolish way o' larnin' myself!"

Pa hadn't forgot. I'd have to take him to school with me. He would take me to school with him. We were going early. I was glad we were going early. If Pa pulled a gun on Professor Herbert there wouldn't be so many of my classmates there to see him.

I knew that Pa wouldn't be at home in the high school. He wore overalls, big boots, a blue shirt and a sheepskin coat, and a slouched black hat gone to seed at the top. He put his gun in its holster. We started trudging toward the high school across the hill.

It was early when we got to the county high school. Professor Herbert had just got there. I just thought as we walked up the steps into the schoolhouse, "Maybe Pa will find out Professor Herbert is a good man. He just doesn't know him. Just like I felt toward the Lambert boys across the hill. I didn't like them until I'd seen them and talked to them. After I went to school with them and talked to them, I liked them and we were friends. It's a lot in knowing the other fellow."

"You're th' Professor here, ain't you?" says Pa.

"Yes," says Professor Herbert, "and you are Dave's father."

"Yes," says Pa, pulling out his gun and laying it on the seat in Professor Herbert's office. Professor Herbert's eyes got big behind his black-rimmed glasses when he saw Pa's gun. Color came into his pale cheeks.

"Jist a few things about this school I want to know," says Pa. "I'm tryin' to make a scholar out'n Dave. He's the only one out'n eleven youngins I've sent to high school. Here he comes in late and leaves me all th' work to do! He said you's all out bug huntin' yesterday and broke a cherry tree down. He had to stay two hours atter school yesterday and work out money to pay on that cherry tree! Is that right?"

"Wwwwy," says Professor Herbert, "I guess it is."

He looked at Pa's gun.

"Well," says Pa, "this ain't no high school. It's a bug school, a lizard school, a snake school! It ain't no school nohow!"

"Why did you bring that gun?" says Professor Herbert to Pa.

"You see that little hole," says Pa as he picked up the long blue forty-four and put his finger on the end of the barrel, "a bullet can come out'n that hole that will kill a schoolteacher same as it will any other man. It will kill a rich man same as a poor man. It will kill a man. But atter I come in and saw you, I know'd I wouldn't need it. This maul [2] of mine could do you up in a few minutes."

Pa stood there, big, hard, brown-skinned, and mighty, beside of Professor Herbert. I didn't know Pa was so much bigger and harder. I'd never seen Pa in a schoolhouse before. I'd seen Professor Herbert. He always looked big before to me. He didn't look big standing beside of Pa.

"I was only doing my duty Mr. Sexton," says Professor Herbert, "and following the course of study the state provided us with."

"Course o' study," says Pa, "what study, bug study? Varmint study? Takin' youngins to th' woods. Boys and girls all out there together a-gallivantin' in the brush and kicking up their heels and their poor old Ma's and Pa's at home a-slavin' to keep 'em in school and give 'em a education! You know that's dangerous, too, puttin' a lot o' boys and girls out together like that!"

Students were coming into the schoolhouse now.

Professor Herbert says, "Close the door, Dave, so others won't hear."

I walked over and closed the door. I was shaking like a leaf in the wind. I thought Pa was going to hit Professor Herbert every minute. He was doing all the talking. His face was getting red. The red color was coming through the brown, weather-beaten skin on Pa's face.

"I was right with these students," says Professor Herbert. "I know what they got into and what they didn't. I didn't send one of the other teachers with them on this field trip. I went myself. Yes, I took the boys and girls together. Why not?"

"It jist don't look good to me," says Pa, "a-takin' all this swarm of youngins out to pillage [3] th' whole deestrict. Breakin' down cherry trees. Keepin' boys in atter school."

---

2. **maul** (môl): a heavy hammer used especially for driving wedges or piles; here, Pa means his hand.

3. **pillage** (pil'ij): to take or destroy property by open violence; to take unlawfully.

"What else could I have done with Dave, Mr. Sexton?" says Professor Herbert. "The boys didn't have any business all climbing that cherry tree after one lizard. One boy could have gone up in the tree and got it. The farmer charged us six dollars. It was a little steep, I think, but we had it to pay. Must I make five boys pay and let your boy off? He said he didn't have the dollar and couldn't get it. So I put it in for him. I'm letting him work it out. He's not working for me. He's working for the school!"

"I jist don't know what you could a-done with 'im," says Pa, "only a-larruped 'im with a withe! That's what he needed!"

"He's too big to whip," says Professor Herbert, pointing at me. "He's a man in size."

"He's not too big fer me to whip," says Pa. "They ain't too big until they're over twenty-one! It jist didn't look fair to me! Work one and let th' rest out because they got th' money. I don't see what bugs has got to do with a high school! It don't look good to me nohow!"

Pa picked up his gun and put it back in its holster. The red color left Professor Herbert's face. He talked more to Pa. Pa softened a little. It looked funny to see Pa in the high school building. It was the first time he'd ever been there.

"We were not only hunting snakes, toads, flowers, butterflies, lizards," says Professor Herbert, "but, Mr. Sexton, I was hunting dry timothy grass [4] to put in an incubator and raise some protozoa." [5]

"I don't know what that is," says Pa. "Th' incubator is th' new-fangled way o' cheatin' th' hens and raisin' chickens. I ain't so sure about th' breed o' chickens you mentioned."

"You've heard of germs, Mr. Sexton, haven't you?" says Professor Herbert.

"Jist call me Luster, if you don't mind," says Pa, very casual like.

"All right, Luster, you've heard of germs, haven't you?"

"Yes," says Pa, "but I don't believe in germs. I'm sixty-five years old and I ain't seen one yet!"

"You can't see them with your naked eye," says Professor Herbert. "Just keep that gun in the holster and stay with me in the high school today. I have a few things I want to show you. That scum on your teeth has germs in it."

"What," says Pa, "you mean to tell me I've got germs on my teeth!"

"Yes," says Professor Herbert. "The same kind as we might be able to find in a living black snake if we dissect it!"

4. **timothy grass:** a fodder grass with long, cylindrical spikes.
5. **protozoa** (prō'tə·zō'ə): one-celled microscopic animals.

"I don't mean to dispute your word," says Pa, "but I don't believe it. I don't believe I have germs on my teeth!"

"Stay with me today and I'll show you. I want to take you through the school anyway! School has changed a lot in the hills since you went to school. I don't guess we had high schools in this county when you went to school!"

"No," says Pa, "jist readin', writin', and cipherin'. We didn't have all this bug larnin', frog larnin', and findin' germs on your teeth and in the middle o' black snakes! Th' world's changin'."

"It is," says Professor Herbert, "and we hope all for the better. Boys like your own there are going to help change it. He's your boy. He knows all of what I've told you. You stay with me today."

"I'll shore stay with you," says Pa. "I want to see th' germs off'n my teeth. I jist want to see a germ. I've never seen one in my life. 'Seein' is believin',' Pap allus told me."

Pa walked out of the office with Professor Herbert. I just hoped Professor Herbert didn't have Pa arrested for pulling his gun. Pa's gun has always been a friend to him when he goes to settle disputes.

The bell rang. School took up. I saw the students when they marched in the schoolhouse look at Pa. They would grin and punch each other. Pa just stood and watched them pass in at the schoolhouse door. Two long lines marched in the house. The boys and girls were clean and well dressed. Pa stood over in the schoolyard under a leafless elm, in his sheepskin coat, his big boots laced in front with buckskin, and his heavy socks stuck above his boot tops. Pa's overalls legs were baggy and wrinkled between his coat and boot tops. His blue work shirt showed at the collar. His big black hat showed his gray-streaked black hair. His face was hard and weather-tanned to the color of a ripe fodder blade. His hands were big and gnarled like the roots of the elm tree he stood beside.

When I went to my first class I saw Pa and Professor Herbert going around over the schoolhouse. I was in my geometry class when Pa and Professor Herbert came in the room. We were explaining our propositions on the blackboard. Professor Herbert and Pa just quietly came in and sat down for a while. I heard Fred Wurts whisper to Glenn Armstrong, "Who is that old man? Lord, he's a rough-looking scamp." Glenn whispered back, "I think he's Dave's Pap." The students in geometry looked at Pa. They must have wondered what he was doing in school. Before the class was over, Pa and Professor Herbert got up and went out. I saw them together down on the playground. Professor Herbert was explaining to Pa. I could see the prints of Pa's gun under his coat when he'd walk around.

At noon in the high school cafeteria Pa and Professor Herbert sat together at the little table where Professor Herbert always ate by himself. They ate together. The students watched the way Pa ate. He ate with his knife instead of his fork. A lot of the students felt sorry for me after they found out he was my father. They didn't have to feel sorry for me. I wasn't ashamed of Pa after I found out he wasn't going to shoot Professor Herbert. I was glad they had made friends. I wasn't ashamed of Pa. I wouldn't be as long as he behaved. He would find out about the high school as I had found out about the Lambert boys across the hill.

In the afternoon when we went to biology Pa was in the class. He was sitting on one of the high stools beside the microscope. We went ahead with our work just as if Pa wasn't in the class. I saw Pa take his knife and scrape tartar from one of his teeth. Professor Herbert put it on the lens and adjusted the microscope for Pa. He adjusted it and worked awhile. Then he says: "Now Luster, look! Put your eye right down to the light. Squint the other eye!"

Pa put his head down and did as Professor Herbert said. "I see 'im," says Pa. "Who'd a ever thought that? Right on a body's teeth! Right in a body's mouth. You're right certain they ain't no fake to this, Professor Herbert?"

"No, Luster," says Professor Herbert. "It's there. That's the germ. Germs live in a world we cannot see with the naked eye. We must use the microscope. There are millions of them in our bodies. Some are harmful. Others are helpful."

Pa holds his face down and looks through the microscope. We stop and watch Pa. He sits upon the tall stool. His knees are against the table. His legs are long. His coat slips up behind when he bends over. The handle of his gun shows. Professor Herbert pulls his coat down quickly.

"Oh, yes," says Pa. He gets up and pulls his coat down. Pa's face gets a little red. He knows about his gun and he knows he doesn't have any use for it in high school.

"We have a big black snake over here we caught yesterday," says Professor Herbert. "We'll chloroform him and dissect him and show you he has germs in his body, too."

"Don't do it," says Pa. "I believe you. I jist don't want to see you kill the black snake. I never kill one. They are good mousers and a lot o' help to us on the farm. I like black snakes. I jist hate to see people kill 'em. I don't allow 'em killed on my place."

The students looked at Pa. They seemed to like him better after he said that. Pa with a gun in his pocket but a tender heart beneath his ribs for snakes, but not for man! Pa won't whip a mule at home. He won't whip his cattle.

"Man can defend hisself," says Pa, "but cattle and mules can't. We have the drop on 'em. Ain't nothin' to a man that'll beat a good pullin' mule. He ain't got th' right kind o' a heart!"

Professor Herbert took Pa through the laboratory. He showed him the different kinds of work we were doing. He showed him our equipment. They stood and talked while we worked. Then they walked out together. They talked louder when they got out in the hall.

When our biology class was over I walked out of the room. It was our last class for the day. I would have to take my broom and sweep two hours to finish paying for the split cherry tree. I just wondered if Pa would want me to stay. He was standing in the hallway watching the students march out. He looked lost among us. He looked like a leaf turned brown on the tree among the treetop filled with growing leaves.

I got my broom and started to sweep. Professor Herbert walked up and says, "I'm going to let you do that some other time. You can go home with your father. He is waiting out there."

I laid my broom down, got my books, and went down the steps. Pa says, "Ain't you got two hours o' sweepin' yet to do?"

I says, "Professor Herbert said I could do it some other time. He said for me to go home with you."

"No," says Pa. "You are goin' to do as he says. He's a good man. School has changed from my day and time. I'm a dead leaf, Dave. I'm behind. I don't belong here. If he'll let me I'll get a broom and we'll both sweep one hour. That pays your debt. I'll hep you pay it. I'll ast 'im and see if he won't let me hep you."

"I'm going to cancel the debt," says Professor Herbert. "I just wanted you to understand, Luster."

"I understand," says Pa, "and since I understand, he must pay for his debt fer th' tree and I'm goin' to hep 'im."

"Don't do that," says Professor Herbert. "It's all on me."

"We don't do things like that," says Pa, "we're just and honest people. We don't want somethin' fer nothin'. Professor Herbert, you're wrong now and I'm right. You'll haf to listen to me. I've larned a lot from you. My boy must go on. Th' world has left me. It changed while I've raised my family and plowed th' hills. I'm a just and honest man. I don't skip debts. I ain't larned 'em to do that. I ain't got much larnin' myself but I do know right from wrong atter I see through a thing."

Professor Herbert went home. Pa and I stayed and swept one hour. It looked funny to see Pa use a broom. He never used one at home. Mom used the broom. Pa used the plow. Pa did hard work. Pa says, "I can't sweep. Durned if I can. Look at th' streaks o' dirt I leave on th' floor! Seems like no work a-tall fer me. Brooms is too light 'r somethin'. I'll jist do th' best I can, Dave. I've been wrong about th' school."

I says, "Did you know Professor Herbert can get a warrant out for you for bringing your pistol to school and showing it in his office! They can railroad [6] you for that!"

"That's all made right," says Pa. "I've made that right. Professor Herbert ain't goin' to take it to court. He likes me. I like 'im. We jist had to get together. He had the remedies. He showed me. You must go on to school. I am as strong a man as ever come out'n th' hills fer my years and th' hard work I've done. But I'm behind, Dave. I'm a little man. Your hands will be softer than mine. Your clothes will be better. You'll allus look cleaner than your old Pap. Jist remember, Dave, to pay your debts and be honest. Jist be kind to animals and don't bother th' snakes. That's all I got agin th' school. Puttin' black snakes to sleep and cuttin' 'em open."

It was late when we got home. Stars were in the sky. The moon was up. The ground was frozen. Pa took his time going home. I couldn't run like I did the night before. It was ten o'clock before we got the work finished, our suppers eaten. Pa sat before the fire and told Mom he was going to take her and show her a germ sometime. Mom hadn't seen one either. Pa told her about the high school and the fine man Professor Herbert was. He told Mom about the strange school across the hill and how different it was from the school in their day and time.

6. **railroad:** *slang,* to have someone imprisoned on false charges or without a fair trial.

Meaning

1. Judging from the story, what kind of man would you say Professor Herbert is? Find specific passages to support any judgment you make. Do you think it was unfair of Professor Herbert to make Dave work off his dollar? Why or why not?
2. The theme of the story might be expressed as "understanding comes through experience." In what way does each of the principal characters come to this realization?
3. How would you describe Dave's relationship with his father? What

worried him about his father's going to the school? What actions of his father change Dave's attitude toward him as the day passes?

4. How do Pa and Professor Herbert represent two different ways of thinking in regard to solving problems in life? This is obviously one of the conflicts in the story. What is the conflict within Pa himself? What is the real conflict in this story?

5. Why does Pa say at the end of the story "I'm a little man"? What are the weak points in Pa's character? What are the good points? Why won't Pa let Professor Herbert cancel Dave's debt?

Method

1. This story is told in the first person. What are the advantages in having the story told from the young boy's point of view? Are there any disadvantages in using the first person in telling a story?

2. The story is not really about a split cherry tree; the incident merely serves to introduce the story. What, then, is the significance of the title? How is it symbolic of the conflict within Dave?

3. The pistol is used as a symbol for Pa, and the microscope represents Professor Herbert. How is each symbol related to the respective character and his approach to solving a problem?

Language: Nonstandard English

Nonstandard is a general term meaning a type of English which is not spoken by the majority of educated persons in the United States. Nonstandard English includes *dialect* and *illiteracies*. Do not confuse intelligence with education. The people who use nonstandard English may have intelligence but lack education.

A *dialect* is a local or provincial form of a language. It may differ from other forms, especially the standard or literary, in pronunciation, intonation, grammar, or vocabulary. Such words and expressions as *cain't, reckon, mebbe, afurst, tain't,* and *yassuh* are examples of dialect.

If you heard someone say, "He hisself brung the package and said it got busted on the way over. He said he ain't got no time for waiting, so he done gone back to the store," you would recognize this as the speech of an uneducated person.

When you're sufficiently sure of your own speech, you will learn to recognize and understand the occasional liveliness of nonstandard English.

Read the following selection from Carl Sandburg's *Abe Lincoln Grows Up*. Notice the vocabulary, the pronunciation, and the grammatical constructions.

His folks talked like other folks in the neighborhood. They called themselves "pore" people. A man learned in books was "eddicated."

What was certain was "sartin." The syllables came through the nose; joints were "j'ints"; fruit "spiled" instead of spoiling; in corn-planting time they "drapped" the seeds. They went on errands and "brung" things back. Their dogs "follered" the coons. Flannel was "flannen," a bandanna a "bandanner," a chimney a "chimbly," a shadow a "shadder," and mosquitoes plain "skeeters." They "gethered" crops. A creek was a "crick," a cover a "kiver."

A man silent was a "say-nothin'." They asked, "Have ye et?" There were dialogues, "Kin ye?" "No, I cain't." And if a woman had an idea of doing something, she said, "I had a idy to." They made their own words. Those who spoke otherwise didn't belong, were "puttin' on." This was their wilderness lingo; it had gnarled bones and gaunt hours of their lives in it.

Words like *independent* bothered the boy. He was hungry to understand the meanings of words. He would ask what *independent* meant, and when he was told the meaning, he lay awake nights thinking about the meaning of the meaning of *independent*. Other words bothered him, such as *predestination*. He asked the meaning of that and lay awake hours at night thinking about the meaning of the meaning.

Composition and Discussion

1. Both the janitor in "Valedictory" and Professor Herbert in this story have understanding and sympathetic natures. Write a composition contrasting and comparing these two men. Consider their appearance, education, speech, and attitudes toward others.

2. Does the "generation gap" still exist? If so, what are some of the most crucial problems? Which are only incidental?

3. How would you answer a classmate who claims, "I can't see studying things that will not be useful to us later in life"? Give reasons and examples to support your reply.

4. What changes would you like to see in the high school curriculum? Are there any courses that you would suggest adding? or dropping?

From *Abe Lincoln Grows Up* by Carl Sandburg. Reprinted by permission of Harcourt, Brace & World, Inc.

Edgar Allan Poe

Edgar Allan Poe was born in Boston, Massachusetts on January 19, 1809. His parents were traveling actors from the southern United States. Upon the death of his mother in 1811, Edgar was taken in by the Allans of Richmond, Virginia. His foster father, John Allan, (from whom Poe took his middle name) was a wealthy merchant. Poe received an extensive education in schools in Richmond and in England, where the Allans lived for five years. He entered the University of Virginia at seventeen, and was an excellent student. While there, he ran up heavy debts which Mr. Allan refused to pay. As a result, Poe withdrew from school and joined the Army. He later entered West Point. After only six months, however, he deliberately brought about his own dismissal when the Army refused to grant him a discharge.

For the next eighteen years of his life, Poe attempted to make a living by writing. His poetry and fiction brought little financial gain. He did essays and reviews for periodicals in Richmond, Philadelphia, and New York, but, though a good editor, he was unable to hold a steady job. He drifted from place to place, suffering extreme poverty. He could not adequately support his child-wife, Virginia Clemm, and was depressed and shattered when she died at twenty-five from tuberculosis. Two years later, in 1849, Poe was found dying on a shabby sidewalk in Baltimore.

Despite his personal failures, Poe did succeed as a poet, short-story writer, and critic. Many books have been written about his work, and no one disputes his creative genius. In 1845, four years before his death, Poe achieved critical recognition and fame with publication of "The Raven," which was reprinted by newspapers throughout the country.

Poe set down original theories on how to write a short story. He insisted that it be short enough to produce a single emotional effect. The writer must decide on the one powerful mood he wishes to create, and every character, incident, and word must then contribute to that pre-established design. Many writers have disagreed with Poe's theories, but his work shows clearly that he followed his own rules.

Poe set the pattern for most of our modern mystery and detective fiction with such stories as "The Gold-Bug" and "The Murders in the Rue Morgue." He also wrote tales of horror and the supernatural, such as "The Fall of the House of Usher," and "The Masque of the Red Death."

Poe holds a unique and honored place in American literature, and his influence on writers both native and foreign has been profound and lasting.

The Masque * of the Red Death

The "Red Death" had long devastated the country. No pestilence had ever been so fatal, or so hideous. Blood was its Avatar [1] and its seal—the redness and the horror of blood. There were sharp pains, and sudden dizziness, and then profuse bleeding at the pores, with dissolution.[2] The scarlet stains upon the body and especially upon the face of the victim were the pest ban [3] which shut him out from the aid and from the sympathy of his fellow men. And the whole seizure, progress, and termination of the disease were the incidents of half an hour.

But the Prince Prospero was happy and dauntless and sagacious. When his dominions were half depopulated, he summoned to his presence a thousand hale and light-hearted friends from among the knights and dames of his court, and with these retired to the deep seclusion of one of his castellated abbeys.[4] This was an extensive and magnificent structure, the creation of the prince's own eccentric yet august taste. A strong and lofty wall girdled it in. This wall had gates of iron. The courtiers, having entered, brought furnaces and massy hammers, and welded the bolts. They resolved to leave means neither of ingress nor egress [5] to the sudden impulses of despair or frenzy from within. The abbey was amply provisioned. With such precautions the courtiers might bid defiance to contagion. The external world could take care of itself. In the meantime, it was folly to grieve or to think. The prince had provided all the appliances of pleasure.

---

* **Masque:** an elaborately staged dramatic performance popular in the sixteenth and seventeenth centuries. The actors wore masks and usually represented mythological or symbolic figures. The acting consisted mostly of dancing and pantomime. Masque also means a masquerade, or a mask.

1. **Avatar** (av'ə·tär'): in Hindu theology, the bodily form taken by a god; the visible sign or indication of something; here, blood is the sign of the "Red Death."

2. **dissolution:** disintegration; decay; hence, death.

3. **pest ban:** the sign by which the disease (*pest*) was recognized and which resulted in the *banning* of the afflicted person.

4. **castellated** (kas'tə·lā'tid) **abbeys:** castle-like monasteries.

5. **ingress** (in'gres) **or egress** (ē'gres): entrance or exit.

There were buffoons, there were improvisatori,[6] there were ballet dancers, there were musicians, there was Beauty, there was wine. All these and security were within. Without was the Red Death.

It was toward the close of the fifth or sixth month of his seclusion, and while the pestilence raged most furiously abroad, that the Prince Prospero entertained his thousand friends at a masked ball of the most unusual magnificence.

It was a voluptuous [7] scene, that masquerade. But first let me tell of the rooms in which it was held. There were seven—an imperial suite. In many palaces, however, such suites form a long and straight vista, while the folding doors slide back nearly to the walls on either hand, so that the view of the whole extent is scarcely impeded. Here the case was very different, as might have been expected from the prince's love of the bizarre. The apartments were so irregularly disposed that the vision embraced but little more than one at a time. There was a sharp turn at every twenty or thirty yards, and at each turn a novel effect. To the right and left, in the middle of each wall, a tall and narrow Gothic window looked out upon a closed corridor which pursued the windings of the suite. These windows were of stained glass, whose color varied in accordance with the prevailing hue of the decorations of the chamber into which it opened. That at the eastern extremity was hung, for example, in blue—and vividly blue were its windows. The second chamber was purple in its ornaments and tapestries, and here the panes were purple. The third was green throughout, and so were the casements.[8] The fourth was furnished and lighted with orange, the fifth was white, the sixth with violet. The seventh apartment was closely shrouded in black velvet tapestries that hung all over the ceiling and down the walls, falling in heavy folds upon a carpet of the same material and hue. But, in this chamber only, the color of the windows failed to correspond with the decorations. The panes here were scarlet—a deep blood-color. Now in no óne of the seven apartments was there any lamp or candelabrum,[9] amid the profusion of golden ornaments that lay scattered to and fro or depended [10] from the roof. There was no light of any kind emanating from lamp or candle within the suite of chambers.

6. **improvisatori** (ēm′prŏv·vē·za·tō′rē): *Italian*, entertainers who improvise or make up songs, poems, or drama as they perform.
7. **voluptuous** (və·lup′chŏō·əs): delightful to the senses; yielding enjoyment through pleasures or luxuries.
8. **casements**: windows having sashes which open on hinges at the side.
9. **candelabrum** (kan′də·lä′brəm): a large, ornamental, branched holder for candles.
10. **depended**: hung.

But in the corridors that followed the suite there stood, opposite each window, a heavy tripod, bearing a brazier [11] of fire, that projected its rays through the tinted glass and so glaringly illumined the room. And thus were produced a multitude of gaudy and fantastic appearances. But in the western or black chamber the effect of the firelight that streamed upon the dark hangings through the blood-tinted panes was ghastly in the extreme, and produced so wild a look upon the countenances of those who entered that there were few of the company bold enough to set foot within its precincts at all.

It was in this apartment, also, that there stood against the western wall a gigantic clock of ebony.[12] Its pendulum swung to and fro with a dull, heavy, monotonous clang; and when the minute hand made the circuit of the face, and the hour was to be stricken, there came from the brazen lungs of the clock a sound which was clear and loud and deep and exceedingly musical, but of so peculiar a note and emphasis that, at each lapse of an hour, the musicians of the orchestra were constrained to pause, momentarily, in their performance, to hearken to the sound; and thus the waltzers perforce [13] ceased their evolutions; and there was a brief disconcert [14] of the whole gay company; and, while the chimes of the clock yet rang, it was observed that the giddiest grew pale, and the more aged and sedate passed their hands over their brows as if in confused revery or meditation. But when the echoes had fully ceased, a light laughter at once pervaded the assembly; the musicians looked at each other and smiled as if at their own nervousness and folly, and made whispering vows, each to the other, that the next chiming of the clock should produce in them no similar emotion; and then, after the lapse of sixty minutes (which embrace three thousand and six hundred seconds of the Time that flies), there came yet another chiming of the clock, and then were the same disconcert and tremulousness and meditation as before.

But, in spite of these things, it was a gay and magnificent revel. The tastes of the prince were peculiar. He had a fine eye for colors and effects. He disregarded the *decora* [15] of mere fashion. His plans were bold and fiery, and his conceptions glowed with barbaric luster. There are some who would have thought him mad. His followers

---

11. **brazier** (brā′zhər): a metal pan for holding burning coals.
12. **ebony** (eb′ə·nē): a rare black wood.
13. **perforce** (per·fôrs′): by force of circumstances; of necessity.
14. **disconcert** (dis′kən·sûrt′): confusion. Explain this word by checking the meaning of its prefix and root.
15. **decora**: *Latin*, plural of *decorum*; that is, observances; proprieties.

felt that he was not. It was necessary to hear and see and touch him to be *sure* that he was not.

He had directed, in great part, the movable embellishments of the seven chambers, upon occasion of this great fete; [16] and it was his own guiding taste which had given character to the masqueraders. Be sure they were grotesque. There were much glare and glitter and piquancy and phantasm [17]—much of what has been since seen in *Hernani*.[18] There were arabesque [19] figures with unsuited [20] limbs and appointments. There were delirious fancies such as the madman fashions. There were much of the beautiful, much of the wanton,[21] much of the bizarre, something of the terrible, and not a little of that which might have excited disgust. To and fro in the seven chambers there stalked, in fact, a multitude of dreams. And these—the dreams —writhed in and about, taking hue from the rooms, and causing the wild music of the orchestra to seem as the echo of their steps. And, anon, there strikes the ebony clock which stands in the hall of the velvet. And then, for a moment, all is still, and all is silent save the voice of the clock. The dreams are stiff-frozen as they stand. But the echoes of the chime die away—they have endured but an instant— and a light, half-subdued laughter floats after them as they depart. And now again the music swells, and the dreams live, and writhe to and fro more merrily than ever, taking hue from the many-tinted windows through which stream the rays from the tripods. But to the chamber which lies most westwardly of the seven, there are now none of the maskers who venture; for the night is waning away, and there flows a ruddier light through the blood-colored panes, and the blackness of the sable drapery appalls; and to him whose foot falls upon the sable carpet, there comes from the near clock of ebony a muffled peal more solemnly emphatic than any which reaches *their* ears who indulge in the more remote gaieties of the other apartments.

But these other apartments were densely crowded, and in them beat feverishly the heart of life. And the revel went whirlingly on, until at length there commenced the sounding of midnight upon the clock. And then the music ceased; as I have told, and the evolutions of the waltzers were quieted, and there was an uneasy cessation of all

16. fete (fāt): a lavish entertainment or festival.
17. piquancy (pē′kən·sē) and phantasm (fan′taz·əm): liveliness and fantasy.
18. *Hernani:* a play by the French author Victor Hugo, 1802–85.
19. arabesque (ar′ə·besk′): a design with an intricate pattern of angular and curved lines. Check your dictionary to find what position this refers to in ballet.
20. unsuited: unmatched.
21. wanton (won′tən): unrestrained; unchaste.

things as before. But now there were twelve strokes to be sounded by the bell of the clock; and thus it happened, perhaps, that more of thought crept, with more of time, into the meditations of the thoughtful among those who reveled. And thus, too, it happened, perhaps, that before the last echoes of the last chime had utterly sunk into silence, there were many individuals in the crowd who had found leisure to become aware of the presence of a masked figure which had arrested the attention of no single individual before. And the rumor of this new presence having spread itself whisperingly around, there arose at length from the whole company a buzz, or murmur, expressive of disapprobation [22] and surprise—then, finally, of terror, of horror, and of disgust.

In an assembly of phantasms such as I have painted, it may well be supposed that no ordinary appearance could have excited such sensation. In truth the masquerade license [23] of the night was nearly unlimited; but the figure in question had out-Heroded Herod,[24] and gone beyond the bounds of even the prince's indefinite decorum. There are chords in the hearts of the most reckless which cannot be touched without emotion. Even with the utterly lost, to whom life and death are equally jests, there are matters of which no jest can be made. The whole company, indeed, seemed now deeply to feel that in the costume and bearing of the stranger neither wit nor propriety existed. The figure was tall and gaunt, and shrouded from head to foot in the habiliments of the grave. The mask which concealed the visage was made so nearly to resemble the countenance of a stiffened corpse that the closest scrutiny must have had difficulty in detecting the cheat. And yet all this might have been endured, if not approved, by the mad revelers around. But the mummer [25] had gone so far as to assume the type of the Red Death. His vesture was dabbled in *blood*—and his broad brow, with all the features of the face, was besprinkled with the scarlet horror.

When the eyes of Prince Prospero fell upon this spectral image (which with a slow and solemn movement, as if more fully to sustain its role, stalked to and fro among the waltzers) he was seen to be con-

22. **disapprobation** (dis′ap·rə·bā′shən): disapproval.
23. **masquerade license:** freedom to act irresponsibly without fear of being recognized.
24. **out-Heroded Herod:** had outdone Herod in violence, outrage, or extravagance. Herod was the king of Judea who is reported to have ordered the slaughter of all the male infants under two years of age in Bethlehem in an attempt to kill the newly born Jesus.
25. **mummer:** one who acts in a disguise or mask, especially during festivals.

vulsed, in the first moment, with a strong shudder either of terror or distaste; but, in the next, his brow reddened with rage.

"Who dares?" he demanded hoarsely of the courtiers who stood near him—"who dares insult us with this blasphemous mockery? Seize him and unmask him—that we may know whom we have to hang at sunrise, from the battlements!"

It was in the eastern or blue chamber in which stood the Prince Prospero as he uttered these words. They rang throughout the seven rooms loudly and clearly—for the prince was a bold and robust man, and the music had become hushed at the waving of his hand.

It was in the blue room where stood the prince, with a group of pale courtiers by his side. At first, as he spoke, there was a slight rushing movement of this group in the direction of the intruder, who at the moment was also near at hand, and now, with deliberate and stately step, made closer approach to the speaker. But from a certain nameless awe with which the mad assumptions of the mummer had inspired the whole party, there were found none who put forth hand to seize him, so that unimpeded, he passed within a yard of the prince's person; and, while the vast assembly, as if with one impulse, shrank from the centers of the rooms to the walls, he made his way uninterruptedly, but with the same solemn and measured step which had distinguished him from the first, through the blue chamber to the purple—through the purple to the green—through the green to the orange—through this again to the white—and even thence to the violet, ere a decided movement had been made to arrest him. It was then, however, that the Prince Prospero, maddening with rage and the shame of his own momentary cowardice, rushed hurriedly through the six chambers, while none followed him on account of a deadly terror that had seized upon all. He bore aloft a drawn dagger, and had approached, in rapid impetuosity, to within three or four feet of the retreating figure, when the latter, having attained the extremity of the velvet apartment, turned suddenly and confronted his pursuer. There was a sharp cry—and the dagger dropped gleaming upon the sable carpet, upon which, instantly afterward, fell prostrate in death the Prince Prospero. Then, summoning the wild courage of despair, a throng of the revelers at once threw themselves into the black apartment, and seizing the mummer, whose tall figure stood erect and motionless within the shadow of the ebony clock, gasped in unutterable horror at finding the grave-cerements [26] and corpse-like mask

26. **cerements** (sir′mants): cloth which is treated with wax and used as wrappings for the dead.

which they handled with so violent a rudeness, untenanted [27] by any tangible form.

And now was acknowledged the presence of the Red Death. He had come like a thief in the night.[28] And one by one dropped the revelers in the blood-bedewed halls of their revel, and died each in the despairing posture of his fall. And the life of the ebony clock went out with that of the last of the gay. And the flames of the tripods expired. And Darkness and Decay and the Red Death held illimitable dominion over all.

27. **untenanted:** Figure out the meaning by breaking this word into its prefix and root.
28. **thief in the night:** a biblical reference (1 Thessalonians 5:2), ". . . the day of the Lord so cometh as a thief in the night."

Meaning and Method

1. The setting of the story, a masked ball, appears in paragraph three. What purposes, then, are served by paragraphs one and two?
2. What does the name Prospero symbolize? What kind of person is the Prince? What is the purpose of all the pleasures he provides for his guests?
3. Describe the effect of the chiming clock on the dancers. Why should the clock, an instrument of time, have this effect upon them? Why is it significant that the clock strikes midnight at precisely the same time that the guests become aware of the uninvited stranger?
4. Why do all the guests fear this strange "mummer"? What do the guests discover when they seize him?
5. Poe makes a strong appeal to our senses, especially to sight and hearing. Find passages where he uses color, particularly red and black. List some of the sounds he wants us to hear. Explain how these things contribute to the mood of horror of the story.
6. "The Masque of the Red Death" is a story of effect rather than one of character or plot. How does Poe create, heighten, and sustain the mood of horror? Refer to specifics from the story. How does the title suggest this is a story of fantasy and horror?
7. The theme may be stated as "Man cannot escape death," or "Death comes for the rich as well as the poor," or "You cannot lock out the ills of mankind through isolation." How would you justify each of these themes?
8. What would you say is the conflict in this story?
9. It has been said that Poe's prose style has many of the characteristics of his poetry. Notice, for example, Poe's use of *alliteration*, that is, the repetition of the same sound or syllable at the beginning of words in the same line or lines close together, in such phrases as "There were much glare and glitter and piquancy and phantasm. . . ."

Notice also the use of *repetition*, not only of the same words but also of the same word sounds. Word repetition is shown in "There were much of the beautiful, much of the wanton, much of the bizarre. . . ." Repetition in sound is shown in ". . . while the chimes of the clock yet rang, it was observed that the giddiest grew pale, and the more aged and sedate passed their hands over their brows as if in confused revery or meditation." Here we have a repetition of a long *i* sound in *while* and in *chimes*, and the long *a* sound in *pale*, *aged*, and *sedate*.

List other examples of Poe's use of alliteration and of repetition of words and sounds.

10. Verses 51 and 52 of Matthew 27 (King James Version) read: "And behold, the veil of the temple was rent in twain from the top to the bottom; and the earth did quake, and the rocks rent; And the graves were opened; and many bodies of the saints which slept arose."

Read the last four sentences of the story. How do they compare in form and content with the King James verses?

Language: The Use of Adjectives

Notice, in the following sentences, the use of adjectives, sometimes three, even four, to achieve a single effect:

1. "Its pendulum swung to and fro with a dull, heavy, monotonous clang. . . ."
2. ". . . a sound which was clear and loud and deep and exceedingly musical. . . ."
3. "His plans were bold and fiery, and his conceptions glowed with barbaric luster."

How do the adjectives in each sentence complement one another? Does each group of adjectives have the same connotative meaning? How does the verb *glowed* in sentence 3 carry out the idea conveyed by the adjectives?

Composition

Think of an event, real or imagined, that would produce a feeling of fear, joy, horror, suspense, pity, or calm. Write a paragraph in which you set the mood and atmosphere for the telling of such an event. Choose words that are rich in their power of suggestion. Construct every sentence with care. Remember that everything must relate to the single effect you wish to create.

Junius Edwards

During the 1960's Junius Edwards established himself in two fields that require creativity and vision: literature and advertising. In 1963 his first novel, *If We Must Die*, was published. And in 1968 he opened one of New York's first Negro-owned general advertising agencies, Junius Edwards, Inc.

Edwards was born in Alexandria, Louisiana, in 1929. His father was a teacher and an insurance salesman. After the death of his parents, he was raised by relatives in Houston and Chicago. In his senior year at a high school in Chicago, he quit school and entered the armed forces. He spent nine years in the Army, and then used the GI Bill to obtain a college education at the University of Oslo in Norway. At thirty, with his wife and two children, he returned to the states and began looking for a copywriter's job in New York City.

While he was a soldier stationed in New Jersey, he had entered and won numerous "twenty-five words or less" contests. These successes influenced his decision to enter the advertising business. His entry into the field itself was a combination of luck and endurance. When he returned from Norway, he compiled a list of advertising firms and wrote to each of them. A leading firm hired him as a copywriter (he had never written copy before), and after eight highly successful years he was able to open his own agency.

He has written many short stories and has won both the Writer's Digest Award and the Eugene Saxton Literary Fellowship Award.

The following excerpt, which consists of the first two chapters from his novel, follows a day in the life of Will Harris, a Negro veteran of the Korean War (1950–1952). The title *If We Must Die* is from the poem of the same name by Claude McKay (1891–1948).

If We Must Die

It was six o'clock. Will Harris knew without looking at the clock. He reached for the clock on his night table and pushed the alarm. He didn't want it to ring at six-thirty and wake Mom sleeping in her room. Will had been awake since five. He had stayed in bed and watched the gray chase the dark and, finally, the sun chase the gray.

It wasn't time to get up. He had plenty of time. He swung his long legs out of bed and smiled when his feet touched the tickling warmth of the pine. He stood, and stretched. He had plenty of time, but he wanted to be ready.

He had shined his shoes last night and brushed his blue suit good. It did not need pressing. Mom had made sure of that, as she had made sure that he had a newly ironed white shirt. He had read until ten o'clock and then he had taken Mom's advice to go to bed.

He could not sleep. Mom was still up and she heard him moving in bed. She came to his door.

"Come in, Mom."

"Can't sleep, son?"

"No."

She didn't switch on the light. She came to his bed and sat on it just as she had done through the years when he was a little boy.

"Come to tuck me in, Mom?"

She laughed. He liked to hear Mom laugh. Her laugh was deep and real, and no matter how he felt, her laugh always did something for him.

"You should sleep," Mom said. "You need it."

"I wish I could."

"Are you worried?"

"A little."

"I know how it is. I'm worried too."

"Do you think it's any use, Mom?"

"Yes," she said quickly. "Yes, I know it is."

"I know, Mom. I know it is. It's just that sometimes, well, sometimes I . . ."

"I know, son. I know." She stood. "It'll be all right. Now, you try and go to sleep. You'll need sleep so you can be ready."

They had said good night and he had thought about it all for a long time, until he fell asleep. He hadn't slept well. He woke up three times and when he woke at five he stayed awake.

Now, he went to the bathroom in his bare feet so he wouldn't wake Mom. After he had washed, he tiptoed back to his room and got dressed. He did not put on his shoes. He went to his bookcase and took out *The Story of the Declaration of Independence* and read.

He read until Mom called him to breakfast. It was seven-thirty. He put on his shoes and went to the kitchen.

"Morning, Mom."

She was putting hot biscuits on the table.

"Morning, son."

She turned around and saw him. She smiled.

"My, you look fine," she said. "Just fine."

"Thanks, Mom."

"How long you been up?"

"Quite a while."

"Reading?"

"Yes."

He sat down.

"Sleep good?"

"Fine."

When Mom had called him in to eat, he had been all set to drink a cup of coffee and tell her he wasn't hungry, but her bacon smelled so good and it was so crisp, the way he liked it, he just dug right in.

"I'm so proud of you, son."

What could he say to that when it came from Mom and with that special sound in her voice?

He attacked that second strip of bacon.

He could never bring himself to say anything when Mom said that to him, not even thank you, because to him thank you wasn't enough. All he could do was smile.

Mom said that only on special occasions in his life. She said it when he graduated from grammar school and high school, when he came home from Korea, and now.

Will turned twenty-one while he was still in Korea. His birthday present was a letter from Mom. She said she considered him a man when he put on the uniform and fighting in Korea made him more a man and being twenty-one confirmed it. She said that now, since he was twenty-one, he had come to the responsibilities of manhood and that he was old enough to vote.

Will Harris knew how Mom felt about voting. He knew, too, that voting was not such a big thing to some people, but to Mom it was something very special. It had always been. As long as he could remember she had been trying to make herself eligible to vote and all the time she had pounded it into Will how important it was. He didn't know how right she was until after he was in the Army and they told him the same thing, but in a different way. He didn't like military life, but he had to admit the Army taught him more about citizenship and made him think more about it than he had ever done before he became a soldier.

He remembered when election time came while he was still in the

Army. The Army told all soldiers who came from states that accepted absentee votes that they were eligible to vote and urged them to send for those ballots and vote. Will sent for a ballot and waited excitedly. It would be his first vote.

Pretty soon those long, official-looking envelopes started to come and it was time to vote. Will knew how some fellow soldiers *looked* like they felt, voting for the first time. He didn't know *how* they felt because he wasn't one of the lucky ones who received ballots. He didn't know what happened. He had sent his request for a ballot. All he knew was that a few soldiers did not get that official-looking envelope and he was one of the few. At first he thought it would come later, but as time passed he realized that it would not come. So many had sent for them, maybe they just couldn't send them to everyone. Red tape. Anyway, he knew he wouldn't miss out next time because he would be out of the Army and nothing in the world was going to keep him from going down and registering and voting.

He didn't tell Mom about sending for the absentee ballot. He had planned to tell her after he had voted. Surprise her. Now he was glad he hadn't told her. After he got out of the Army and went back home, he told her he was going to register and vote in the next election.

Mom told him voting would be easy. She knew that even though she had never voted. The hard thing, she said, was to get registered. The whole thing, registering and voting, she said, was very easy in some states, but not in their state. That was why Mom never made it. It was not easy. Mom wasn't dumb, but they always had some pretty tough questions to be answered when she went down to register. There was always one that stumped her.

Will studied for two years after he was out of the Army. Mom helped him. She helped him by steadily asking him questions that might come. She asked him any time, anyplace. They asked all the people they could find who had ever been down to try to register to tell them what questions they were asked and they wrote them all down and Will learned the answers to them. He got books about the state government, federal government, history, and an almanac, and he studied them all. He also studied newspapers, periodicals, pamphlets from the state capitol, and anything else he could get his hands on. He even studied the Constitution of the United States and his state's constitution.

Then, to top all that, Mom went down to see a lawyer and had their house put in Will's name so he could be even better qualified to vote as a property owner.

Will thought of himself as a funny sort of eater. Most people eat their cereal first and then bacon and eggs. Not Will. He couldn't do that. He always ate two slices of bacon first and then two slices of toast or two biscuits with two eggs, sunny side up, lots of pepper (Mom always said it was too much pepper), a little jam and butter (Mom always said it was too little butter). After that, he would eat his cereal before lingering over that last crisp slice of bacon. Then he would take a cigarette and drink his coffee, fast.

That's the way he ate that morning. He wasn't a bit nervous. Mom was. He could tell Mom was nervous. She didn't eat at all. She just sat there, silent, over a cup of black coffee.

They sat at the breakfast table in silence until Will put out his cigarette.

"You got your birth certificate?"

"Yes."

"Deed to the house?"

"Yes."

"Discharge papers?"

"Yes, Mom."

"High school diploma?"

"Yes, Mom. I have everything."

"Don't be nervous, son."

"I'm not, Mom."

"Remember. Go in there and sit till they call you in, now."

"Yes, Mom."

"No matter how long you have to wait."

"Okay."

"Even if they take other people before you who came in after you."

"Don't worry, Mom."

"No matter how hot you get in there, don't you take off your jacket."

"I won't, Mom."

"Don't forget, now, no matter how good you know the answer, take it slow. Don't give them too fast."

"All right, Mom."

"And son. I don't think you better take along any books to read while you wait. And don't buy a newspaper, neither. I don't think it's a good idea to let them see you reading. They might count it against you."

Mom sure is nervous, thought Will.

"And smoking, son. I . . . ."

"I'll hold up from smoking while I'm waiting, Mom."

"That's good, son. That's good. Now, don't forget to . . ."

Yes, Mom was nervous. She went on reminding him about things that he had spent two years learning. It was Mom's way. He just let her go on and she was still telling him things to remember when he went out the front door.

She followed him out.

"Son. I want you to remember, no matter what happens down there today. I'm proud of you. Real proud."

Will kissed her forehead.

He held her shoulders and smiled.

People are sort of funny-acting things, Will thought, they really are. But no matter how funny they act sometimes, most people are all right. Every family in his block knew what he was going to do that day and as he walked down to the bus stop, they waved and smiled. Even people with whom he had never had a word. Some came and shook his hand and smiled up to him. It was like when he came home from Korea.

Will felt pretty good when he got on the bus. He went on back to that big, wide seat in the back of the bus. It was a hot day, anyway, and sitting over the motor made it even hotter back there, so he took off his jacket. He sweated easy. He didn't want to be all sweated up when he got down to the courthouse.

When he got off the bus he still had two blocks to walk, so he decided to smoke a cigarette. He liked cigarettes. Mom said he smoked too much, but he kept it up. It was one reason why he didn't like to see double-feature movies. He just couldn't sit that long without a smoke.

He hadn't finished his smoke by the time he got to the courthouse so he stood outside and smoked and then he put on his jacket and straightened his tie and went on up to the second floor.

There was a sign there that told him what to do. He was to go into the waiting room and sit there until he was called in to register. He opened the door to the waiting room and went in. The room was empty. It made him glad. Maybe he wouldn't have to wait long. He closed the door and looked around the room. He didn't know when it was swept last. It had one window over to his left and if it hadn't been opened he didn't know whether the sun would have gotten in through those dirty windowpanes or not. At his right there were two benches. He sat down on the back bench.

He had just finished a cigarette downstairs, but he hadn't been sitting there ten minutes before he felt the urge. All those cigarette butts on the floor don't help, he thought. He looked out the window. There was nothing to see out there. He wondered how long he would have to sit and wait.

He sat there for an hour. During that time, four men came in. He noticed that when the first man came in he didn't bother about the sign and the benches. He just walked right on in the inner office and when he came out he put something in his pocket. Will knew the man had registered. When the first man came and went right on in like that, Will was surprised. By the time the second, third, and fourth men came and did the same thing Will wanted to forget that sign and walk on in and get registered, too, so he could get out of there and have a smoke.

No.

He remembered Mom's words. He sat there. He waited.

Waited. . . .

Pretty soon, three men came in. The first man was little and he had a smile that Will thought was bigger than the man himself; the kind of smile that made Will feel good from seeing it. The two men who followed him weren't smiling so big. One had a camera. It was easy for Will to see that it was a press camera. The other man had a pencil and pad.

"You all stand over by the door," the man with the camera said, "like you was being interviewed."

The little man and the man with the pencil and pad went over to the door to the inner office and the man with the camera told them how he wanted them to pose and then he took two pictures.

Will sat there and watched them. As he watched them, he had the idea that he had seen the little man before. They had all gone into the inner office when Will remembered. A few days ago, he had seen the little man's picture in the newspaper. The man had just gotten his citizenship papers. The story told how the little man had, a few years ago, escaped from one of the Iron Curtain countries and come to America to live. It told how he had been shot while escaping. Will wondered whether the little man had been shot with a burp gun,[1] the way he had been shot over in Korea. Seeing the little man made Will feel kind of close to him. It must be because both of us have been wounded by Communists, thought Will.

1. burp gun: a small submachine gun; its name is based on the sound it makes when it is fired.

The door opened and the man with the camera backed out. His camera was up to his face as he took two more pictures.

"One more with the registrar," he said. He took a picture while the little man and the registrar shook hands.

"How you feel now that you all registered and ready to vote like all other Americans?" the man with the pencil and pad asked.

Will listened and watched.

The little man smiled and Will thought he was searching for words.

"I cannot, how do you say, describe, yes. Describe. I cannot describe the feeling. Not with, not with the words. I got the papers, yes. Yes. I got the papers. Yes. But when I come down here today. Down here to the courthouse to register to vote, it make me feel more like the citizen than when I got the papers. When I got the papers, I knew I was a citizen. I'm so happy. I'm so proud. I'm American. Just like you. Just like you all. I'm American. I tell myself all the time. I'm American. Yes, I do. I hear myself speak and I don't hear myself speak American, but that's all right. That's all right. I learn. Every day, I learn the English."

"You doing fine with English," the photographer said. "Fact is, you talk almost good as us."

"Thank you. Thank you. I don't worry about the speech so much. I learn. I just want to do my, how do you say, duty. Yes, duty. I want to do my duty as a citizen. That's what I want to do. My duty. I could never do my duty as I saw it in the old country. I had to do what they say. But here? It's America. America. Government here, they don't tell you where to live, how to live, and what to do. And you know why? Because the government is for you and me. Me, too. Me, too. America means freedom. Today I come down here to do the biggest thing that any American can do, register and vote."

The man spoke slowly and Will was sure that the reporter was able to get everything written down.

"And do you care to tell us how you're going to vote?" the reporter asked.

"In America, nobody stops you from voting. Nobody tells you how to vote. You don't have to day, I mean, to say, to nobody who you vote for. Nobody. I like that about America. You don't have to be born here to be a citizen and vote and enjoy the freedom. I come here election day and I vote. I vote the way I want to vote. Nobody gets angry. Nobody tells me how. I do it the way I want to do it. I know for sure I am American."

Will watched the three men go on out the door. That smile was as big as ever on the little man's face. He was so proud to be an American citizen. That little man and his big smile sure made Will feel good.

It made Will smile too.

Will Harris sat on the bench in the waiting room for another hour. His pride was not the only thing that hurt. He wanted them to call him in and get him registered so he could get out of there. Twice, he started to go into the inner office and tell them, but he thought better of it. He had counted ninety-six cigarette butts on the floor when a fat man came out of the office and spoke to him.

"What you want, boy?"

Will Harris got to his feet.

"I came to register."

"Oh, you did, did you?"

"Yes, sir."

The fat man stared at Will for a second and then turned his back to him.

As he turned his back, he said, "Come on in here."

Will went in.

It was a little office, and dirty, but not so dirty as the waiting room. There were no cigarette butts on the floor here. Instead, there was paper. It looked like candy wrappers to Will. There were two desks jammed in there, and a bony little man sat at one of them, his head down, his fingers fumbling with some papers. The fat man went around the empty desk and pulled up a chair. The bony man did not look up.

Will stood in front of the empty desk and watched the fat man sit down behind it. The fat man swung his chair around until he faced the little man.

"Charlie," he said.

"Yeah, Sam," Charlie said, not looking up from his work.

"Charlie. This boy here says he come to register."

"You sure? You sure that's what he said, Sam?" Still not looking up. "You sure? You better ask him again."

"I'm sure, Charlie."

"You better be sure, Sam."

"All right, Charlie. All right. I'll ask him again," the fat man said. He looked up at Will. "Boy. What you come here for?"

"I came to register."

The fat man stared up at him. He didn't say anything. He just stared, his lips a thin line, his eyes wide open. His left hand searched behind him and came up with a handkerchief. He raised his left arm and mopped his face with the handkerchief, his eyes still on Will.

The odor from under his sweat-soaked arm made Will step back. Will held his breath until the fat man finished mopping his face. The fat man put his handkerchief away. He pulled a desk drawer open and then he took his eyes off Will. He reached in the desk drawer and took out a bar of candy. He took the wrapper off the candy and threw the wrapper on the floor at Will's feet. He looked at Will and ate the candy.

Will stood there and tried to keep his face straight. He kept telling himself: I'll take anything. I'll take anything. I'll take anything to get it done.

The fat man kept his eyes on Will and finished the candy. He took out his handkerchief and wiped his mouth. He grinned.

Will held his breath.

The fat man put his handkerchief back.

Will breathed again.

"Charlie."

"Yeah, Sam."

"He says he come to register."

"Sam, are you sure?"

"Pretty sure, Charlie."

"Well, explain to him what it's about." The bony man still had not looked up.

"All right, Charlie," Sam said and looked up at Will. "Boy. When folks come here, they intend to vote, so they register first."

"That's what I want to do," Will said.

"What's that? Say that again."

I'll take anything, Will thought.

"That's what I want to do. Register and vote."

The fat man turned his head to the bony man.

"Charlie."

"Yeah, Sam."

"He says . . . Charlie, this boy says that he wants to register and vote."

The bony man looked up from his desk for the first time. He looked at Sam, then both of them looked at Will.

Will looked from one of them to the other, one to the other. It was hot and he wanted to sit down. Anything. I'll take anything. I'll take anything. Anything, thought Will.

The man called Charlie turned back to his work and Sam swung his chair around until he faced Will.

"You got a job?" he asked.

"Yes, sir."

"Boy, you know what you're doing?"

"Yes, sir."

"All right," Sam said. "All right."

Just then, Will heard the door open behind him and someone came in. It was a man.

"How, you all? How about registering?"

Sam smiled. Charlie looked up and smiled.

"Take care of you right away," Sam said, and then to Will, "Boy. Wait outside."

As Will went out he heard Sam's voice: "Take a seat. Take a seat. Have you fixed up in a little while. Now, what's your name?"

"Thanks," the man said, and Will heard the scrape of a chair.

Will closed the door and went back to his bench.

Anything. Anything. Anything. Anything. Anything. Anything. I'll take it all. All.

Pretty soon the man came out. Sam came out behind him and he called Will and told him to come in. When Will went in and stood before the desk, Sam told him he wanted to see his papers: Discharge, high school diploma, birth certificate, Social Security card, and some other papers. Will had them all. He felt good when he handed them to Sam.

"You belong to any organization?"

"No, sir."

"Pretty sure about that?"

"Yes, sir."

"You ever heard of the Fifteenth Amendment?"

"Yes, sir."

"What does that one say?"

"It's the one that says all citizens can vote."

"You like that, don't you, boy? Don't you?"

"Yes, sir. I like them all."

Sam's eyes got big. He slammed his right fist down on his desk top. "I didn't ask you that. I asked you if you liked the Fifteenth Amendment. Now, if you can't answer my questions . . ."

"I like it," Will put in, and watched Sam catch his breath.

Sam sat there looking up at Will. He opened and closed his desk-pounding fist. His mouth hung open.

"Charlie."

"Yeah, Sam." Not looking up.

"You hear that?" Looking wide-eyed at Will. "You hear that?"

"I heard it, Sam."

Will had to work to keep his face straight.

"Boy," Sam said. "You born in this town?"

You got my birth certificate right there in front of you. "Yes, sir."

"You happy here?"

"Yes, sir."

"You got nothing against the way things go around here?"

"No, sir."

"Can you read?"

"Yes, sir."

"Are you smart?"

"No, sir."

"Where you get that suit?"

"New York."

"New York?" Sam asked, and looked over at Charlie. Charlie's head was still down. Sam looked back to Will.

"Yes, sir."

"Boy, what you doing there?"

"I got out of the Army there."

"You believe in what them folks do in New York?"

"I don't know what you mean."

"You know what I mean. Boy, you know good and well what I mean. You know how folks carry on in New York. You believe in that?"

Will knew what answer Sam wanted.

"No, sir," he said.

"You pretty sure about that?"

"Yes, sir."

"What year did they make the Fifteenth Amendment?"

No matter how good you know the answer, take it slow, don't give them too fast. Mom's words rang in Will's ears.

". . . Eighteen . . . seventy. Eighteen-seventy," said Will.

"Boy, what year is this, now?"

"This is nineteen . . ."

Sam cut him off with: "Name a signer of the Declaration of Independence who became President."

". . . John Adams."

"Boy, what did you say?" Sam's eyes were wide again.

Will thought. Then he said, "John Adams."

Sam's eyes got wider. He looked to Charlie and spoke to a bowed head. "Now, too much is too much." Then he turned back to Will.

He didn't say anything to Will. He narrowed his eyes first, then spoke.

"Boy. Did you say *just* John Adams?"

How stupid can I get, Will asked himself.

"Mr. John Adams," he said.

"That's more like it," Sam smiled. "Now, why do you want to vote?"

"I want to vote because it is my duty as an American citizen to vote."

"Hah," Sam said real loud, and pushed back from his desk and turned to the bony man.

"Charlie."

"Yeah, Sam."

"Hear that?"

"I heard, Sam."

Sam leaned back in his chair, keeping his eyes on Charlie. He locked his hands across his round stomach and sat there.

"Charlie."

"Yeah, Sam."

"Think you and Elnora be coming over tonight?"

"Don't know, Sam," said the bony man, not looking up. "You know Elnora."

"Well, you welcome if you can."

"Don't know, Sam."

"You ought to, if you can. Drop on in, if you can. Come on over and we'll split a corn."

The bony man looked up.

"Now, that's different, Sam."

"Thought it would be."

"Can't turn down corn, if it's good."

"You know my corn."

"Sure do. I'll drag Elnora, if I have to."

The bony man went back to work.

Sam turned his chair around to his desk. He opened a desk drawer and took out a package of cigarettes. He tore it open and put a cigarette in his mouth. He looked up at Will, then he lit the cigarette and took a long drag and then he blew smoke, very slowly, up toward Will's face.

The smoke floated up toward Will's face. It came up in front of his eyes and nose and hung there, then it danced and played around his face and disappeared.

Will didn't move, but he was glad he hadn't been asked to sit down.

Anything. Anything.

"You have a car?"

"No, sir."

"Don't you have a job?"

"Yes, sir."

"You like that job?"

"Yes, sir."

"You like it, but you don't want it."

Will put his hand up to his mouth and coughed from the smoke.

"What do you mean?" Will asked.

"Don't get smart, boy," said Sam, wide-eyed. "I'm asking the questions here. You understand that?"

"Yes, sir."

"All right. All right. Be sure you do."

"I understand it."

"You a Communist?"

"No sir."

"What party do you want to vote for?"

"I wouldn't go by parties. I'd read about the men and vote for a man, not a party."

"Hah," said Sam and looked over at Charlie's bowed head. "Hah," he said again, and turned back to Will.

"Boy, you pretty sure you can read?"

"Yes, sir."

"All right. All right. We'll see about that." Sam took a book out of his desk and flipped some pages. He gave the book to Will.

"Read that loud," he said.

"Yes sir," Will said, and began, " 'When in the course of human events it becomes necessary for one people to dissolve the political bonds which have connected them with another, and to assume among the powers of the earth the separate and equal station to which the laws of nature and of nature's God entitle them, a decent respect to the opinions of mankind requires that they should declare the causes which impel them to the separation.' "

Will cleared his throat and read on. He tried to be distinct with each syllable. He didn't need the book. He could have recited the whole thing without the book.

" 'We hold these truths to be self-evident, that all men are created equal, that they—' "

"Wait a minute, boy," Sam said. "Wait a minute. You believe that? You believe that about 'created equal'?"

"Yes, sir," Will said, knowing that was the wrong answer.

"You really believe that?"

"Yes, sir." Will couldn't make himself say the answer Sam wanted to hear.

Sam stuck out his right hand and Will put the book in it. Then Sam turned to the other man.

"Charlie."

"Yeah, Sam."

"Charlie, did you hear that?"

"What was it, Sam?"

"This boy, here, Charlie. He says he really believes it."

"Believes what, Sam? What you talking about?"

"This boy, here. Believes that all men are equal, like it says in the Declaration."

"Now, Sam. Now, you know that's not right. You know good and well that's not right. You heard him wrong. Ask him again, Sam. Ask him again, will you?"

"I didn't hear him wrong, Charlie," said Sam and turned to Will. "Did I, boy? Did I hear you wrong?"

"No, sir."

"I didn't hear you wrong?"

"No, sir."

Sam turned to Charlie.

"Charlie."

"Yeah, Sam."

"It's just like I told you. I heard right."

The man called Charlie looked up from his desk and at the man called Sam. Then they looked at Will. For a full minute Will just looked from one to the other, one to the other.

"Charlie."

"Yeah, Sam."

"Charlie. You think this boy trying to be smart?"

"Sam. I think he might be. Just might be. He looks like one of them that don't know his place."

Sam narrowed his eyes.

"Boy," he said. "You know your place?"

"I don't know what you mean."

"Boy, you know good and well what I mean."

"What do you mean?"

"Boy, who's . . ." He leaned forward, on his desk. "Boy. Just who's asking questions, here?"

"You are. Sir."

"Charlie. You think he really is trying to be smart?"

"Sam. I think you better ask him."

"Boy."

"Yes, sir."

"Boy. You trying to be smart with me?"

"No, sir."

"Sam."

"Yeah, Charlie."

"Sam. Ask him if he thinks he's good as you and me."

"Now, Charlie. Now, you heard what he said about the Declaration."

"Ask anyway, Sam."

"All right," Sam said. "Boy. You think you good as me and Mister Charlie?"

What the heck, thought Will. Give them the answer they want to hear.

"No, sir," Will said.

They smiled and Charlie turned away.

Will wanted to take off his jacket. It was hot and he felt a drop of sweat roll down his right side. He pressed his right arm against his side to wipe out the sweat. He thought he had it, but it rolled again and he felt another drop come behind that one. He pressed his arm in again. It was no use. He gave it up.

"How many states make up this country?"

". . . Fifty."

"How many stars did the first flag have?"

". . . Thirteen."

"What's the name of the mayor of this town?"

". . . Mr. Roger Phillip Thornedyke Jones."

"Spell Thornedyke."

". . . Capital T-h-o-r-n-e-d-y-k-e, Thornedyke."

"How long has he been Mayor?"

". . . Ten years." Too long, thought Will.

"Who was the biggest hero in the War Between the States?"

". . . General Robert E. Lee."

"What does the *E* stand for?"

". . . Edward."

"Think you pretty smart, don't you?"

"No, sir."

"Well, boy, you been giving these answers too slow. I want them fast. Understand? Fast."

"Yes, sir."

"What's your favorite song?"

" 'Dixie,' " Will said, and prayed Sam would not ask him to sing it.

"Do you like your job?"

"Yes, sir."

"What was the last state into the forty-eight?"

"Arizona."

"What year?"

"1912."

"There was another state in 1912."

"New Mexico, but it came in January and Arizona came in February."

"You think you smart, don't you?"

"No, sir."

"Don't you think you smart? Don't you?"

"No, sir."

"Oh, yes, you do, boy."

Will said nothing.

"Boy, you make good money on your job?"

"I make enough."

"Oh. Oh, you're not satisfied with it?"

"Yes, sir. I am."

"You don't act like it, boy. You know that? You don't act like it."

"What do you mean?"

"You getting smart again, boy. Just who's asking questions here?"

"You are."

"That's right. That's right."

The bony man made a noise with his lips and slammed his pencil down on his desk. He looked at Will, then at Sam.

"Sam," he said. "Sam, you having trouble with that boy? Don't you let that boy give you no trouble, now, Sam. Don't you do it."

"Charlie," Sam said. "Now, Charlie, you know better than that. You know better. This boy here know better than that, too."

"You sure about that, Sam? You sure?"

"I better be sure, if this boy here knows what's good for him."

"Does he know, Sam?"

"Do you know, boy?" Sam asked Will.

"Yes, sir."

Charlie turned back to his work.

"Boy," Sam said. "You sure you're not a member of any organization?"

"Yes, sir. I'm sure."

Sam gathered up all Will's papers and he stacked them very neatly and placed them in the center of his desk. He took the cigarette out of his mouth and put it out in the full ash tray. He picked up Will's papers and gave them to him.

"You've been in the Army. That right?"

"Yes, sir."

"You served two years. That right?"

"Yes, sir."

"You have to do six years in the Reserve. That right?"

"Yes, sir."

"You're in the Reserve now. That right?"

"Yes, sir."

"You lied to me here, today. That right?"

"No, sir."

"Oh, yes, you did, boy. Oh, yes, you did. You told me you wasn't in any organization. That right?"

"Yes, sir."

"Then, you lied, boy. You lied to me because you're in the Army Reserve. That right?"

"Yes, sir. I'm in the Reserve, but I didn't think you meant that. I'm just in it and I don't have to go to meetings or anything like that. I thought you meant some kind of civilian organization."

"When you said you wasn't in an organization, that was a lie. Now, wasn't it, boy?"

He had Will there. When Sam had asked him about organizations the first thing to pop in Will's mind had been the Communists, or something like them.

"Now, wasn't it a lie?"

"No, sir."

Sam narrowed his eyes.

Will went on.

"No, sir, it wasn't a lie. There's nothing wrong with the Army Reserve. Everybody has to be in it. I'm not in it because I want to be in it."

"I know there's nothing wrong with it," Sam said. "Point is, you lied to me here today."

"I didn't lie. I just didn't understand the question," Will said.

"You understood the question, boy. You understood good and well, and you lied to me. Now, wasn't it a lie?"

"No, sir."

"Boy. You going to stand right there in front of me, big as anything, and tell me it wasn't a lie?" Sam almost shouted. "Now, wasn't it a lie?"

"Yes, sir," Will said, and put his papers in his jacket pocket.

"You right, it was."

Sam pushed back from his desk.

"That's it, boy. You can't register. You don't qualify. Liars don't qualify."

"But . . ."

"That's it." Sam spat the words out and looked at Will hard for a second and then he swung his chair around until he faced Charlie.

"Charlie."

"Yeah, Sam."

"Charlie. You want to go out to eat first today?"

Will opened the door and went out. As he walked down the stairs, he took off his jacket and his tie and opened his collar and rolled up his shirt sleeves. He stood on the courthouse steps and took a deep breath and heard a noise come from his throat when he breathed out. He looked up at the flag in the courtyard. The flag hung from its staff, still and quiet, the way he hated to see it; but it was there, waiting, and he knew that a little push from the right breeze would lift it and send it flying and waving and whipping from its staff, proud, the way he liked to see it.

He took out a cigarette and lit it and took a slow, deep drag. He blew the smoke out. He saw the cigarette burning in his right hand, turned it between his thumb and forefinger, made a face, and let the cigarette drop to the courthouse steps.

He threw his jacket over his left shoulder and walked on down to the bus stop, swinging his arms.

Meaning and Method

1. Judging by their speech and behavior, how do you think Will and his mother feel toward each other? Why might they feel this way?
2. Does Will's mother want him to register because she feels it is her duty as a mother to see that he does, or does her desire concern the welfare of other people outside her immediate family? Explain your answer.
3. How has Will prepared himself for the voter registration examination?

Why is it necessary for him to study many hours for an examination which millions of Americans prepare very little for? To what extent have his past experiences in the Army and the information given by his mother provided encouragement for the task he will shortly undertake? Is he optimistic or pessimistic as he leaves home to register?

4. Compare the goals of the immigrant from the Iron Curtain country with Will's. In light of the outcome of the story, what is ironic about the foreigner's words and their effect on Will? Point out passages to illustrate your answer.

5. What methods do the two registrars use to undermine Will both physically and mentally? Why is it ironic that Will should be disqualified on a technicality concerning the Army Reserve? Where is the irony in the fact that the registrar calls Will a liar?

6. The flag, of course, is usually used as a symbol of one's country. Reread the last three paragraphs of the story. What else is the author using the flag as a symbol for? What is Edwards referring to when he writes "and he knew that a little push from the right breeze would lift it and send it flying and waving and whipping from its staff, proud, the way he liked to see it."

7. A *short story* is a brief fictional prose narrative that employs suspense, plot, conflict, characterization, theme, atmosphere, setting, tone, foreshadowing, and point of view. Its main characteristic is its aim: to produce a single, unified effect in the mind of the reader. A *novel*, like a short story, is an invented prose narrative. Because of its greater length, a novel is able to show character developing as the result of a complicated series of actions and under the impact of several events.

Although this selection consists of the first two chapters of a novel, it still may be classified as a short story. (a) Show how the author has achieved a unified treatment of a single action. (b) What is the single effect?

Composition and Discussion

1. To write an explanation of a procedure you must: (a) begin with a statement of its purpose and tell when and by whom it is performed; (b) present the important steps in the process in the order in which they are to be accomplished, making sure to give the specific details of each stage and to clarify technical terms or unfamiliar words; (c) use transitional expressions such as *when, first, on the average, after a certain period, next, then,* and *finally* to provide easy transitions between the steps; and (d) conclude by explaining the results that follow when the steps are followed carefully.

Write a clear and accurate explanation of the voting procedure in your state. What reforms, if any, can you suggest?

2. For a book report, write a review of Junius Edwards's entire novel, *If We Must Die*, which narrates additional happenings in Will Harris's day. Include in your critical examination (a) a statement of the author's overall attitude toward the subject of the Negro's right to vote, (b) a description of some of the events in Will Harris's day that reveal this attitude, and (c) a discussion of whether you agree or disagree with the attitude the author adopts in this book.

3. In a panel discussion or debate, consider the following: *Should an elementary or high school diploma from an American or English-speaking school be a requirement for voting or should proof of literacy in a foreign language (any language) be considered sufficient?*

H. G. Wells
[1866–1946]

Clifton Fadiman, an American literary critic, referred to this writer as "Wells the world-citizen, Wells the world-planner, Wells the world-encyclopedist." And *The London Times* spoke of him as a "nonstop genius."

Herbert George Wells was born at Bromley, Kent, England. His father was an unsuccessful shopkeeper and a professional cricket player. His mother worked as a housekeeper on a large country estate. Since his parents were unable to finance his education, Wells was left to provide for himself. He earned money to attend Midhurst Grammar School by working as a dry-goods apprentice and a chemist's [that is, druggist's] assistant. Upon graduation he worked in a London dry-goods firm. He later won a scholarship to the Royal College of Science at London University, from which he graduated with honors at twenty-one.

Wells was a self-made prophet, as well as a biologist, a journalist, and a writer. He had a vision of a World State which could be achieved through science if man used inventions intelligently. However, his view of man became increasingly pessimistic as he grew older, losing for him the great popularity he once held.

His writings, which numbered about a hundred volumes, included history, science, politics, sociology, and fiction. Among his better known works are *The Time Machine*, a science-fiction story about a machine that transported its inventor into the far future, and *The War of the Worlds*, which tells of the invasion of England by the Martians. His novel *Tono-Bungay*, which satirized the dishonest practices common in the commercial and advertising fields of his time, is the story of a man who made a fortune by manufacturing and selling a quack medicine, Tono-Bungay.

"The Magic Shop" is from his short-story collection *Twelve Stories and a Dream*, published in 1903.

The Magic Shop

I had seen the Magic Shop from afar several times; I had passed it once or twice, a shop window of alluring little objects, magic balls, magic hens, wonderful cones, ventriloquist dolls, the material of the basket trick, packs of cards that *looked* all right, and all that sort of

"The Magic Shop" from *Short Stories of H. G. Wells.* Reprinted by permission of A. P. Watt & Son for the Executors of H. G. Wells.

thing, but never had I thought of going in until one day, almost without warning, Gip hauled me by my finger right up to the window, and so conducted himself that there was nothing for it but to take him in. I had not thought the place was there, to tell the truth—a modest-sized frontage in Regent Street, between the picture shop and the place where the chicks run about just out of patent incubators—but there it was sure enough. I had fancied it was down nearer the Circus, or around the corner in Oxford Street, or even in Holborn; [1] always over the way and a little inaccessible it had been, with something of the mirage [2] in its position; but here it was now quite indisputably, and the fat end of Gip's pointing finger made a noise upon the glass.

"If I was rich," said Gip, dabbing a finger at the Disappearing Egg, "I'd buy myself that. And that"—which was The Crying Baby, Very Human—"and that," which was a mystery, and called, so a neat card asserted, "Buy One and Astonish Your Friends."

"Anything," said Gip, "will disappear under one of those cones. I have read about it in a book.

"And there, Dadda, is the Vanishing Halfpenny—only they've put it this way up so's we can't see how it's done."

Gip, dear boy, inherits his mother's breeding, [3] and he did not propose to enter the shop or worry in any way; only, you know, quite unconsciously he lugged my finger doorward, and he made his interest clear.

"That," he said, and pointed to the Magic Bottle.

"If you had that?" I said; at which promising inquiry he looked up with a sudden radiance.

"I could show it to Jessie," he said, thoughtful as ever of others.

"It's less than a hundred days to your birthday, Gibbles," I said, and laid my hand on the door handle.

Gip made no answer, but his grip tightened on my finger, and so we came into the shop.

It was no common shop this; it was a magic shop, and all the prancing precedence [4] Gip would have taken in the matter of mere

1. **Holborn:** a large district or borough in London; also mentioned are *Regent Street*, noted for its variety of shops and business offices, the *Circus* (meaning Picadilly Circus), and *Oxford Street*, well-known commercial thoroughfares.
2. **mirage** (mi·räzh′): an optical illusion; anything that appears to be real.
3. **breeding:** manner of conducting one's self; manners.
4. **prancing precedence** (pres′ə·dəns): *Prancing* is the act of springing from the hind legs, usually used in reference to the motions of a high-spirited horse. *Precedence* is the ceremonial order or placing of persons of different ranks in formal occasions according to the rules of diplomatic etiquette. Here, the words are a humorous reference to the usual behavior of the boy in the presence of toys.

toys was wanting. He left the burthen [5] of the conversation to me.

It was a little, narrow shop, not very well lit, and the doorbell pinged again with a plaintive [6] note as we closed it behind us. For a moment or so we were alone and could glance about us. There was a tiger in *papier-mâché* [7] on the glass case that covered the low counter—a grave, kind-eyed tiger that waggled his head in a methodical manner; there were several crystal spheres, a china hand holding magic cards, a stock of magic fishbowls in various sizes, and an immodest magic hat that shamelessly displayed its springs. On the floor were magic mirrors; one to draw you out long and thin, one to swell your head and vanish your legs, and one to make you short and fat like a dwarf; and while we were laughing at these the shopman, as I suppose, came in.

At any rate, there he was behind the counter—a curious, sallow, dark man, with one ear larger than the other and a chin like the toe cap [8] of a boot.

"What can we have the pleasure?" he asked, spreading his long, magic fingers on the glass case; and so with a start we were aware of him.

"I want," I said, "to buy my little boy a few simple tricks."

"Legerdemain [9]?" he asked. "Mechanical? Domestic?"

"Anything amusing," said I.

"Um!" said the shopman, and scratched his head for a moment as if thinking. Then, quite distinctly, he drew from his head a glass ball. "Something in this way?" he said, and held it out.

The action was unexpected. I had seen the trick done at entertainments endless times before—it's part of the common stock of conjurers—but I had not expected it here. "That's good," I said, with a laugh.

"Isn't it?" said the shopman.

Gip stretched out his disengaged hand to take this object and found merely a blank palm.

"It's in your pocket," said the shopman, and there it was!

"How much will that be?" I asked.

"We make no charge for glass balls," said the shopman politely.

---

5. **burthen** (bûr'thən): burden.
6. **plaintive**: expressive of sadness; mournful.
7. **papier-mâché** (pā'pər·mə·shā'): a material made of paper pulp mixed with glue or other adhesives that can be molded when wet and that hardens when dry.
8. **toe cap**: a small, permanently applied cap of leather or other material covering the toe of a shoe or boot.
9. **Legerdemain** (lej'ər·də·mān'): a magician's trick so skillfully done that the method of performance escapes observation; also called "sleight of hand."

"We get them"—he picked out one of his elbow as he spoke—"free." He produced another from the back of his neck, and laid it beside its predecessor on the counter. Gip regarded his glass ball sagely,[10] then directed a look of inquiry at the two on the counter and finally brought his round-eyed scrutiny to the shopman, who smiled. "You may have those too," said the shopman, "and if you *don't* mind, one from my mouth. *So!*"

Gip counseled [11] me mutely for a moment, and then in a profound silence put away the four balls, resumed my reassuring finger, and nerved himself for the next event.

"We get all our smaller tricks in that way," the shopman remarked.

I laughed in the manner of one who subscribes to a jest.[12] "Instead of going to the wholesale shop," I said. "Of course, it's cheaper."

"In a way," the shopman said. "Though we pay in the end. But not so heavily—as people suppose. . . . Our larger tricks, and our daily provisions, and all the other things we want, we get out of that hat. . . . And you know, sir, if you'll excuse my saying it, there *isn't* a wholesale shop, not for Genuine Magic goods, sir. I don't know if you noticed our inscription—the Genuine Magic shop." He drew a business card from his cheek and handed it to me. "Genuine," he said, with his finger on the word, and added, "There is absolutely no deception, sir."

He seemed to be carrying out the joke pretty thoroughly, I thought.

He turned to Gip with a smile of remarkable affability. "You, you know, are the Right Sort of Boy."

I was surprised at his knowing that, because, in the interests of discipline, we keep it rather a secret even at home; but Gip received it in unflinching silence, keeping a steadfast eye on him.

"It's only the Right Sort of Boy gets through that doorway."

And, as if by way of illustration, there came a rattling at the door, and a squeaking little voice could be faintly heard. "Nyar! I *warn* 'a go in there, Dadda, I WARN 'a go in there. Ny-a-a-ah!" and then the accents of a downtrodden parent, urging consolations and propitiations.[13] "It's locked, Edward," he said.

"But it isn't," said I.

"It is, sir," said the shopman, "always—for that sort of child," and as he spoke we had a glimpse of the other youngster, a little, white

10. **sagely** (sāj′lē): solemnly.
11. **counseled**: consulted.
12. **subscribes . . . jest**: agrees to a joke.
13. **propitiations** (prō·pish′ē·ā′shəns): mollifications, appeasements.

face, pallid from sweet-eating and over-sapid [14] food, and distorted by evil passions, a ruthless little egotist, pawing at the enchanted pane. "It's no good, sir," said the shopman, as I moved, with my natural helpfulness, doorward, and presently the spoilt child was carried off howling.

"How do you manage that?" I said, breathing a little more freely.

"Magic!" said the shopman, with a careless wave of the hand, and behold! sparks of colored fire flew out of his fingers and vanished into the shadows of the shop.

"You were saying," he said, addressing himself to Gip, "before you came in, that you would like one of our 'Buy One and Astonish Your Friends' boxes?"

Gip, after a gallant effort, said, "Yes."

"It's in your pocket."

And leaning over the counter—he really had an extraordinarily long body—this amazing person produced the article in the customary conjurer's manner. "Paper," he said, and took a sheet out of the empty hat with the springs; "string," and behold his mouth was a string-box, from which he drew an unending thread, which when he had tied his parcel he bit off—and, it seemed to me, swallowed the ball of string. And then he lit a candle at the nose of one of the ventriloquist's dummies, stuck one of his fingers (which had become sealing-wax red) into the flame, and so sealed the parcel. "Then there was the Disappearing Egg," he remarked, and produced one from within my coat-breast and packed it, and also The Crying Baby, Very Human. I handed each parcel to Gip as it was ready, and he clasped them to his chest.

He said very little, but his eyes were eloquent; the clutch of his arms was eloquent. He was the playground of unspeakable emotions. These, you know, were *real* Magics.

Then, with a start, I discovered something moving about in my hat—something soft and jumpy. I whipped it off, and a ruffled pigeon —no doubt a confederate—dropped out and ran on the counter, and went, I fancy, into a cardboard box behind the *papier-mâché* tiger.

"Tut, tut!" said the shopman, dexterously relieving me of my head-dress; "careless bird, and—as I live—nesting!"

He shook my hat, and shook out into his extended hand two or three eggs, a large marble, a watch, about half a dozen of the inevitable glass balls, and then crumpled, crinkled paper, more and more

14. **over-sapid** (sap'id): over-seasoned.

and more, talking all the time of the way in which people neglect to brush their hats *inside* as well as out, politely, of course, but with a certain personal application. "All sorts of things accumulate, sir. . . . Not *you*, of course, in particular. . . . Nearly every customer. . . . Astonishing what they carry about with them. . . ." The crumpled paper rose and billowed on the counter more and more and more, until he was nearly hidden from us, until he was altogether hidden, and still his voice went on and on. "We none of us know what the fair semblance [15] of a human being may conceal, sir. Are we all then no better than brushed exteriors, whited sepulchers—" [16]

His voice stopped—exactly like when you hit a neighbor's gramophone with a well-aimed brick, the same instant silence, and the rustle of the paper stopped, and everything was still. . . .

"Have you done with my hat?" I said, after an interval.

There was no answer.

I stared at Gip, and Gip stared at me, and there were our distortions in the magic mirrors, looking very rum, and grave, and quiet.

"I think we'll go now," I said. "Will you tell me how much all this comes to? . . .

"I say," I said, on a rather louder note, "I want the bill; and my hat, please."

It might have been a sniff from behind the paper pile. . . .

"Let's look behind the counter, Gip," I said. "He's making fun of us."

I led Gip around the head-wagging tiger, and what do you think there was behind the counter? No one at all! Only my hat on the floor, and a common conjurer's lop-eared white rabbit lost in meditation, and looking as stupid and crumpled as only a conjurer's rabbit can do. I resumed my hat, and the rabbit lolloped [17] a lollop or so out of my way.

"Dadda!" said Gip, in a guilty whisper.

"What is it, Gip?" said I.

"I *do* like this shop, Dadda."

"So should I," I said to myself, "if the counter wouldn't suddenly extend itself to shut one off from the door." But I didn't call Gip's attention to that. "Pussy!" he said, with a hand out to the rabbit as it came lolloping past us; "Pussy, do Gip a magic!" and his eyes followed it as it squeezed through a door I had certainly not re-

---

15. semblance (sem′bləns): outward appearance; aspect.
16. sepulchers (sep′əl·kers): burial places, often made of stone; tombs.
17. lolloped (läl′əpt): moved with a bounding or bobbing motion.

marked [18] a moment before. Then this door opened wider, and the man with one ear larger than the other appeared again. He was smiling still, but his eye met mine with something between amusement and defiance. "You'd like to see our show room, sir," he said, with an innocent suavity.[19] Gip tugged my finger forward. I glanced at the counter and met the shopman's eye again. I was beginning to think the magic just a little too genuine. "We haven't *very* much time," I said. But somehow we were inside the show room before I could finish that.

"All goods of the same quality," said the shopman, rubbing his flexible hands together, "and that is the Best. Nothing in the place that isn't genuine Magic, and warranted [20] thoroughly rum. Excuse me, sir!"

I felt him pull at something that clung to my coat sleeve, and then I saw he held a little, wriggling red demon by the tail—the little creature bit and fought and tried to get at his hand—and in a moment he tossed it carelessly behind a counter. No doubt the thing was only an image of twisted india rubber, but for the moment—! And his gesture was exactly that of a man who handles some petty, biting bit of vermin. I glanced at Gip, but Gip was looking at a magic rocking horse. I was glad he hadn't seen the thing. "I say," I said, in an undertone, and indicating Gip and the red demon with my eyes, "you haven't many things like *that* about, have you?"

"None of ours! Probably brought it with you," said the shopman— also in an undertone, and with a more dazzling smile than ever. "Astonishing what people *will* carry about with them unawares!" And then to Gip, "Do you see anything you fancy here?"

There were many things that Gip fancied there.

He turned to this astonishing tradesman with mingled confidence and respect. "Is that a Magic Sword?" he said.

"A Magic Toy Sword. It neither bends, breaks, nor cuts the fingers. It renders the bearer invincible in battle against any one under eighteen. Half-a-crown to seven and sixpence, according to size. These panoplies [21] on cards are for juvenile knights errant [22] and very useful —shield of safety, sandals of swiftness, helmet of invisibility."

"Oh, Dadda!" gasped Gip.

18. **remarked:** noticed.
19. **suavity** (swä′və·tē): smoothness of manner.
20. **warranted:** guaranteed.
21. **panoplies** (pan′ə·plēz): battle outfits for warriors.
22. **knights errant** (nīts′ er′ənt): wandering knights who went forth in search of adventure.

I tried to find out what they cost, but the shopman did not heed me. He had got Gip now; he had got him away from my finger; he had embarked upon the exposition of all his confounded stock, and nothing was going to stop him. Presently I saw with a qualm [23] of distrust and something very like jealousy that Gip had hold of this person's finger as usually he has hold of mine. No doubt the fellow was interesting, I thought, and had an interesting faked lot of stuff, really *good* faked stuff. Still—

I wandered after them, saying very little, but keeping an eye on this prestidigital [24] fellow. After all, Gip was enjoying it. And no doubt when the time came to go we should be able to go quite easily.

It was a long, rambling place, that show room, a gallery broken up by stands and stalls and pillars, with archways leading off to other departments, in which the queerest-looking assistants loafed and stared at one, and with perplexing mirrors and curtains. So perplexing, indeed, were these that I was presently unable to make out the door by which we had come.

The shopman showed Gip magic trains that ran without steam or clockwork, just as you set the signals, and then some very, very valuable boxes of soldiers that all came alive directly you took off the lid and said—. I myself haven't a very quick ear and it was a tongue-twisting sound, but Gip—he has his mother's ear—got it in no time. "Bravo!" said the shopman, putting the men back into the box unceremoniously and handing it to Gip. "Now," said the shopman, and in a moment Gip had made them all alive again.

"You'll take that box?" asked the shopman.

"We'll take that box," said I, "unless you charge its full value. In which case it would need a Trust Magnate—"

"Dear heart! *No!*" and the shopman swept the little men back again, shut the lid, waved the box in the air, and there it was, in brown paper, tied up and—*with Gip's full name and address on the paper!*

The shopman laughed at my amazement.

"This is the genuine magic," he said. "The real thing."

"It's almost too genuine for my taste," I said again.

After that he fell to showing Gip tricks, odd tricks, and still odder the way they were done. He explained them, he turned them inside out, and there was the dear little chap nodding his busy bit of a head in the sagest manner.

23. **qualm** (kwäm): a sudden misgiving or fear.
24. **prestidigital** (pres·tə·dij′ə·təl): quick-fingered.

I did not attend [25] as well as I might. "Hey, presto!" said the Magic Shopman, and then would come the clear, small "Hey, presto!" of the boy. But I was distracted by other things. It was being borne in upon me just how tremendously rum this place was; it was, so to speak, inundated [26] by a sense of rumness. There was something a little rum about the fixtures even, about the ceiling, about the floor, about the casually distributed chairs. I had a queer feeling that whenever I wasn't looking at them straight they went askew,[27] and moved about, and played a noiseless puss-in-the-corner behind my back. And the cornice [28] had a serpentine [29] design with masks—masks altogether too expressive for proper plaster.

Then abruptly my attention was caught by one of the odd-looking assistants. He was some way off and evidently unaware of my presence—I saw a sort of three-quarter length of him over a pile of toys and through an arch—and, you know, he was leaning against a pillar in an idle sort of way doing the most horrid things with his features! The particular horrid thing he did was with his nose. He did it just as though he was idle and wanted to amuse himself. First of all it was a short, blobby nose, and then suddenly he shot it out like a telescope, and then out it flew and became thinner and thinner until it was like a long, red, flexible whip. Like a thing in a nightmare it was! He flourished it about and flung it forth as a fly-fisher flings his line.

My instant thought was that Gip mustn't see him. I turned about, and there was Gip quite preoccupied with the shopman, and thinking no evil. They were whispering together and looking at me. Gip was standing on a little stool, and the shopman was holding a sort of big drum in his hand.

"Hide and seek, Dadda!" cried Gip. "You're He!"

And before I could do anything to prevent it, the shopman had clapped the big drum over him.

I saw what was up directly. "Take that off," I cried, "this instant! You'll frighten the boy. Take it off!"

The shopman with the unequal ears did so without a word, and held the big cylinder toward me to show its emptiness. And the little stool was vacant! In that instant my boy had utterly disappeared! . . .

25. attend: pay attention.
26. inundated (in'un·dāt·əd): overflowing with, as in a flood; overwhelmed by.
27. askew (ə·skyoo'): to one side; awry.
28. cornice (kôr'nis): a decorative molding around the walls of a room, close to the ceiling.
29. serpentine (sûr'pən·tēn): resembling a serpent; that is, wavy, twisted.

You know, perhaps, that sinister something that comes like a hand out of the unseen and grips your heart about. You know it takes your common self away and leaves you tense and deliberate, neither slow nor hasty, neither angry nor afraid. So it was with me.

I came up to this grinning shopman and kicked his stool aside. "Stop this folly!" I said. "Where is my boy?"

"You see," he said, still displaying the drum's interior, "there is no deception—"

I put out my hand to grip him, and he eluded me by a dexterous movement. I snatched again, and he turned from me and pushed open a door to escape. "Stop!" I said, and he laughed, receding. I leapt after him—into utter darkness.

Thud!

"Lor' bless my 'eart! I didn't see you coming, sir!"

I was in Regent Street, and I had collided with a decent-looking workingman; and a yard away, perhaps, and looking a little perplexed [30] with himself, was Gip. There was some sort of apology, and then Gip had turned and come to me with a bright little smile, as though for a moment he had missed me.

And he was carrying four parcels in his arm!

He secured immediate possession of my finger.

For a second I was rather at a loss. I stared around to see the door of the magic shop, and, behold, it was not there! There was no door, no shop, nothing, only the common pilaster [31] between the shop where they sell pictures and the window with the chicks! . . .

I did the only thing possible in that mental tumult; [32] I walked straight to the kerbstone and held up my umbrella for a cab.

" 'Ansoms [33]," said Gip, in a note of culminating exultation.

I helped him in, recalled my address with an effort, and got in also. Something unusual proclaimed itself in my tail-coat pocket, and I felt and discovered a glass ball. With a petulant expression I flung it into the street.

Gip said nothing.

For a space neither of us spoke.

"Dadda!" said Gip, at last, "that *was* a proper shop!"

I came around with that to the problem of just how the whole

30. **perplexed:** confused; bewildered.
31. **pilaster** (pi·las′tər): a rectangular column, built into but projecting from a wall.
32. **tumult** (tōō′mult): commotion; violent agitation.
33. **'Ansoms:** that is, *hansoms* (han′səms), two-wheeled, one-horse carriages with the driver's seat elevated behind, formerly used as taxis in London.

thing had seemed to him. He looked completely undamaged—so far, good; he was neither scared nor unhinged, he was simply tremendously satisfied with the afternoon's entertainment, and there in his arms were the four parcels.

Confound it! what could be in them?

"Um!" I said. "Little boys can't go to shops like that every day."

He received this with his usual stoicism,[34] and for a moment I was sorry I was his father and not his mother, and so couldn't suddenly there, *coram publico*,[35] in our hansom, kiss him. After all, I thought, the thing wasn't so very bad.

But it was only when we opened the parcels that I really began to be reassured. Three of them contained boxes of soldiers, quite ordinary lead soldiers, but of so good a quality as to make Gip altogether forget that originally these parcels had been Magic Tricks of the only genuine sort, and the fourth contained a kitten, a little living white kitten, in excellent health and appetite and temper.

I saw this unpacking with a sort of provisional[36] relief. I hung about in the nursery for quite an unconscionable[37] time. . . .

That happened six months ago. And now I am beginning to believe it is all right. The kitten had only the magic natural to all kittens, and the soldiers seem as steady a company as any colonel could desire. And Gip—?

The intelligent parent will understand that I have to go cautiously with Gip. But I went so far as this one day. I said, "How would you like your soldiers to come alive, Gip, and march about by themselves?"

"Mine do," said Gip. "I just have to say a word I know before I open the lid."

"Then they march about alone?"

"Oh *quite*, Dadda. I shouldn't like them if they didn't do that."

I displayed no unbecoming surprise, and since then I have taken occasion to drop in upon him once or twice, unannounced, when the soldiers were about, but so far I have never discovered them performing in anything like a magical manner. . . .

It's so difficult to tell.

There's also a question of finance. I have an incurable habit of paying bills. I have been up and down Regent Street several times,

34. **stoicism** (stō′ə·siz′əm): the state of being unaffected or indifferent to pleasure or pain.
35. **coram publico**: *Latin expression*, in public.
36. **provisional**: temporary; tentative.
37. **unconscionable** (un·kon′shən·ə·bəl): excessive; unreasonable.

looking for that shop. I am inclined to think, indeed, that in that matter honor is satisfied, and that, since Gip's name and address are known to them, I may very well leave it to these people, whoever they may be, to send in their bill in their own time.

Meaning and Method

1. How does Gip react to the "magic shop"? How does the father react? How do you explain the difference?
2. From whose point of view are the story incidents seen? What reason can you give for the author's using this point of view?
3. Point out different details the author includes to achieve a sense of reality in this story.
4. How does the magician's speech differ in tone, manner, and content when he talks to the boy and when he addresses the father?
5. By what different means does Wells maintain the sense of magic?
6. Why do the four packages Gip carries away make the story more effective?
7. What does the remark, "It's only the Right Sort of Boy gets through that doorway" suggest about the whole story?
8. Today's fantasy or magic is often tomorrow's reality. Can you think of some things we now accept as realities which we would formerly have called magic?

Wells's "fantasies" were often used to make serious comments on the future. Let us assume that the magic shop represents the technological world of tomorrow. Whom, then, do the shopkeeper, the father, and Gip represent?

Language: Differences in British and American Words, Spellings, and Pronunciations

British and Americans sometimes have different words to express similar ideas. In this story, Gip's father feels there is something "tremendously rum," about the magic London shop. He says, "There was something a little *rum* about the fixtures even." The American equivalent of this British slang word is "odd" or "strange." The face of the youngster who can't get into the shop is white from *sweet-eating*. In England, *sweets* means *candy*. Gip's father hails a cab from the *kerbstone*, not the *curb*.

There are also some differences in British and American spellings. The British write *labour*, not *labor*, and the letter *s* is often used for *z*, as in the words *recognise* and *patronise*. And sometimes, even when the spelling is the same, the pronunciation is different. For example, the British pronunciation of *tomato* is tə·mä′tō with a broad *a*, and the words *lab-oratory* and *schedule* are pronounced lə·bor′ə·trē and shed′yōōl.

See if you can find out the American equivalents of the following British expressions:

1. *telly*   3. *cinema*   5. *casual office worker*
2. *bobby*   4. *underground*   6. *diversion* (a road sign)

Composition

1. Children often have a keen sense of wonder and imagination. As they grow to adulthood, many lose these qualities. Write an essay discussing the possible reasons for this situation.

2. Write a composition comparing and contrasting the imaginary worlds created in "The Magic Shop" and "The Masque of the Red Death." Start with an explanation of the situation the author wishes you to believe in. Then describe the vivid and exact details that each uses to make his world believable.

Saki (H. H. Munro)

"There is no greater compliment to be paid the right kind of friend than to hand him Saki, without comment. Particularly to those less familiar with the mysterious jungles of English humor, a savage country with birds of unexpected plumage. . . . Delicate, airy, lucid, precise, with the inconspicuous agility of perfect style, he can pass into the uncanny, the tragic, into mocking fairy tales grimmer than Grimm."

These words of praise about Hector Hugh Munro, a British humorist and satirist, were written by Christopher Morley, an American writer and journalist, in his Introduction to *The Short Stories of Saki*, published in 1930. Mr. Morley compares Saki to O. Henry, calling them both "instinctive storytellers."

Munro was born in 1870 in Burma, where his Scottish father was the inspector-general of the police force. His mother died shortly before his second birthday and he was sent to Devonshire, England, to be reared by two spinster English aunts. The aunts, harsh disciplinarians with fierce tempers, strictly regulated the boy's life. Many of his stories, for example "Shredni Vashtar" and "The Story-Teller," study the relationship between aunts and nephews.

At the age of twenty-five, Munro began his writing career as a political satirist for the *Westminster Gazette*. He then worked for six years as a foreign correspondent for the *Morning Post*, traveling to the Balkans, Russia, and Paris. In 1904 the publication of *Reginald* established his fame as a writer of whimsical stories, and in 1908 Munro ended his foreign travels and settled near London. At the outbreak of World War I he enlisted in the British army and was subsequently sent to France, where he was killed in 1916.

Among the short-story collections that appeared during his lifetime are *Reginald in Russia*, *The Chronicles of Clovis*, and *Beasts and Super-Beasts*. He also wrote two novels and a history of Russia. A posthumous collection of Munro's short stories, *The Square Egg*, appeared in 1924 under his pen name Saki, a pseudonym he adopted early in his career. He loved Persian poetry and Eastern stories and chose the name Saki from the "cup-bearer" or "wine-bringer" in *The Rubáiyát*.*

* **The Rubáiyát** (roo′bī·yät) **of Omar Khayyám** (kī·äm′) : a book of verses written in the eleventh century by Omar Khayyám, a Persian poet and astronomer. It contains the poet's meditations on life and his counsel to eat, drink, and be merry while life lasts. A translation by Edward FitzGerald (1809–1883) appeared in England in 1859. *Rubáiyát* is the Arabic word for quatrains, or four-lined stanzas. *Saki* is the Arabic word meaning "one who gives to drink."

The Story-Teller

It was a hot afternoon, and the railway carriage was correspondingly sultry, and the next stop was at Templecombe, nearly an hour ahead. The occupants of the carriage were a small girl, and a smaller girl, and a small boy. An aunt belonging to the children occupied one corner seat, and the further corner seat on the opposite side was occupied by a bachelor who was a stranger to their party, but the small girls and the small boy emphatically occupied the compartment. Both the aunt and the children were conversational in a limited, persistent way, reminding one of the attentions of a housefly that refused to be discouraged. Most of the aunt's remarks seemed to begin with "Don't," and nearly all of the children's remarks began with "Why?" The bachelor said nothing out loud.

"Don't, Cyril, don't," exclaimed the aunt, as the small boy began smacking the cushions of the seat, producing a cloud of dust at each blow.

"Come and look out of the window," she added.

The child moved reluctantly to the window. "Why are those sheep being driven out of that field?" he asked.

"I expect they are being driven to another field where there is more grass," said the aunt weakly.

"But there is lots of grass in that field," protested the boy; "there's nothing else but grass there. Aunt, there's lots of grass in that field."

"Perhaps the grass in the other field is better," suggested the aunt fatuously.[1]

"Why is it better?" came the swift, inevitable question.

"Oh, look at those cows!" exclaimed the aunt. Nearly every field along the line had contained cows or bullocks, but she spoke as though she were drawing attention to a rarity.

"Why is the grass in the other field better?" persisted Cyril.

The frown on the bachelor's face was deepening to a scowl. He was a hard, unsympathetic man, the aunt decided in her mind. She was utterly unable to come to any satisfactory decision about the grass in the other field.

The smaller girl created a diversion by beginning to recite "On the Road to Mandalay."[2] She only knew the first line, but she put her

1. **fatuously:** foolishly, stupidly.
2. **"On the Road to Mandalay":** a poem by the English author and poet, Rudyard Kipling (1865–1936).

limited knowledge to the fullest possible use. She repeated the line over and over again in a dreamy but resolute and very audible voice; it seemed to the bachelor as though someone had had a bet with her that she could not repeat the line aloud two thousand times without stopping. Whoever it was who had made the wager was likely to lose his bet.

"Come over here and listen to a story," said the aunt, when the bachelor had looked twice at her and once at the communication cord.[3]

The children moved listlessly toward the aunt's end of the carriage. Evidently her reputation as a storyteller did not rank high in their estimation.

In a low, confidential voice, interrupted at frequent intervals by loud, petulant questions from her listeners, she began an unenterprising and deplorably uninteresting story about a little girl who was good, and made friends with every one on account of her goodness, and was finally saved from a mad bull by a number of rescuers who admired her moral character.

"Wouldn't they have saved her if she hadn't been good?" demanded the bigger of the small girls. It was exactly the question that the bachelor had wanted to ask.

"Well, yes," admitted the aunt lamely, "but I don't think they would have run quite so fast to her help if they had not liked her so much."

"It's the stupidest story I've ever heard," said the bigger of the small girls, with immense conviction.

"I didn't listen after the first bit, it was so stupid," said Cyril.

The smaller girl made no actual comment on the story, but she had long ago recommenced a murmured repetition of her favorite line.

"You don't seem to be a success as a storyteller," said the bachelor suddenly from his corner.

The aunt bristled in instant defense at this unexpected attack.

"It's a very difficult thing to tell stories that children can both understand and appreciate," she said stiffly.

"I don't agree with you," said the bachelor.

"Perhaps *you* would like to tell them a story," was the aunt's retort.

"Tell us a story," demanded the bigger of the small girls.

"Once upon a time," began the bachelor, "there was a little girl called Bertha, who was extraordinarily good."

3. **communication cord**: emergency cord.

The children's momentarily aroused interest began at once to flicker; all stories seemed dreadfully alike, no matter who told them.

"She did all that she was told, she was always truthful, she kept her clothes clean, ate milk puddings as though they were jam tarts, learned her lessons perfectly, and was polite in her manners."

"Was she pretty?" asked the bigger of the small girls.

"Not as pretty as any of you," said the bachelor, "but she was horribly good."

There was a wave of reaction in favor of the story; the word *horrible* in connection with goodness was a novelty that commended itself. It seemed to introduce a ring of truth that was absent from the aunt's tales of infant life.

"She was so good," continued the bachelor, "that she won several medals for goodness, which she always wore, pinned on to her dress. There was a medal for obedience, another medal for punctuality, and a third for good behavior. They were large metal medals and they clinked against one another as she walked. No other child in the town where she lived had as many as three medals, so everybody knew that she must be an extra good child."

"Horribly good," quoted Cyril.

"Everybody talked about her goodness, and the Prince of the country got to hear about it, and he said that as she was so very good she might be allowed once a week to walk in his park, which was just outside the town. It was a beautiful park, and no children were ever allowed in it, so it was a great honor for Bertha to be allowed to go there."

"Were there any sheep in the park?" demanded Cyril.

"No," said the bachelor, "there were no sheep."

"Why weren't there any sheep?" came the inevitable question arising out of that answer.

The aunt permitted herself a smile, which might almost have been described as a grin.

"There were no sheep in the park," said the bachelor, "because the Prince's mother had once had a dream that her son would either be killed by a sheep or else by a clock falling on him. For that reason the Prince never kept a sheep in his park or a clock in his palace."

The aunt suppressed a gasp of admiration.

"Was the Prince killed by a sheep or by a clock?" asked Cyril.

"He is still alive so we can't tell whether the dream will come true," said the bachelor unconcernedly; "anyway, there were no sheep in the park, but there were lots of little pigs running all over the place."

"What color were they?"

"Black with white faces, white with black spots, black all over, gray with white patches, and some were white all over."

The storyteller paused to let a full idea of the park's treasures sink into the children's imaginations; then he resumed:

"Bertha was rather sorry to find that there were no flowers in the park. She had promised her aunts, with tears in her eyes, that she would not pick any of the kind Prince's flowers, and she had meant to keep her promise, so of course it made her feel silly to find that there were no flowers to pick."

"Why weren't there any flowers?"

"Because the pigs had eaten them all," said the bachelor promptly. "The gardeners had told the Prince that you couldn't have pigs and flowers, so he decided to have pigs and no flowers."

There was a murmur of approval at the excellence of the Prince's decision; so many people would have decided the other way.

"There were lots of other delightful things in the park. There were ponds with gold and blue and green fish in them, and trees with beautiful parrots that said clever things at a moment's notice, and humming birds that hummed all the popular tunes of the day. Bertha walked up and down and enjoyed herself immensely, and thought to herself: 'If I were not so extraordinarily good I should not have been allowed to come into this beautiful park and enjoy all that there is to be seen in it,' and her three medals clinked against one another as she walked and helped to remind her how very good she really was. Just then an enormous wolf came prowling into the park to see if it could catch a fat little pig for its supper."

"What color was it?" asked the children, amid an immediate quickening of interest.

"Mud-color all over, with a black tongue and pale gray eyes that gleamed with unspeakable ferocity. The first thing that it saw in the park was Bertha; her pinafore was so spotlessly white and clean that it could be seen from a great distance. Bertha saw the wolf and saw that it was stealing toward her, and she began to wish that she had never been allowed to come into the park. She ran as hard as she could, and the wolf came after her with huge leaps and bounds. She managed to reach a shrubbery of myrtle bushes and she hid herself in one of the thickest of the bushes. The wolf came sniffing among the branches, its black tongue lolling out of its mouth and its pale gray eyes glaring with rage. Bertha was terribly frightened, and thought to herself: 'If I had not been so extraordinarily good, I should have been safe in the town at this moment.' However, the scent of the myrtle was so strong that the wolf could not sniff out where Bertha was hiding, and the bushes were so thick that he might have hunted about in them for a long time without catching sight of her, so he thought he might as well go off and catch a little pig instead. Bertha was trembling very much at having the wolf prowling and sniffing so near her, and as she trembled the medal for obedience clinked against the medals for good conduct and punctuality. The wolf was just moving away when he heard the sound of the medals clinking and stopped to listen; they clinked again in a bush quite near him. He dashed into the bush, his pale gray eyes gleaming with ferocity and triumph, and dragged Bertha out and devoured her to the last morsel. All that was left of her were her shoes, bits of clothing, and the three medals for goodness."

"Were any of the little pigs killed?"

"No, they all escaped."

"The story began badly," said the smaller of the small girls, "but it had a beautiful ending."

"It is the most beautiful story that I ever heard," said the bigger of the small girls, with immense decision.

"It is the *only* beautiful story I have ever heard," said Cyril.

A dissentient [4] opinion came from the aunt.

"A most improper story to tell to young children! You have undermined the effect of years of careful teaching."

"At any rate," said the bachelor, collecting his belongings preparatory to leaving the carriage, "I kept them quiet for ten minutes, which was more than you were able to do."

"Unhappy woman!" he observed to himself as he walked down the platform of Templecombe station; "for the next six months or so those children will assail her in public with demands for an improper story!"

4. **dissentient** (di·sen′shənt): dissenting; expressing disagreement.

Meaning and Method

1. The theme of the bachelor's story is an unconventional one. Why? (Review the discussion of conventional and unconventional themes on page 7.) Why do the children find a "ring of truth" in the bachelor's story "that was absent from the aunt's tales of infant life?"

2. Which do you think is more annoying to the bachelor—the children's behavior or the aunt's? Give reasons for your answer. What double purpose does his story serve?

3. How does the bachelor appeal to the children's senses of sight and sound in his story?

4. What is ironic about the way the "horribly good girl" met her end?

5. Why is the railway car setting essential to the plot of this story? What is the function of setting in the bachelor's story?
6. Compare and contrast the aunt's story and the bachelor's story. How are they alike? How do they differ?
7. In the aunt's opinion the bachelor's "improper story" has "undermined the effect of years of careful teaching." Do you agree or disagree? Give reasons for your answer. What kind of stories do you think should be told to children?
8. Both the aunt and the bachelor are storytellers. To whom, then, does the title refer? Give reasons for your answer.
9. Sometimes to create a humorous or dramatic effect a writer will deliberately exaggerate or overstate a fact. An extravagantly exaggerated statement is called *hyperbole* (hī·pûr′bə·lē). Saki uses hyperbole in "The Story-Teller" when he writes, "It seemed to the bachelor as though someone had had a bet with her [the smaller girl] that she could not repeat the line aloud two thousand times without stopping. Whoever it was who had made the wager was likely to lose his bet."

Other ways of achieving humor include the use of unusual wording or word choice, irony of statement or situation, and ambiguity or double meaning which may occur when the same word has two or more meanings.

Explain which of these methods each of the following quotations from "The Story-Teller" involves:
(a) "The gardeners had told the Prince that you couldn't have pigs and flowers, so he decided to have pigs and no flowers."
(b) "[The little pigs were] black with white faces, white with black spots, black all over, gray with white patches, and some were white all over."
(c) "She had promised her aunts, with tears in her eyes, that she would not pick any of the kind Prince's flowers, . . . so of course it made her feel silly to find that there were no flowers to pick."
(d) ". . . and humming birds that hummed all the popular tunes of the day."
(e) "The wolf was just moving away when he heard the sound of the medals clinking and stopped to listen; they clinked again in a bush quite near him."
(f) ". . . for the next six months or so those children will assail her in public with demands for an improper story!"

Language: Repetition for Effect

One of several literary devices at an author's disposal, besides simile and metaphor, is repetition. Although this is more common in poetry than in any other form of writing, it can be effectively used by a prose writer or a dramatist. In *Julius Caesar*, Shakespeare has Mark Antony repeat several times that Brutus is an honorable man. Each time the word *honorable* is spoken, it changes meaning because of the examples Antony uses. Finally, the mob he is addressing rages at the word, taking it to mean the greatest treachery, and screams for Brutus's life.

In "The Story-Teller" there is a great deal of repetition. Throughout the story Munro employs the words "small" and "smaller" in connection with the children. How do these words help to characterize them?

What reaction do the children show when the bachelor links the word "horribly" with "good girl?" The boy Cyril even echoes the phrase "horribly good" for emphasis. The bachelor's constant repetition of the phrase "medals for goodness," or some variation of it, eventually makes the entire idea of the "metal medals" sound ludicrous.

What other words or phrases are repeated in his story until they reach the point where they sound absurd?

Composition

Satire is the use of ridicule, sarcasm, wit, or irony to expose or discredit foolish customs or ideas.

Write a composition in which you tell how Saki, through the story-teller, is satirizing the stories adults usually tell to children. Give examples of the techniques that he uses to ridicule his subject.

Guy de Maupassant *

"You must scrutinize whatever you want to express, so long and so attentively, as to enable you to find some aspect of it which no one has yet seen and expressed. There is an unexplored side to everything, because we are wont never to use our eyes but with the memory of what others before us have thought of the things we see. The smallest thing has something unknown in it; we must find it. To describe a blazing fire, a tree on a plain, we must stand face to face with that fire or that tree, till to us they are wholly unlike any other fire or tree. Thus we may become original. . . ."

These are the words of advice given to Guy de Maupassant (1850–1893) by Gustave Flaubert (1821–1880), another French writer. Seven years of training from Flaubert enabled Maupassant to perfect a skill which helped him become France's most famous short-story writer.

Maupassant spent his youth in Normandy but lived the greater part of his life in Paris. He served in the French army and also worked as a government clerk. Despite a severe nervous disorder, which ended in insanity and death in his early forties, Maupassant wrote more than two hundred short stories and six novels. Among his works are the short-story collections *La Maison Tellier* (*The House of Mme Tellier*), *Mademoiselle Fifi*, and *Contes and Nouvelles* (*Stories and Novels*), and the novels *Une Vie* (*A Life*), *Bel Ami* (*Good Friend*), *Pierre et Jean* (*Peter and John*), and *Notre Coeur* (*Our Hearts*).

A shrewd observer of people, Maupassant fashioned his characters with sharp, clean lines—like photographs taken with a well-focused camera. With a minimum of details and with unusual objectivity, he presented to his readers realistic accounts of episodes and events in his characters' lives. His style has served as a model for many writers.

"The Necklace," one of the most famous of his stories, looks with cold objectivity into the life of a vain young Frenchwoman who pays a tragic price for one night of social triumph.

* Guy de Maupassant (gē də mō·pà·sän′).

The Necklace

She was one of those pretty and charming girls, born, as if by an accident of fate, into a family of clerks. With no dowry,[1] no prospects, no way of any kind of being met, understood, loved, and married by a man both prosperous and famous, she was finally married to a minor clerk in the Ministry of Education.

She dressed plainly because she could not afford fine clothes, but was as unhappy as a woman who has come down in the world; for women have no family rank or social class. With them, beauty, grace, and charm take the place of birth and breeding. Their natural poise, their instinctive good taste, and their mental cleverness are the sole guiding principles which make daughters of the common people the equals of ladies in high society.

She grieved incessantly, feeling that she had been born for all the little niceties and luxuries of living. She grieved over the shabbiness of her apartment, the dinginess of the walls, the worn-out appearance of the chairs, the ugliness of the draperies. All these things, which another woman of her class would not even have noticed, gnawed at her and made her furious. The sight of the little Breton [2] girl who did her humble housework roused in her disconsolate [3] regrets and wild daydreams. She would dream of silent chambers, draped with Oriental tapestries and lighted by tall bronze floor lamps, and of two handsome butlers in knee breeches, who, drowsy from the heavy warmth cast by the central stove,[4] dozed in large overstuffed armchairs.

She would dream of great reception halls hung with old silks, of fine furniture filled with priceless curios, and of small, stylish, scented sitting rooms just right for the four o'clock chat with intimate friends, with distinguished and sought-after men whose attention every woman envies and longs to attract.

When dining at the round table, covered for the third day with the same cloth, opposite her husband who would raise the cover of the soup tureen, declaring delightedly, "Ah! a good stew! There's nothing

1. **dowry** (dou′rē): money or property that a woman brings to her husband at marriage.
2. **Breton** (bret′n): a native of Brittany, a province in northwestern France.
3. **disconsolate** (dis·kon′sə·lit): inconsolable; hopelessly depressing.
4. **central stove**: a large stove for heating placed in the center of a room, used in France at the time this story takes place.

"The Necklace" by Guy de Maupassant, translated by Newbury LeB. Morse from *Adventures in Reading*: Olympic Edition, copyright © 1958 by Harcourt, Brace & World, Inc. Reprinted by permission of the publisher.

I like better. . . ." she would dream of fashionable dinner parties, of gleaming silverware, of tapestries making the walls alive with characters out of history and strange birds in a fairyland forest; she would dream of delicious dishes served on wonderful china, of gallant compliments whispered and listened to with a sphinxlike smile as one eats the rosy flesh of a trout or nibbles at the wings of a grouse.

She had no evening clothes, no jewels, nothing. But those were the things she wanted; she felt that was the kind of life for her. She so much longed to please, be envied, be fascinating and sought after.

She had a well-to-do friend, a classmate of convent school days, whom she would no longer go to see, simply because she would feel so distressed on returning home. And she would weep for days on end from vexation, regret, despair, and anguish.

Then one evening, her husband came home proudly holding out a large envelope.

"Look," he said, "I've got something for you."

She excitedly tore open the envelope and pulled out a printed card bearing these words:

"The Minister of Education and Mme Georges Ramponneau [5] beg M. and Mme Loisel [6] to do them the honor of attending an evening reception at the ministerial mansion on Friday, January 18."

Instead of being delighted, as her husband had hoped, she scornfully tossed the invitation on the table, murmuring, "What good is that to me?"

"But, my dear, I thought you'd be thrilled to death. You never get a chance to go out, and this is a real affair, a wonderful one! I had an awful time getting a card. Everybody wants one; it's much sought after, and not many clerks have a chance at one. You'll see all the most important people there."

She gave him an irritated glance, and burst out impatiently, "What do you think I have to go in?"

He hadn't given that a thought. He stammered, "Why, the dress you wear when we go to the theater. That looks quite nice, I think."

He stopped talking, dazed and distracted to see his wife burst out weeping. Two large tears slowly rolled from the corners of her eyes to the corners of her mouth. He gasped, "Why, what's the matter? What's the trouble?"

By sheer will power she overcame her outburst and answered in a calm voice while wiping the tears from her wet cheeks:

5. **Mme Georges Ramponneau** (mȧ·dȧm′ zhȏrzh rȧm′pə·nō).
6. **M. . . . Loisel** (mə·syûr′ . . . lwȧ·zĕl′).

"Oh, nothing. Only I don't have an evening dress and therefore I can't go to that affair. Give the card to some friend at the office whose wife can dress better than I can."

He was stunned. He resumed, "Let's see, Mathilde.[7] How much would a suitable outfit cost—one you could wear for other affairs too —something very simple?"

She thought it over for several seconds, going over her allowance and thinking also of the amount she could ask for without bringing an immediate refusal and an exclamation of dismay from the thrifty clerk.

Finally, she answered hesitatingly, "I'm not sure exactly, but I think with four hundred francs [8] I could manage it."

He turned a bit pale, for he had set aside just that amount to buy a rifle so that, the following summer, he could join some friends who were getting up a group to shoot larks on the plain near Nanterre.[9]

However, he said, "All right. I'll give you four hundred francs. But try to get a nice dress."

As the day of the party approached, Mme Loisel seemed sad, moody, and ill at ease. Her outfit was ready, however. Her husband said to her one evening, "What's the matter? You've been all out of sorts for three days."

And she answered, "It's embarrassing not to have a jewel or a gem —nothing to wear on my dress. I'll look like a pauper: I'd almost rather not go to that party."

He answered, "Why not wear some flowers? They're very fashionable this season. For ten francs you can get two or three gorgeous roses."

She wasn't at all convinced. "No . . . There's nothing more humiliating than to look poor among a lot of rich women."

But her husband exclaimed, "My, but you're silly! Go see your friend Mme Forestier [10] and ask her to lend you some jewelry. You and she know each other well enough for you to do that."

She gave a cry of joy, "Why, that's so! I hadn't thought of it."

The next day she paid her friend a visit and told her of her predicament.

Mme Forestier went toward a large closet with mirrored doors,

---

7. **Mathilde** (ma·tēld').
8. **four hundred francs**: at that time, about eighty dollars.
9. **Nanterre** (nän·târ'): a French town near Paris.
10. **Forestier** (fô·rə·styā').

took out a large jewel box, brought it over, opened it, and said to Mme Loisel: "Pick something out, my dear."

At first her eyes noted some bracelets, then a pearl necklace, then a Venetian cross, gold and gems, of marvelous workmanship. She tried on these adornments in front of the mirror, but hesitated, unable to decide which to part with and put back. She kept on asking, "Haven't you something else?"

"Oh, yes, keep on looking. I don't know just what you'd like."

All at once she found, in a black satin box, a superb diamond necklace: and her pulse beat faster with longing. Her hands trembled as she took it up. Clasping it around her throat, outside her high-necked dress, she stood in ecstasy looking at her reflection.

Then she asked, hesitatingly, pleading, "Could I borrow that, just that and nothing else?"

"Why, of course."

She threw her arms around her friend, kissed her warmly, and fled with her treasure.

The day of the party arrived. Mme Loisel was a sensation. She was the prettiest one there, fashionable, gracious, smiling, and wild with joy. All the men turned to look at her, asked who she was, begged to be introduced. All the cabinet officials wanted to waltz with her. The minister took notice of her.

She danced madly, wildly, drunk with pleasure, giving no thought to anything in the triumph of her beauty, the pride of her success, in a kind of happy cloud composed of all the adulation,[11] of all the admiring glances, of all the awakened longings, of a sense of complete victory that is so sweet to a woman's heart.

She left around four o'clock in the morning. Her husband, since midnight, had been dozing in a small empty sitting room with three other gentlemen whose wives were having too good a time.

He threw over her shoulders the wraps he had brought for going home, modest garments of everyday life whose shabbiness clashed with the stylishness of her evening clothes. She felt this and longed to escape, unseen by the other women who were draped in expensive furs.

Loisel held her back.

"Hold on! You'll catch cold outside. I'll call a cab."

But she wouldn't listen to him and went rapidly down the stairs. When they were on the street, they didn't find a carriage; and they

---

11. **adulation** (aj′ōō·lā′shən): excessive flattery or admiration.

set out to hunt for one, hailing drivers whom they saw going by at a distance.

They walked toward the Seine,[12] disconsolate and shivering. Finally on the docks they found one of those carriages that one sees in Paris only after nightfall, as if they were ashamed to show their drabness during daylight hours.

It dropped them at their door in the Rue des Martyrs,[13] and they climbed wearily up to their apartment. For her, it was all over. For him, there was the thought that he would have to be at the ministry at ten o'clock.

Before the mirror, she let the wraps fall from her shoulders to see herself once again in all her glory. Suddenly she gave a cry. The necklace was gone.

Her husband, already half-undressed, said, "What's the trouble?"

She turned toward him despairingly, "I . . . I . . . I don't have Mme Forestier's necklace."

"What! You can't mean it! It's impossible!"

They hunted everywhere, through the folds of the dress, through the folds of the coat, in the pockets. They found nothing.

He asked, "Are you sure you had it when leaving the dance?"

"Yes, I felt it when I was in the hall of the ministry."

"But, if you had lost it on the street we'd have heard it drop. It must be in the cab."

"Yes. Quite likely. Did you get its number?"

"No. Didn't you notice it either?"

"No."

They looked at each other aghast. Finally Loisel got dressed again. "I'll retrace our steps on foot," he said, "to see if I can find it."

And he went out. She remained in her evening clothes, without the strength to go to bed, slumped in a chair in the unheated room, her mind a blank.

Her husband came in about seven o'clock. He had had no luck.

He went to the police station, to the newspapers to post a reward, to the cab companies, everywhere the slightest hope drove him.

That evening Loisel returned, pale, his face lined; still he had learned nothing.

"We'll have to write your friend," he said, "to tell her you have broken the catch and are having it repaired. That will give us a little time to turn around."

12. **Seine** (sān): a river which runs through Paris.
13. **Rue des Martyrs**: Street of the Martyrs.

She wrote to his dictation.

At the end of a week, they had given up all hope.

And Loisel, looking five years older, declared, "We must take steps to replace that piece of jewelry."

The next day they took the case to the jeweler whose name they found inside. He consulted his records. "I didn't sell that necklace, madame," he said. "I only supplied the case."

Then they went from one jeweler to another hunting for a similar necklace, going over their recollections, both sick with despair and anxiety.

They found, in a shop in Palais Royal,[14] a string of diamonds which seemed exactly like the one they were seeking. It was priced at forty thousand francs. They could get it for thirty-six.[15]

They asked the jeweler to hold it for them for three days. And they reached an agreement that he would take it back for thirty-four thousand if the lost one was found before the end of February.

Loisel had eighteen thousand francs he had inherited from his father. He would borrow the rest.

He went about raising the money, asking a thousand francs from one, four hundred from another, a hundred here, sixty there. He signed notes, made ruinous deals, did business with loan sharks, ran the whole gamut [16] of moneylenders. He compromised the rest of his life, risked his signature without knowing if he'd be able to honor it, and then, terrified by the outlook for the future, by the blackness of despair about to close around him, by the prospect of all the privations [17] of the body and tortures of the spirit, he went to claim the new necklace with the thirty-six thousand francs which he placed on the counter of the shopkeeper.

When Mme Loisel took the necklace back, Mme Forestier said to her frostily, "You should have brought it back sooner; I might have needed it."

She didn't open the case, an action her friend was afraid of. If she had noticed the substitution, what would she have thought? What would she have said? Would she have thought her a thief?

Mme Loisel experienced the horrible life the needy live. She played her part, however, with sudden heroism. That frightful debt had to

14. **Palais Royal** (pà·lā′ rwà·yàl′): an area with many shops.
15. **thirty-six [thousand francs]**: in 1884, the year of "The Necklace," about seven thousand two hundred dollars.
16. **gamut** (gam′ət): the whole range of something.
17. **privations** (prī·vā′shəns): the lack of what is essential for existence.

be paid. She would pay it. She dismissed her maid; they rented a garret under the eaves.

She learned to do the heavy housework, to perform the hateful duties of cooking. She washed dishes, wearing down her shell-pink nails scouring the grease from pots and pans; she scrubbed dirty linen, shirts, and cleaning rags, which she hung on a line to dry; she took the garbage down to the street each morning and brought up water, stopping on each landing to get her breath. And, clad like a peasant woman, basket on arm, guarding sou [18] by sou her scanty allowance, she bargained with the fruit dealers, the grocer, the butcher, and was insulted by them.

Each month notes had to be paid, and others renewed to give more time.

Her husband labored evenings to balance a tradesman's accounts, and at night, often, he copied documents at five sous a page.

And this went on for ten years.

Finally, all was paid back, everything including the exorbitant [19] rates of the loan sharks and accumulated compound interest.

Mme Loisel appeared an old woman, now. She became heavy, rough, harsh, like one of the poor. Her hair untended, her skirts askew, her hands red, her voice shrill, she even slopped water on her floors and scrubbed them herself. But, sometimes, while her husband was at work, she would sit near the window and think of that long-ago evening when, at the dance, she had been so beautiful and admired.

What would have happened if she had not lost that necklace? Who knows? Who can say? How strange and unpredictable life is! How little there is between happiness and misery!

Then one Sunday when she had gone for a walk on the Champs Elysées [20] to relax a bit from the week's labors, she suddenly noticed a woman strolling with a child. It was Mme Forestier, still young-looking, still beautiful, still charming.

Mme Loisel felt a rush of emotion. Should she speak to her? Of course. And now that everything was paid off, she would tell her the whole story. Why not?

She went toward her. "Hello, Jeanne."

The other, not recognizing her, showed astonishment at being spoken to so familiarly by this common person. She stammered,

18. **sou** (sōō): a coin at that time worth about a penny.
19. **exorbitant** (ig·zôr′bə·tənt): excessive.
20. **Champs Élysées** (shän zā·lē·zā′): a fashionable avenue in Paris.

"But . . . madame . . . I don't recognize . . . You must be mistaken."

"No, I'm Mathilde Loisel."

Her friend gave a cry, "Oh, my poor Mathilde, how you've changed!"

"Yes, I've had a hard time since last seeing you. And plenty of misfortunes—and all on account of you!"

"Of me . . . How do you mean?"

"Do you remember that diamond necklace you lent me to wear to the dance at the ministry?"

"Yes, but what about it?"

"Well, I lost it."

"You lost it! But you returned it."

"I brought you another just like it. And we've been paying for it for ten years now. You can imagine that wasn't easy for us who had nothing. Well, it's over now, and I am glad of it."

Mme Forestier stopped short. "You mean to say you bought a diamond necklace to replace mine?"

"Yes. You never noticed, then? They were quite alike."

And she smiled with proud and simple joy.

Mme Forestier, quite overcome, clasped her by the hands, "Oh, my poor Mathilde. But mine was only paste.[21] Why, at most it was worth only five hundred francs!" [22]

21. **paste:** a brilliant glass used in making imitation diamonds.
22. **five hundred francs:** about one hundred dollars then.

Meaning and Method

1. What kind of persons are Mathilde and her husband at the beginning of the story? Do they change after the necklace is lost? If so, how? Are their actions consistent with their characteristics and values? Why or why not?
2. Why did it never occur to the Loisels that the necklace might be paste?
3. The things we value are the things by which we set our goals and make our decisions. What comment on values does this story make? How does the necklace serve as a symbol of Mathilde's values?
4. What is the theme of the story?
5. Why didn't Maupassant end the story by giving Mathilde's feelings when she learned the necklace was false? How would this have changed the story?

Language: Forming Adjectives and Adverbs

In addition to those suffixes which give us noun forms (see p. 120), there are other suffixes which can change the roots to adjective or adverb forms. The following sample words are taken from "The Necklace."

Adjective Suffix	Meaning	Adjective
1. *-able, -ible*	able, fit, likely	suitable
2. *-ful*	full of, marked by	wonderful
3. *-like*	like, similar	sphinxlike
4. *-ous*	marked by, given to	prosperous
5. *-y*	showing, suggesting, apt to	drowsy, moody

Adverb Suffix	Meaning	Adverb
-ly	like, of the nature of, in the manner of	finally, plainly

Add a suffix to each of the following words to form an adjective or an adverb. Write a sentence for each word you form.

1. translate	8. peace	15. distinguish
2. dirt	9. like	16. laugh
3. marvel	10. soul	17. eat
4. quiet	11. courage	18. hope
5. simple	12. notice	19. cat
6. play	13. war	20. prosper
7. joy	14. show	21. float

Composition and Discussion

1. Maupassant is noted for the simplicity and straightforward presentation of his stories as well as for their objectivity. (Remember O. Henry as an example of an author who intruded into his story.) Discuss these qualities of Maupassant's writing as they apply to the story.

2. This story is an excellent example of irony. In order for the irony to be effective, it was necessary for the author to create a certain combination of circumstances. Mme Loisel had to decide (a) to go to the ball, (b) to replace the necklace, and (c) to speak to Mme Forestier when she met her on the street. How does the author prepare us to accept these decisions?

3. The author writes, "What would have happened if she had not lost that necklace? Who knows? Who can say? How strange and unpredictable life is! How little there is between happiness and misery!"

Consider Mathilde's reactions to her friendship with Mme Forestier, her husband's getting the invitation, her having a dress but no jewels, and her hasty departure from the ball. Then, by giving reasons, develop a paragraph in which you give what you think were Mathilde's chances for happiness had she not lost the necklace.

4. Write a composition, pro or con, on one of the following topics: "Clothes don't make the man." "It's not what you know, it's whom you know." Give reasons for your choice, and support your argument with facts, examples, and incidents.

Selma Lagerlöf *
[1858–1940]

The 1909 Nobel prize winner, Selma Lagerlöf, is considered Sweden's greatest storyteller, and shares with Hans Christian Andersen the highest popularity among Scandinavian authors. She was born in Värmland, southern Sweden, a region noted for its beautiful lakes and its folk culture of song, dance, and colorful costumes. At three she was afflicted by infantile paralysis, which left her in frail health but did not prohibit a long, creative life. She was first educated at home and later studied to be a teacher in her country's rural schools.

Two of the author's favorite interests were her grandmother's storytelling (Miss Lagerlöf later used many of these stories in her books) and her ancestral home, Mårbacka, which she reclaimed and remodeled with her Nobel prize money. In her book *Mårbacka,* she has pictured her childhood and related how an old housekeeper continued to tell her legends and ghost stories after her grandmother's death. The romantic stories of her childhood are also told in *The Story of Gösta Berling.*

Simplicity, dignity, and idealism mark her writings, which echo the qualities of her beloved folk tales. Her birthplace, Värmland, and Dalecarlia, where she taught school, are the backgrounds for most of her stories. Dalecarlia, the setting for "The Silver Mine," is a region rich in mineral resources.

* **Lagerlöf** (lä'yər·lœf).

The Silver Mine

King Gustaf III [1] was traveling through Dalecarlia.[2] He was pressed for time, and all the way he wanted to drive like lightning. Although they drove with such speed that the horses were extended like stretched rubber bands and the coach cleared the turns on two

1. **Gustaf III** (gōōs'täf).
2. **Dalecarlia** (dal'ə·kar'li·ä): a region in west central Sweden.

wheels, the King poked his head out of the window and shouted to the postilion,[3] "Why don't you go ahead? Do you think you are driving over eggs?"

Since they had to drive over poor country roads at such a mad pace, it would have been almost a miracle had the harness and wagon held together! And they didn't, either; for at the foot of a steep hill the pole broke—and there the King sat! The courtiers sprang from the coach and scolded the driver, but this did not lessen the damage done. There was no possibility of continuing the journey until the coach was mended.

When the courtiers looked around to try to find something with which the King could amuse himself while he waited, they noticed a church spire looming high above the trees in a grove a short distance ahead. They intimated to the King that he might step into one of the coaches in which the attendants were riding and drive up to the church. It was a Sunday, and the King might attend services to pass the time until the royal coach was ready.

The King accepted the proposal and drove toward the church. He had been traveling for hours through dark forest regions, but here it looked more cheerful, with fairly large meadows and villages, and with the Dal River gliding on light and pretty, between thick rows of alder bushes.

But the King had ill luck to this extent: the bell ringer took up the recessional chant just as the King was stepping from the coach on the church knoll [4] and the people were coming out from the service. But when they came walking past him, the King remained standing, with one foot in the wagon and the other on the footstep. He did not move from the spot—only stared at them. They were the finest lot of folk he had ever seen. All the men were above the average height, with intelligent and earnest faces, and the women were dignified and stately, with an air of Sabbath peace about them.

The whole of the preceding day the King had talked only of the desolate tracts he was passing through, and had said to his courtiers again and again, "Now I am certainly driving through the very poorest part of my kingdom!" But now, when he saw the people, garbed in the picturesque dress of this section of the country, he forgot to think of their poverty; instead his heart warmed, and he remarked to himself, "The King of Sweden is not so badly off as his enemies

3. **postilion** (pŏs·til′yən): a rider or guide on one of the leading horses in a team attached to a coach.
4. **knoll** (nōl): a small round hill; mound.

think. So long as my subjects look like this, I shall probably be able to defend both my faith and my country."

He commanded the courtiers to make known to the people that the stranger who was standing among them was their King and that they should gather around him, so he could talk to them.

And then the King made a speech to the people. He spoke from the high steps outside the vestry,[5] and the narrow step upon which he stood is there even today.

The King gave an account of the sad plight in which the kingdom was placed. He said that the Swedes were threatened with war by both Russians and Danes. Under ordinary circumstances it would not be such a serious matter, but now the army was filled with traitors, and he did not dare depend upon it. Therefore there was no other course for him to take than to go himself into the country settlements and ask his subjects if they would be loyal to their King and help him with men and money, so he could save the Fatherland.

The peasants stood quietly while the King was speaking, and when he had finished they gave no sign either of approval or disapproval.

The King himself thought that he had spoken well. The tears had sprung to his eyes several times while he was speaking. But when the peasants stood there all the while, troubled and undecided, and could not make up their minds to answer him, the King frowned and looked displeased.

The peasants understood that it was becoming monotonous for the King to wait, and finally one of them stepped out from the crowd.

"Now, you must know, King Gustaf, that we were not expecting a royal visit in the parish today," said the peasant, "and therefore we are not prepared to answer you at once. I advise you to go into the vestry and speak with our pastor, while we discuss among ourselves this matter which you have laid before us."

The King apprehended [6] that a more satisfactory response was not to be had immediately, so he felt that it would be best for him to follow the peasant's advice.

When he came into the vestry, he found no one there but a man who looked like a peasant. He was tall and rugged, with big hands, toughened by labor, and he wore neither cassock nor collar, but leather breeches and a long white homespun coat, like all the other men.

5. **vestry** (ves′trē): a room in a church where altar linens, sacred vessels, and the vestments of the clergy are kept.
6. **apprehended** (ap′rə·hend·əd): understood. To *apprehend* can also mean to *arrest,* and to *dread.*

He rose and bowed to the King when the latter entered.

"I thought I should find the parson in here," said the King.

The man grew somewhat red in the face. He thought it annoying to mention the fact that he was the parson of this parish, when he saw that the King had mistaken him for a peasant. "Yes," said he, "the parson is usually on hand in here."

The King dropped into a large armchair which stood in the vestry at that time and which stands there today, looking exactly like itself, with this difference: the congregation has had a gilded crown attached to the back of it.

"Have you a good parson in this parish?" asked the King, who wanted to appear interested in the welfare of the peasants.

When the King questioned him in this manner, the parson felt that he couldn't possibly tell who he was. "It's better to let him go on believing that I'm only a peasant," thought he, and replied that the parson was good enough. He preached a pure and clear gospel and tried to live as he taught.

The King thought that this was a good commendation but he had a sharp ear and marked a certain doubt in the tone. "You sound as if you were not quite satisfied with the parson," said the King.

"He's a bit arbitrary," said the man, thinking that if the King should find out later who he was, he would not think that the parson had been standing here and blowing his own horn. Therefore he wished to come out with a little faultfinding also. "There are some, no doubt, who say the parson wants to be the only one to counsel and rule in this parish," he continued.

"Then, at all events, he has led and managed in the best possible way," said the King. He didn't like it that the peasant complained of one who was placed above him. "To me it appears as though good habits and old-time simplicity were the rule here."

"The people are good enough," said the curate, "but then they live in poverty and isolation. Human beings here would certainly be no better than others if this world's temptations came closer to them."

"But there's no fear of anything of the sort happening," said the King, with a shrug.

He said nothing further, but began thrumming on the table with his fingers. He thought he had exchanged a sufficient number of gracious words with this peasant and wondered when the others would be ready with their answer.

"These peasants are not very eager to help their King," thought he.

"If I only had my coach, I would drive away from them and their palaver!" [7]

The pastor sat there troubled, debating with himself as to how he should decide an important matter which he must settle. He was beginning to feel happy because he had not told the King who he was. Now he felt that he could speak with him about matters which otherwise he could not have placed before him.

After a while the parson broke the silence and asked the King if it was an actual fact that enemies were upon them and that the kingdom was in danger.

The King thought this man ought to have sense enough not to trouble him further. He simply glared at him and said nothing.

"I ask because I was standing in here and could not hear very well," said the parson. "But if this is really the case, I want to say to you that the pastor of this congregation might perhaps be able to procure for the King as much money as he will need."

"I thought that you said just now that everyone here was poor," said the King, thinking that the man did not know what he was talking about.

"Yes, that's true," replied the rector, "and the parson has no more than any of the others. But if the King would condescend to listen to me for a moment, I will explain how the pastor happens to have the power to help him."

"You may speak," said the King. "You seem to find it easier to get the words past your lips than your friends and neighbors out there, who never will be ready with what they have to tell me."

"It is not so easy to reply to the King! I'm afraid that, in the end, it will be the parson who must undertake this on behalf of the others."

The King crossed his legs, folded his arms, and let his head sink down on his breast. "You may begin now," he said, in the tone of one already asleep.

"Once upon a time there were five men from this parish who were out on a moose hunt," began the clergyman. "One of them was the parson of whom we are speaking. Two of the others were soldiers, named Olaf and Eric Svärd; the fourth man was the innkeeper in this settlement, and the fifth was a peasant named Israel Per Persson."

"Don't go to the trouble of mentioning so many names," muttered the King, letting his head droop to one side.

"Those men were good hunters," continued the parson, "who usually had luck with them, but that day they had wandered long and

7. **palaver** (pə·lav′ər): public discussion, especially of an empty, lengthy nature.

far without getting anything. Finally they gave up the hunt altogether and sat down on the ground to talk. They said there was not a spot in the whole forest fit for cultivation; all of it was only mountain and swampland. 'Our Lord has not done right by us in giving us such a poor land to live in,' said one. 'In other localities people can get riches for themselves in abundance, but here, with all our toil and drudgery we can scarcely get our daily bread.' "

The pastor paused a moment, as if uncertain that the King heard him, but the latter moved his little finger to show that he was awake.

"Just as the hunters were discussing this matter, the parson saw something that glittered at the base of the mountain, where he had kicked away a moss tuft. 'This is a queer mountain,' he thought, as he kicked off another moss tuft. He picked up a sliver of stone that came with the moss and which shone exactly like the other. 'It can't be possible that this stuff is lead,' said he.

"Then the others sprang up and scraped away the turf with the butt ends of their rifles. When they did this, they saw plainly that a broad vein of ore followed the mountain.

" 'What do you think this might be?' asked the parson.

"The men chipped off bits of stone and bit into them. 'It must be lead, or zinc at least,' said they.

" 'And the whole mountain is full of it,' added the innkeeper."

When the parson had got thus far in his narrative, the King's head was seen to straighten up a little and one eye opened. "Do you know if any of these persons knew anything about ore and minerals?" he asked.

"They did not," replied the parson.

Then the King's head sank and both eyes closed.

"The clergyman and his companions were very happy," continued the speaker, without letting himself be disturbed by the King's indifference; "they fancied that now they had found that which would give them and their descendants wealth. 'I'll never have to do any more work,' said one. 'Now I can afford to do nothing at all the whole week through, and on Sundays I shall drive to church in a golden chariot!' They were otherwise sensible men, but the great find had gone to their heads, and they talked like children. Still they had enough presence of mind to put back the moss tufts and conceal the vein of ore. Then they carefully noted the place where it was, and went home. Before they parted company, they agreed that the parson should travel to Falun and ask the mining expert what kind of ore this was. He was to return as soon as possible, and until then they promised one another on oath not to reveal to a single soul where the ore was to be found."

The King's head was raised again a trifle, but he did not interrupt the speaker with a word. It appeared as though he was beginning to believe that the man actually had something of importance he wished to say to him, since he didn't allow himself to be disturbed by his indifference.

"Then the parson departed with a few samples of ore in his pocket. He was just as happy in the thought of becoming rich as the others were. He was thinking of rebuilding the parsonage, which at present was no better than a peasant's cottage, and then he would marry a dean's [8] daughter whom he liked. He had thought that he might have to wait for her many years. He was poor and obscure and knew that it would be a long while before he should get any post that would enable him to marry.

"The parson drove over to Falun in two days, and there he had to wait another whole day because the mining expert was away. Finally he ran across him and showed him the bits of ore. The mining expert took them in his hand. He looked at them first, then at the parson. The parson related how he had found them in a mountain at home in his parish, and wondered if it might not be lead.

" 'No, it's not lead,' said the mining expert.

" 'Perhaps it is zinc, then?' asked the parson.

" 'Nor is it zinc,' said the mineralogist.

"The parson thought that all the hope within him sank. He had not been so depressed in many a long day.

" 'Have you many stones like these in your parish?' asked the mineralogist.

" 'We have a whole mountainful,' said the parson.

"Then the mineralogist came up closer, slapped the parson on the shoulder, and said, 'Let us see that you make such good use of this that it will prove a blessing both to yourselves and to the country, for this is silver.'

" 'Indeed?' said the parson, feeling his way. 'So it is silver!'

"The mineralogist began telling him how he should go to work to get legal rights to the mine and gave him many valuable suggestions; but the parson stood there dazed and did not listen to what the mineralogist was saying. He was thinking how wonderful it was that at home in his poor parish stood a whole mountain of silver ore, waiting for him."

8. **dean's:** A dean is the head of a cathedral or collegiate church.

The King raised his head so suddenly that the parson stopped short in his narrative. "It turned out, of course, that when he got home and began working the mine, he saw that the mineralogist had only been fooling him." said the King.

"Oh, no, the mineralogist had not fooled him," said the parson.

"You may continue," said the King as he settled himself more comfortably in the chair to listen.

"When the parson was at home again and was driving through the parish," continued the clergyman, "he thought that first of all he should inform his partners of the value of their find. And as he drove alongside the innkeeper Sten Stensson's place, he intended to drive up to the house to tell him they had found silver. But when he stopped outside the gate, he noticed that a broad path of evergreen was strewn all the way up to the doorstep.

" 'Who has died in this place?' asked the parson of a boy who stood leaning against the fence.

" 'The innkeeper himself,' answered the boy. Then he let the clergyman know that the innkeeper had drunk himself full every day for a week. 'Oh, so much brandy, so much brandy, has been drunk here!'

" 'How can that be?' asked the parson. 'The innkeeper used never to drink himself full.'

" 'Oh,' said the boy, 'he drank because he said he had found a mine. He was very rich. He should never have to do anything now but drink, he said. Last night he drove off, full as he was, and the wagon turned over and he was killed.'

"When the parson heard this, he drove homeward, distressed over what he had heard. He had come back so happy, rejoicing because he could tell the great news.

"When the parson had driven a few paces, he saw Israel Per Persson walking along. He looked about as usual, and the parson thought it was well that fortune had not gone to his head too. Him he would cheer at once with the news that he was a rich man.

" 'Good day!' said Per Persson. 'Do you come from Falun now?'

" 'I do,' said the parson. 'And now I must tell you that it has turned out even better than we had imagined. The mineralogist said it was silver ore that we had found.'

"That instant Per Persson looked as though the ground had opened under him. 'What are you saying, what are you saying? Is it silver?'

" 'Yes,' answered the parson. 'We'll all be rich men now, all of us, and can live like gentlemen.'

" 'Oh, is it silver?' said Per Persson once again, looking more and more mournful.

" 'Why, of course it is silver,' replied the parson. 'You mustn't think that I want to deceive you. You mustn't be afraid to be happy.'

" 'Happy!' said Per Persson. 'Should I be happy? I believed it was only glitter that we had found, so I thought it would be better to take the certain for the uncertain; I have sold my share in the mine to Olaf Svärd for a hundred dollars.'

"He was desperate, and when the parson drove away from him, he stood on the highway and wept.

"When the clergyman got back to his home, he sent a servant to Olaf Svärd and his brother to tell them that it was silver they had found. He thought that he had had quite enough of driving around and spreading the good news.

"But in the evening, when the parson sat alone, his joy asserted itself again. He went out in the darkness and stood on a hillock upon which he contemplated building the new parsonage. It should be imposing, of course, as fine as a bishop's palace. He stood there long that night; nor did he content himself with rebuilding the parsonage! It occurred to him that, since there were such riches to be found in the parish, throngs of people would pour in, and finally a whole city would be built around the mine. And then he would have to erect a new church in place of the old one. Toward this object a large portion of his wealth would probably go. And he was not content with this, either, but fancied that, when his church was ready, the King and many bishops would come to the dedication. Then the King would be pleased with the church, but he would remark that there was no place where a king might put up, and then he would have to erect a castle in the new city."

Just then one of the King's courtiers opened the door of the vestry and announced that the big royal coach was mended.

At the first moment the King was ready to withdraw, but on second thought he changed his mind. "You may tell your story to the end," he said to the parson. "But you can hurry it a bit. We know all about how the man thought and dreamed. We want to know how he acted."

"But while the parson was still lost in his dreams," continued the clergyman, "word came to him that Israel Per Persson had made away with himself. He had not been able to bear the disappointment of having sold his share in the mine. He had thought, no doubt, that he could not endure to go about every day seeing another enjoying the wealth that might have been his."

The King straightened up a little. He kept both eyes open. "Upon my word," he said, "if I had been that parson, I should have had enough of the mine!"

"The King is a rich man," said the parson. "He has quite enough, at all events. It is not the same thing with a poor curate who possesses nothing. The unhappy wretch thought instead, when he saw that God's blessing was not with his enterprise, 'I will dream no more of bringing glory and profit to myself with these riches, but I can't let the silver lie buried in the earth! I must take it out, for the benefit of the poor and needy. I will work the mine, to put the whole parish on its feet.'

"So one day the parson went out to see Olaf Svärd, to ask him and his brother what should be done immediately with the silver mountain. When he came in the vicinity of the barracks he met a cart surrounded by armed peasants, and in the cart sat a man with his hands tied behind him and a rope around his ankles.

"When the parson passed by, the cart stopped and he had time to regard the prisoner, whose head was tied up so it was not easy to see who he was. But the parson thought he recognized Olaf Svärd. He heard the prisoner beg those who guarded him to let him speak a few words with the parson.

"The parson drew nearer, and the prisoner turned toward him. 'You will soon be the only one who knows where the silver mine is,' said Olaf.

" 'What are you saying, Olaf?' asked the parson.

" 'Well, you see, parson, since we have learned that it was a silver mine we had found, my brother and I could no longer be as good friends as before. We were continually quarreling. Last night we got into a controversy over which one of us five it was who first discovered the mine. It ended in strife between us, and we came to blows. I have killed my brother and he has left me with a souvenir across the forehead to remember him by. I must hang now, and then you will be the only one who knows about the mine; therefore I wish to ask something of you.'

" 'Speak out!' said the parson. 'I'll do what I can for you.'

" 'You know that I am leaving several little children behind me,' began the soldier, but the parson interrupted him.

" 'As regards this, you can rest easy. That which comes to your share in the mine they shall have, exactly as if you yourself were living.'

" 'No,' said Olaf Svärd, 'it was another thing I wanted to ask of you. Don't let them have any portion of that which comes from the mine!'

"The parson staggered back a step. He stood there dumb and could not answer.

" 'If you do not promise me this, I cannot die in peace,' said the prisoner.

" 'Yes,' said the parson slowly and painfully. 'I promise you what you ask of me.'

"Thereupon the murderer was taken away, and the parson stood on the highway thinking how he should keep the promise he had given him. On the way home he thought of the wealth which he had been so happy over. What if it really were true that the people in this community could not stand riches? Already four were ruined who hitherto had been dignified and excellent men. He seemed to see the whole community before him, and he pictured to himself how this silver mine would destroy one after another. Was it befitting that he, who had been appointed to watch over these poor human beings' souls, should let loose upon them that which would be their destruction?"

All of a sudden the King sat bolt upright in his chair. "I declare!" said he, "you'll make me understand that a parson in this isolated settlement must be every inch a man."

"Nor was what had already happened enough," continued the parson, "for as soon as the news about the mine spread among the parishioners, they stopped working and went about in idleness, waiting for the time when great iiches should pour in on them. All the ne'er-do-wells there were in this section streamed in, and drunkenness and fighting were what the parson heard talked of continually. A lot of people did nothing but tramp around in the forest searching for the mine, and the parson marked that as soon as he left the house people followed him stealthily to find out if he wasn't going to the silver mountain and to steal the secret from him.

"When matters were come to this pass, the parson called the peasants together to vote. To start with, he reminded them of all the misfortunes which the discovery of the mountain had brought upon them, and he asked them if they were going to let themselves be ruined or if they would save themselves. Then he told them that they must not expect him, who was their spiritual adviser, to help on their destruction. Now he had decided not to reveal to anyone where the silver mine was, and never would he himself take riches from it. And then he asked the peasants how they would have it henceforth. If they wished to continue their search for the mine and wait upon riches, then he would go so far away that no word of their misery could reach him; but if they would give up thinking about the silver mine and be as heretofore, he would remain with them. 'Whichever way you may choose,' said the parson, 'remember this, that from me no one shall ever know anything about the silver mountain.' "

"Well," said the King, "how did they decide?"

"They did as their pastor wished," said the parson. "They understood that he meant well by them when he wanted to remain poor for their sakes. And they commissioned him to go to the forest and conceal the vein of ore with evergreen and stone, so that no one would be able to find it—neither they themselves nor their posterity." [9]

"And ever since the parson has been living here just as poor as the rest?"

"Yes," answered the curate, "he has lived here just as poor as the rest."

"He has married, of course, and built a new parsonage?" said the King.

"No, he couldn't afford to marry, and he lives in the old cabin."

"It's a pretty story that you have told me," said the King. After a few seconds he resumed, "Was it of the silver mountain that you were thinking when you said that the parson here would be able to procure for me as much money as I need?"

"Yes," said the other.

"But I can't put the thumbscrews [10] on him," said the King. "Or how would you advise that I get such a man to show me the mountain—a man who has renounced his sweetheart and all the allurements of life?"

"Oh, that's a different matter," said the parson. "But if it's the Fatherland that is in need of the fortune, he will probably give in."

"Will you answer for that?" asked the King.

"Yes, that I will answer for," said the clergyman.

"Doesn't he care, then, what becomes of his parishioners?"

"That can rest in God's hands."

The King rose from his chair and walked over to the window. He stood for a moment and looked upon the group of people outside. The longer he looked, the clearer his large eyes shone; and his figure seemed to grow. "You may greet the pastor of this congregation and say that for Sweden's King there is no sight more beautiful than to see a people such as this!"

Then the King turned from the window and looked at the clergyman. He began to smile. "Is it true that the pastor of this parish is so

9. **posterity** (pos·ter′ə·tē): descendants; all future generations.
10. **thumbscrews**: instruments of torture for compressing the thumbs.

poor that he removes his black clothes as soon as the service is over and dresses himself like a peasant?" asked the King.

"Yes, so poor is he," said the curate, and a crimson flush leaped into his roughhewn face.

The King went back to the window. One could see that he was in his best mood. All that was noble and great within him had been quickened into life. "You must let that mine lie in peace," said the King. "Inasmuch as you have labored and starved a lifetime to make this people such as you would have it, you may keep it as it is."

"But if the kingdom is in danger?" said the parson.

"The kingdom is better served with men than with money," remarked the King. When he had said this, he bade the clergyman farewell and went out from the vestry.

Without stood the group of people, as quiet and taciturn [11] as they were when he went in. As the King came down the steps, a peasant stepped up to him.

"Have you had a talk with our pastor?" said the peasant.

"Yes," said the King. "I have."

"Then of course you have our answer?" said the peasant. "We asked you to go in and talk with our parson, that he might give you an answer from us."

"I have the answer," said the King.

11. **taciturn** (tas′ə·tûrn): not inclined to talk.

Meaning and Method

1. The silver mine brought many evils to the village. What were the causes of the death of the two soldiers, the innkeeper, and the peasant? How was the parson tempted? What major vice spread among the parishioners?

2. How did the pastor persuade the people to forego using the mine? What effect did the decision have on the lives of the people? of the pastor?

3. A *frame story* is one which is placed inside another story. For some reason embodied in the outer story, there is occasion to narrate the inner story, which is usually the more important of the two.

   Point out the boundaries of the inner story in "The Silver Mine." What is the advantage for the author of having someone "inside" the story tell what happened?

4. What is the author's purpose in having the mine discovered by persons with such varied occupations?

5. How does the author prepare you at the beginning of the story for the King's final decision?
6. What is the theme of the story?
7. Think of the once-upon-a-time stories you heard in your childhood. What folktale qualities does this story have?

Language: Synonyms

The English word *synonym* comes from the Greek prefix *syn*, meaning together or associated with or like, and *onyma*, the Greek word for name. Synonyms are words similar in meaning.

In "The Silver Mine" the author refers to the storyteller as a *parson*, a *curate*, a *pastor*, and a *clergyman*. If you were to consult a thesaurus (thə·sôr′əs), a book or "treasury" of words, especially of synonyms and antonyms, you would find these four words listed under the same entry. Along with these four synonyms, you would find such other synonyms as *ecclesiastic*, *churchman*, *cleric*, *minister*, and *the Reverend*.

Although there is a relationship among synonyms, each word is still highly individual and brings its own force to the context. For example, look up the origin and meaning of *curate* and *pastor* and compare the shades of meaning each word has.

The following sentences, taken from the story, describe the parson or his actions. Consult a thesaurus to find synonyms for the italicized words. Could you substitute any of the synonyms for these words and still keep the present meaning?

1. " 'There are some, no doubt, who say the parson wants to be the only one to *counsel* and rule in the parish,' he continued."
2. "[He was] *distressed* over what he had heard."
3. "The parson staggered back a step. He stood there *dumb* and could not answer."
4. ". . . —a man who has *renounced* his sweetheart. . . ."
5. ". . . a crimson flush leaped into his *roughhewn* face."

Composition

Write a character sketch about the King, the parson, or the general nature of the villagers. Begin by describing in detail his, or their, particular characteristics. Illustrate your description by referring to what the character(s) say and do.

As part of your sketch, tell which episode in the story shows you the most about the subject you choose. Be sure to explain the specific qualities illustrated by the passage you select.

William Melvin Kelley

"An American writer who happens to have brown skin faces this unique problem: Solutions and answers to The Negro Problem are very often read into his work. . . . At this time, let me say for the record that I am not a sociologist or a politician or a spokesman. Some people try to give answers. A writer, I think, should ask questions. He should depict people, not symbols or ideas disguised as people."

These objectives are stated by William Melvin Kelley in his Preface to *Dancers on the Shore* (1964), a collection of short stories which includes "Enemy Territory."

Kelley was born in New York City in 1937. He attended Fieldston School, a private high school in New York City, and Harvard University. He says that his "desire to write was really a vague undergraduate yearning," but after leaving Harvard he decided to make it his career. When he was twenty-five, his first novel, *A Different Drummer*, was published and was widely praised. It won the Richard and Hinda Rosenthal Award of the National Institute of Arts and Letters. Two other novels have followed: *A Drop of Patience* in 1965 and *dem* in 1967. Many of his short stories have appeared in such magazines as *The Saturday Evening Post, Esquire, The Negro Digest*, and *Mademoiselle*.

On the dedication page of *Dancers on the Shore*, he explains that the person who listened to and encouraged his ambition to write rather than choosing "a more secure and respectable occupation" was his grandmother, Jessie Garcia, "who was the only family I had." It is to her that he dedicates his collection with "admiration, gratitude, and love."

Enemy Territory

I peered over a rotting tree stump and saw him moving, without a helmet, in the bushes. I got his forehead in my sights, squeezed the trigger, and imagined I saw the bullet puncture his head and blood trickle out. "I got you, Jerome. I got you!"

"Awh, you did not."

"I got you; you're dead."

I must have sounded very definite because he compromised. "You only wounded me."

"Tommy? Tommy! Come here." Her voice came from high above me.

I scrambled to my knees. "What, Ma?" She was on the porch of our house, next to the vacant lot where we were playing.

"Come here a minute, dear. I want you to do something for me." She was wearing a yellow dress. The porch was red brick.

I hopped up and ran to the foot of our steps. She came to the top. "Mister Bixby left his hat."

As I had waited in ambush for Jerome, I had seen Mister Bixby climb and, an hour later, chug down the steps. He was one of my father's poker-playing friends. It was only after she mentioned it that I remembered Mister Bixby had been wearing, when he arrived, a white, wide-brimmed Panama hat with a black band.

Entering my parents' room on the second floor, I saw it on their bed. My mother picked it up. "Walk it around to his house. Now walk, I say. Don't run because you'll probably drop it and ruin it." It was so white a speck of dirt would have shone like a black star in a white sky. "So walk! Let me see your hands."

I extended them palms up and she immediately sent me to the bathroom to wash. Then she gave me the hat. I did not really grip it; rather, with my finger in the crown, I balanced it, as if about to twirl it.

When I stepped onto the porch again, I saw them playing on their corner—Valentine's Gang. Well, in this day of street gangs organized like armies, I cannot rightly call Joey Valentine, who was eight, and his acquaintances, who ranged in age from five to seven, a gang. It was simply that they lived on the next block, and since my friends and I were just at the age when we were allowed to cross the street, but were not yet used to this new freedom, we still stood on opposite sides of the asphalt strip that divided us and called each other names. It was not until I got onto the porch that I realized, with a sense of dread that only a six-year-old can conjure up, that Mister Bixby lived one block beyond Valentine's Territory.

Still, with faith that the adult nature of my mission would give me unmolested passage, I approached the corner, which was guarded by a red fire alarm box, looked both ways for the cars that seldom came, and, swallowing, began to cross over.

They were playing with toy soldiers and tin tanks in the border of dry yellow dirt that separated the flagstones from the gutter. I was in the middle of the street when they first realized I was invading; they were shocked. At the time, I can remember thinking they must have been awed that I should have the unequaled courage to cross into their territory. But looking back, I realize it probably had little to do with me. It was the hat, a white Panama hat. A more natural target for abuse has never existed.

I was two steps from the curb when Joey Valentine moved into my path. "Hey, what you got?"

Since he was obviously asking the question to show off, I bit my lips and did not answer. I saw myself as one of my radio heroes resisting Japanese interrogation. I was aloof. However, the white Panama hat was not at all aloof. Before I knew it, Joey Valentine reached out a mud-caked hand and knocked the hat off my finger to a resounding chorus of cheers and laughter.

I scooped up the hat before any of them, retreated at a run across the street, and stopped beside the red alarm box. Wanting to save some small amount of my dignity, I screamed at them: "I'll get you guys! I'll get you. I'm not really an American. I'm an African and Africans are friends of the Japs and I'll get them to *bomb your house!*"

But even as I ranted at them, I could see I was doing so in vain. Across the way, Valentine's Gang lounged with the calm of movie Marines listening to Japanese propaganda on the radio. I turned toward my house, inspecting the hat for smudges. There were none; it was as blinding white as ever. Already I felt tears inching down my cheeks.

Not until I was halfway up the porch steps did I see my grandmother sitting in her red iron chair. But before I could say anything, before I could appeal for understanding and comfort, she lifted herself out of the chair and disappeared into the house. She had seen it all—I knew that—and she was too ashamed of me to face me.

Suddenly she was coming back, holding a broom handle. She had never before lifted a hand to me, but in my state, I felt sure that many things would change. I closed my eyes and waited.

Instead of the crunch of hard wood on bone, I heard her chair creak. I opened my eyes and found the end of the broom handle under my nose.

"You know if you don't go back and deliver that hat, you'll feel pretty bad tonight."

I nodded.

"Well, take this. We don't like you fighting. But sometimes you have to. So now you march down there and tell those boys if they don't let you alone, you'll have to hit them with this. Here." She pushed the broom handle at me.

I took it, but was not very happy about it. I studied her; she looked the same, her white hair bunned at her neck, her blue eyes large behind glasses, her skin the color of unvarnished wood. But something inside must have changed for her actually to tell me to hit someone. I had been in fights, fits and starts of temper that burned out in a second. But to walk deliberately down to the corner, threaten someone, and hit him if he did not move aside, this was completely different, and, as my parents and grandmother had raised me, downright evil. She must have realized what I was thinking.

"You know who Teddy Roosevelt was?"

I nodded.

"Well, he once said: *Speak softly and carry a big stick; you will go far.*" [1]

I understood her, but to do something like this was still alien to my nature. I held back.

"Come on." She stood abruptly and took my hand. We went into the house, down the hall, and into her bedroom. "I have to see to the mulatto rice. You sit on my bed and look at the picture on the wall." She went on to the kitchen. I was still holding the broom handle and now put it down across the bed, and climbed up beside it, surrounded by her room, an old woman's room with its fifty years of perfume, powder, and sweet soap. I felt a long way from the corner and Valentine's Gang.

There were three pictures on the wall and I was not certain which she wanted me to study. The smallest was of my granduncle Wilfred, who lived on Long Island and came to Thanksgiving dinner. The largest was of Jesus, the fingers of his right hand crossed and held up, his left hand baring his chest, in the middle of which was his heart, red and dripping blood. In the cool darkness of the room, he looked at me with gentle eyes, a slight smile on his lips. The third was my grandmother's husband, who had died so long before that I had never known him and had no feeling for him as my grandfather. He was light, like my grandmother, but more like some of the short, sallow Italian men who lived on the block. His black hair was parted in the middle. He wore a big mustache which hid his mouth. His

---

1. *Speak . . . far!*: During the years of his presidency (1901–09), Theodore Roosevelt (1858–1919), used this slogan to describe his attitude toward the governments of countries in South America and the Caribbean.

jaw was square and dimpled. With black eyes, he seemed to look at something just above my head.

"Well, all right now." My grandmother came in, sweating from standing over the stove, and sat in a small armchair beside the bed. "Did you look at the picture?"

"I didn't know which one." I looked at Jesus again.

"No, not him this time. This one." She indicated her husband. "I meant him."

Now Pablo [Cortés], your grandfather—she started—was just like you, as gentle as a milkweed flower settling into honey, and as friendly as ninety-seven puppy dogs. He was from Cuba, which is an island in the Atlantic Ocean.

He was so kind that he'd meet every boat coming in from Cuba and talk to all of the people getting off, and if he found that one of them didn't have a place to stay, and no money for food, he'd bring him home. He'd lead this new friend into the kitchen and say: "Jennie, this is a countryman. He got no place to sleep, and he's hungry." And I'd sigh and say: "All right. Dinner'll be ready in ten minutes." They'd go into the living room and sing and roll cigars.

That's what he did for a living, roll cigars, working at home. The leaves were spread out all over the floor like a rug and I never did like cigars because I know somebody's been walking all over the leaves, sometimes in bare feet like your mother did when she was a little girl.

Pablo was so friendly he gave a party every day while I was at work. I'd come home and open the door and the cigar smoke would tumble out and through the haze I would see twenty drunken Cubans, most with guitars, others rolling cigars, and all of them howling songs.

So now fifty years ago, I'd come from down South to stay with my brother Wilfred, and I was so dumb that the first time I saw snow I thought somebody upstairs'd broken open a pillow out the window. So my brother Wilfred had to explain a lot of things to me. And the first thing was about the neighborhoods. In those days, New York was all split up into neighborhoods. The Italians lived in one neighborhood, and the Polish in another, and the Negroes and Cubans someplace else. After Pablo and I got married, we lived with the Negroes. And if you walked two blocks one way, you'd come to the Irish neighborhood, and if you were smart, you'd turn around and come back because if the Irish caught you, they'd do something terrible to you.

I don't know if Pablo knew this or not, or if he just thought he was so friendly that everybody would just naturally be friendly right back. But one day he went for a walk. He got over into the Irish neighborhood and got a little thirsty—which he did pretty often—so he went into an Irish bar and asked for a drink. I guess they thought he was new in this country because the bartender gave him his drink. So Pablo, smiling all the time, and waiting for them to smile back, stood there in that Irish bar and drank slow. When he was finished, the bartender took the glass and instead of washing it, he smashed it down on the floor and stepped on it and crushed the pieces under his heel. What he meant was that it was pretty bad to be a Cuban and no Irishman would want to touch a glass a Cuban had drunk from.

I don't know if Pablo knew that either. He asked for another drink. And he got it. And after he finished this one, the bartender smashed it in the sink and glared at him.

Pablo was still thirsty and ordered again.

The bartender came and stood in front of him. He was a big man, with a face as red as watermelon. "Say, buddy, can't you take a hint?"

Pablo smiled. "What hint?"

The bartender was getting pretty mad. "Why you think I'm breaking them glasses?"

"I thought you like to break glasses. You must got a high bill on glasses."

The bartender got an axhandle from under the bar. "Get out of here, Cuban!"

So now Pablo knew the bartender didn't want him in the bar. "Now, let me get this straight. If I ask you for drink, and you give me drink, you would break that glass too?"

"That's right. But you better not order again."

Pablo sighed. He was sad. "Well, then we will pretend I got drunk in this bar." And the next thing anybody knew Pablo was behind the bar, breaking all the glasses he could reach.

"And we will pretend that I look at myself in your mirror." He picked up a bottle and cracked the big mirror they had.

By now there was a regular riot going on, with all the men in the bar trying to catch and hold him, and Pablo running around, breaking chairs and tables. Finally, just before they caught and tied him up, he tipped over their piano. "We will pretend I played a Cuban song on this piano!"

They called the police and held him until the wagon came. And the next time I saw him was in court the next morning, where the judge kept looking at Pablo like he really didn't believe that a man who seemed so kind and gentle could do such things. But it was plain Pablo had wrecked the Irishman's bar. The judge sentenced him to thirty days in the city jail, and fifty dollars damages, which Pablo couldn't pay. So the judge gave him thirty extra days.

I didn't see Pablo for the next two months. When he came home, he was changed. He wasn't smiling at all, and you remember that he used to smile all the time. As soon as he came in the house he told me he was going out again. I knew where and I got mad. "Do you want to spend another two months in jail? Is that what you want?"

He didn't understand me. "Why you ask me that?"

"Why! You're going over there to that white man's bar and get into a fight and go on back to jail. Did you like it that much? Did jail change you so much?"

"Jennie, don't you see? I try not to change." He picked up five boxes of cigars he'd made before he went to jail and put them into a brown paper bag, and tucked the bag under his arm.

I watched him go out the door and then started to cry. I loved him, you see, and didn't want him back in jail. And I cried because I didn't understand him now and was afraid of that.

When the Irishmen saw him coming into their bar, they were stunned. Their mouths dropped open and they all got very quiet. Pablo didn't pay them any mind, just walked up to the bar and put his foot on the brass rail.

The bartender picked up his axhandle. "What you want here, Cuban? Ain't you had enough?"

"No." Pablo didn't smile. He took the brown paper bag and put it gently on the counter. Cigars, he said, are delicate and shouldn't be tossed around.

The bartender looked at the bag. "What you got there?"

"Maybe you find out." He touched the box with his fingers. "I like a drink."

The bartender stared at him for a second and then at the paper bag for a long time. He started to sweat. "All right." He set the drink down in front of Pablo.

For a minute Pablo just looked at it. Then he lifed it to his lips and drank it down and pushed it across the bar to the bartender.

The bartender picked it up and studied it. Finally, he looked at Pablo again. "What the hell! I had to close up for a week after you was here the first time." He took the glass to the sink, washed it with soap and water, and put it with the other clean glasses. Then he looked at Pablo again. "Satisfied?"

"Not yet." Pablo grabbed the paper bag and started to open it.

"Watch out, fellows!" The bartender yelled in his ear. When Pablo looked up, all the men in the bar were lying on their stomachs covering their heads. The bartender was behind the bar on his knees, his hands over his ears.

Pablo took a cigar box out of the bag, opened it, pulled himself up and across the bar, and reached the box down to the bartender. "Hey, you want fine, handmade Havana cigar?" He was smiling.

"Are you going back down to that corner?" My grandmother took my hand.

I looked into her face and then at the picture of her husband. He was still studying something just above my head. "I guess so." I did not really want to do it.

"You may not even have to use that." She pointed at the broom handle. "But you should know you can."

I knew this was true and climbed off the bed and picked up the white hat and the broom handle. "Okay."

"I'll be waiting on the porch for you." She smiled, got up, and sighing, went out to the kitchen.

For a while, I listened to pots knocking and being filled with water. Then I stood in her room and practiced what I would say to Valentine's Gang: "If you guys don't let me go by, I'll have to hit you with this." There was a quake in my voice the first time I said it out loud, but if I had to, I thought I would actually be able to say it and then use the stick. I went down the hall, onto the porch, and looked down toward the corner.

It was empty. The mothers of the members of Valentine's Gang had summoned them home to supper.

Meaning

1. State in your own words what Teddy Roosevelt's slogan means to Tommy's grandmother. Why is the meaning so "alien" to the boy's nature? Why does the grandmother's insistence that Tommy carry a broomstick with him create a conflict within the boy?

2. What generalization does the grandmother make about Pablo's character before she begins to tell his story? How are his actions during the first visit to the bar related to Roosevelt's slogan? What admirable trait of character does Pablo exhibit during his second visit? What lesson is Tommy's grandmother trying to teach by telling the boy this incident in Pablo's life?

3. Is Tommy's problem with the children on the next block the same as

Pablo's conflict with the adults in the bar? Why or why not? Why does the grandmother think it is so important for Tommy to be able to cross into "enemy territory" at such an early age? What is the theme of this story?

4. What is ironic about the ending of "Enemy Territory?" What good reason might the author have for not giving a more definite solution to the problem with which the story begins?

Method

1. Where in the story does the author indicate that he is looking back at a childhood event?
2. What would you say is the author's attitude toward the grandmother? Find passages where he uses description, dialogue, or action to express this attitude.
3. How does the inner story concerning Pablo build suspense for the climax of the outer story concerning Tommy?
4. How does the story illustrate the conflict of man against society and man against himself?

Composition

1. Use "Enemy Territory" to reveal your understanding of the conflict of "man versus society." Choose either Pablo or Tommy as your main subject. Include in your essay (a) a summary of his character, (b) a description of the society he opposes, (c) an explanation of the causes of the conflict, and (d) your feelings on the outcome of the conflict.

2. Do you approve of the methods Pablo used to solve his problem? In a panel discussion, be prepared to examine (a) the methods he used, (b) the alternatives he had, (c) what you would have done. Be prepared to discuss whether you approve or disapprove of the methods the grandmother suggests that Tommy use to solve his problem.

William Faulkner

[1897–1962]

In November 1950 William Faulkner received the news that he had won the 1949 Nobel prize for literature. The next month he traveled to Stockholm to deliver his now-famous acceptance speech.

In it he spoke of the duties of a writer and affirmed that "man will not merely endure; he will prevail. He is immortal, not because he alone among creatures has an inexhaustible voice, but because he has a soul, a spirit capable of compassion and sacrifice and endurance. The poet's, the writer's, duty is to write about these things. It is his privilege to help man endure by lifting his heart, by reminding him of the courage and honor and hope and pride and compassion and pity and sacrifice which have been the glory of his past." *

Early in his writing career Faulkner decided that his native Mississippi would be the best source of his material. He was born in New Albany, Mississippi. In 1902 his family moved to Oxford, Mississippi, in the northwestern part of the state, where, except for a few short absences, he settled for most of his life. During World War I he went to Canada and enlisted in the Canadian Air Force. After the war he spent brief periods in New Orleans, New York, and Europe.

Following the Nobel prize recognition, he lectured at such places as the University of Virginia and, in 1955, Japan. Most of the time, however, he lived quietly in Oxford, producing, in depth and variety, novels and short stories about his land and its people.

Faulkner's subjects are the decadent Southern aristocracy (his own family were once wealthy landowners ruined by the Civil War), and the world of poor whites and Negroes. His style, with its lengthy sentences and vague time sequences, and his penetrating and conscientious exploration of character, often make difficult reading.

Like most of Faulkner's stories, "Two Soldiers" is set in Yoknapatawpha County,† his fictional name for Lafayette County, Mississippi. It illustrates on a small scale his compassion and his sensitivity to the feelings of a child.

† **Yoknapatawpha** (yök′nə·pä·tôw·fä).

Two Soldiers

Me and Pete would go down to Old Man Killegrew's and listen to his radio. We would wait until after supper, after dark, and we would stand outside Old Man Killegrew's parlor window, and we could hear it because Old Man Killegrew's wife was deaf, and so he run the radio as loud as it would run, and so me and Pete could hear it plain as Old Man Killegrew's wife could, I reckon, even standing outside with the window closed.

And that night I said, "What? Japanese? What's a pearl harbor?" and Pete said, "Hush."

And so we stood there, it was cold, listening to the fellow in the radio talking, only I couldn't make no heads nor tails out of it. Then the fellow said that would be all for a while, and me and Pete walked back up the road to home, and Pete told me what it was. Because he was nigh twenty and he had done finished the Consolidated [1] last June and he knowed a heap: about them Japanese dropping bombs on Pearl Harbor and that Pearl Harbor was across the water.

"Across what water?" I said. "Across that Government reservoy up at Oxford?"

"Naw," Pete said. "Across the big water. The Pacific Ocean."

We went home. Maw and pap was already asleep, and me and Pete laid in bed, and I still couldn't understand where it was, and Pete told me again—the Pacific Ocean.

"What's the matter with you?" Pete said. "You're going on nine years old. You been in school now ever since September. Ain't you learned nothing yet?"

"I reckon we ain't got as fer as the Pacific Ocean yet," I said.

We was still sowing the vetch [2] then that ought to been all finished by the fifteenth of November, because pap was still behind, just like he had been ever since me and Pete had knowed him. And we had firewood to git in, too, but every night me and Pete would go down to Old Man Killegrew's and stand outside his parlor window in the cold and listen to his radio; then we would come back home and lay

1. **Consolidated**: combined in one body or system. In some suburban and rural areas, one large high school, called a consolidated high school, which combines the facilities of several communities, serves the entire area.
2. **vetch** (vech): a plant of the pea and bean family used as a winter cover crop; some varieties are grown as food for cattle.

"Two Soldiers" from *Collected Stories of William Faulkner,* copyright 1942 by The Curtis Publishing Company. Reprinted by permission of Random House, Inc.

in bed and Pete would tell me what it was. That is, he would tell me for a while. Then he wouldn't tell me. It was like he didn't want to talk about it no more. He would tell me to shut up because he wanted to go to sleep, but he never wanted to go to sleep.

He would lay there, a heap stiller than if he was asleep, and it would be something, I could feel it coming out of him, like he was mad at me even, only I knowed he wasn't thinking about me, or like he was worried about something, and it wasn't that neither, because he never had nothing to worry about. He never got behind like pap, let alone stayed behind. Pap give him ten acres when he graduated from the Consolidated, and me and Pete both reckoned pap was durn glad to get shut of at least ten acres, less to have to worry about himself; and Pete had them ten acres all sowed to vetch and busted out and bedded for the winter, and so it wasn't that. But it was something. And still we would go down to Old Man Kille- grew's every night and listen to his radio, and they was at it in the Philippines now, but General MacArthur was holding um. Then we would come back home and lay in bed, and Pete wouldn't tell me nothing or talk at all. He would just lay there still as an ambush and when I would touch him, his side or his leg would feel hard and still as iron, until after a while I would go to sleep.

Then one night—it was the first time he had said nothing to me except to jump on me about not chopping enough wood at the wood tree where he was cutting—he said, "I got to go."

"Go where?" I said.

"To that war," Pete said.

"Before we even finish gettin' in the firewood?"

"Firewood, hell," Pete said.

"All right," I said. "When we going to start?"

But he wasn't even listening. He laid there, hard and still as iron in the dark. "I got to go," he said. "I jest ain't going to put up with no folks treating the Unity [3] States that way."

"Yes," I said. "Firewood or no firewood, I reckon we got to go."

This time he heard me. He laid still again, but it was a different kind of still.

"You?" he said. "To a war?"

"You'll whup the big uns and I'll whup the little uns," I said.

Then he told me I couldn't go. At first I thought he just never wanted me tagging after him, like he wouldn't leave me go with him

3. Unity (yōō·nī′tē).

when he went sparking [4] them girls of Tull's. Then he told me the
Army wouldn't leave me go because I was too little, and then I
knowed he really meant it and that I couldn't go nohow noways. And
somehow I hadn't believed until then that he was going himself, but
now I knowed he was and that he wasn't going to leave me go with
him a-tall.

"I'll chop the wood and tote the water for you-all then!" I said.
"You got to have wood and water!"

Anyway, he was listening to me now. He wasn't like iron now.

He turned onto his side and put his hand on my chest because it
was me that was laying straight and hard on my back now.

"No," he said. "You got to stay here and help pap."

"Help him what?" I said. "He ain't never caught up nohow. He
can't get no further behind. He can sholy take care of this little
shirttail of a farm while me and you are whupping them Japanese. I
got to go too. If you got to go, then so have I."

"No," Pete said. "Hush now. Hush." And he meant it, and I
knowed he did. Only I made sho from his own mouth. I quit.

"So I just can't go then," I said.

"No," Pete said. "You just can't go. You're too little, in the first
place, and in the second place—"

"All right," I said. "Then shut up and leave me go to sleep."

So he hushed then and laid back. And I laid there like I was
already asleep, and pretty soon he was asleep and I knowed it was
the wanting to go to the war that had worried him and kept him
awake, and now that he had decided to go, he wasn't worried any
more.

The next morning he told maw and pap. Maw was all right. She
cried.

"No," she said, crying, "I don't want him to go. I would rather go
myself in his place, if I could. I don't want to save the country. Them
Japanese could take it all and keep it, so long as they left me and
my family and my children alone. But I remember my brother Marsh
in that other war. He had to go to that one when he wasn't but
nineteen and our mother couldn't understand it then any more than
I can now. But she told Marsh if he had to go, he had to go. And so,
if Pete's got to go to this one, he's got to go to it. Jest don't ask me
to understand why."

But pap was the one. He was the feller. "To the war?" he said.

4. **sparking:** courting.

"Why I don't see a bit of use in that. You ain't old enough for the draft, and the country ain't being invaded. Our President in Washington, D.C., is watching the conditions and he will notify us. Besides, in that other war your ma just mentioned, I was drafted and sent clean to Texas and was held there nigh eight months until they finally quit fighting. It seems to me that that, along with your Uncle Marsh who received a actual wound on the battlefields of France, is enough for me and mine to have to do to protect the country, at least in my lifetime. Besides, what'll I do for help on the farm with you gone? It seems to me I'll get mighty far behind."

"You been behind as long as I can remember," Pete said. "Anyway I'm going. I got to."

"Of course he's got to go," I said. "Them Japanese—"

"You hush your mouth!" maw said, crying. "Nobody's talking to you! Go and get me a armful of wood! That's what you can do!"

So I got the wood. And all the next day, while me and Pete and pap was getting in as much wood as we could in that time because Pete said how pap's idea of plenty of wood was one more stick laying against the wall that maw ain't put on the fire yet, maw was getting Pete ready to go. She washed and mended his clothes and cooked him a shoe box of vittles. And that night me and Pete laid in the bed and listened to her packing his grip and crying, until after a while Pete got up in his nightshirt and went back there, and I could hear them talking, until at last maw said, "You ought to go, and so I want you to go. But I don't understand it, and I won't never, and so don't expect me to." And Pete come back and got into bed again and laid again still and hard as iron on his back, and then he said, and he wasn't talking to me, he wasn't talking to nobody: "I got to go. I just got to."

"Sho you got to," I said. "Them Japanese—" He turned over hard, he kind of surged over onto his side, looking at me in the dark.

"Anyway, you're all right," he said. "I expected to have more trouble with you than with all the rest of them put together."

"I reckon I can't help it neither," I said. "But maybe it will run a few years longer and I can get there. Maybe someday I will jest walk in on you."

"I hope not," Pete said. "Folks don't go to wars for fun. A man don't leave his maw crying just for fun."

"Then why are you going?" I said.

"I got to," he said. "I just got to. Now you go on to sleep. I got to ketch that early bus in the morning."

"All right," I said, "I hear tell Memphis is a big place. How will you find where the Army's at?"

"I'll ask somebody where to go to join it," Pete said. "Go on to sleep now."

"Is that what you'll ask for? Where to join the Army?" I said.

"Yes," Pete said. He turned onto his back again. "Shut up and go to sleep."

We went to sleep. The next morning we et breakfast by lamplight because the bus would pass at six o'clock. Maw wasn't crying now. She jest looked grim and busy, putting breakfast on the table while we et it. Then she finished packing Pete's grip, except he never wanted to take no grip to the war, but maw said decent folks never went nowhere, not even to a war, without a change of clothes and something to tote them in. She put in the shoe box a fried chicken and biscuits and she put the Bible in, too, and then it was time to go. We didn't know until then that maw wasn't going to the bus. She jest brought Pete's cap and overcoat, and still she didn't cry no more, she jest stood with her hands on Pete's shoulders and she didn't move, but somehow, and just holding Pete's shoulders, she looked as hard and fierce as when Pete had turned toward me in the bed last night and tole me that anyway I was all right.

"They could take the country and keep the country, as long as they never bothered me and mine," she said. Then she said, "Don't never forget who you are. You ain't rich and the rest of the world outside of Frenchman's Bend never heard of you. But your blood is good as any blood anywhere, and don't you never forget it."

Then she kissed him, and then we was out of the house, with pap toting Pete's grip whether Pete wanted him to or not. There wasn't no dawn even yet, not even after we had stood on the highway by the mailbox awhile. Then we seen the lights of the bus coming and I was watching the bus until it come up and Pete flagged it, and then, sho enough, there was daylight—it had started while I wasn't watching. And now me and Pete expected pap to say something else foolish, like he done before, about how Uncle Marsh getting wounded in France and that trip to Texas pap had taken in 1918 ought to be enough to save the Unity States in 1942, but he never. He done all right too. He jest said, "Good-by, son. Always remember what your ma tole you and write her whenever you find the time." Then he shaken Pete's hand, and Pete looked at me for a minute and put his hand on my head and rubbed my head durn nigh hard enough to wring my neck off and jumped into the bus, and the feller wound the door shut and the bus began to hum; then it was moving, humming and grinding and whining louder and louder; it was going fast, with two little red lights behind it that never seemed to get no littler, but jest seemed to be running together until pretty soon they would touch and just be one light. But they never did, and then the bus was gone, and even like it was, I could have pretty nigh busted out crying, nigh to nine years old and all.

Me and pap went back to the house. All that day we worked at the wood tree, and so I never had no good chance until about middle of the afternoon. Then I taken my slingshot and I would have liked to took all my bird eggs, too, because Pete had give me his collection and he holp me with mine, and he would like to git the box out and look at them as good as I would, even if he was nigh twenty years old. But the box was too big to tote a long ways and have to worry with, so I just taken the shikepoke [5] egg, because it was the best un, and wropped it up good into a matchbox and hid it and the slingshot under the corner of the barn. Then we et supper and went to bed, and I thought then how if I would 'a' had to stayed in that room and that bed like that even for one more night, I jest couldn't 'a' stood it. Then I could hear pap snoring, but I never heard no sound from maw, whether she was asleep or not, and I don't reckon she was. So I taken my shoes and drapped them out the window, and then I clumb out like I used to watch Pete do when he was still jest seventeen and pap wouldn't leave him out, and I put on my shoes and went to the barn and got the slingshot and the shikepoke egg and went to the highway.

It wasn't cold, it was just durn confounded dark, and that highway stretched on in front of me like, without nobody using it, it had stretched out half again as fer, just like a man does when he lays down, so that for a time it looked like full sun was going to ketch me before I had finished them twenty-two miles to Jefferson. But it didn't. Daybreak was jest starting when I walked up the hill into town. I could smell breakfast cooking in the cabins and I wished I had thought to brought me a cold biscuit, but that was too late now. And Pete had told me Memphis was a piece beyond Jefferson, but I never knowed it was no eighty miles. So I stood there on that empty square, with daylight coming and coming and the street lights still burning and that Law [6] looking down at me, and me still eighty miles from Memphis, and it had took me all night to walk jest twenty-two

5. shikepoke: a heron.
6. Law: *colloquial*, a policeman.

miles, and so, by the time I got to Memphis at that rate, Pete would
'a' done already started for Pearl Harbor.

"Where do you come from?" the Law said.

And I told him again, "I got to git to Memphis. My brother's
there."

"You mean you ain't got any folks around here?" the Law said.
"Nobody but that brother? What are you doing way off down here
and your brother in Memphis?"

And I told him again, "I got to git to Memphis. I ain't got no time
to waste talking about it and I ain't got time to walk it. I got to git
there today."

"Come on here," the Law said.

We went down another street. And there was the bus, jest like
when Pete got into it yestiddy morning, except there wasn't no lights
on it now and it was empty. There was a regular bus dee-po like a
railroad dee-po, with a ticket counter and a feller behind it, and the
Law said, "Set down over there," and I set down on the bench, and
the Law said, "I want to use your telephone," and he talked into
the telephone a minute and put it down and said to the feller behind
the ticket counter, "Keep your eye on him. I'll be back as soon as
Mrs. Habersham can arrange to get herself up and dressed." He went
out. I got up and went to the ticket counter.

"I want to go to Memphis," I said.

"You bet," the feller said. "You set down on the bench now.
Mr. Foote will be back in a minute."

"I don't know no Mr. Foote," I said. "I want to ride that bus to
Memphis."

"You got some money?" he said. "It'll cost you seventy-two cents."

I taken out the matchbox and unwropped the shikepoke egg. "I'll
swap you this for a ticket to Memphis," I said.

"What's that?" he said.

"It's a shikepoke egg," I said. "You never seen one before. It's
worth a dollar. I'll take seventy-two cents fer it."

"No," he said, "the fellers that own that bus insist on a cash basis.
If I started swapping tickets for bird eggs and livestock and such,
they would fire me. You go and set down on the bench now, like
Mr. Foote—"

I started for the door, but he caught me, he put one hand on the
ticket counter and jumped over it and caught up with me and
reached his hand out to ketch my shirt. I whupped out my pocketknife and snapped it open.

"You put a hand on me and I'll cut it off," I said.

I tried to dodge him and run at the door, but he could move quicker than any grown man I ever see, quick as Pete almost. He cut me off and stood with his back against the door and one foot raised a little, and there wasn't no other way to get out. "Get back on that bench and stay there," he said.

And there wasn't no other way out. And he stood there with his back against the door. So I went back to the bench. And then it seemed like to me that dee-po was full of folks. There was that Law again, and there was two ladies in fur coats and their faces already painted. But they still looked like they had got up in a hurry and they still never liked it, a old one and a young one, looking down at me.

"He hasn't got an overcoat!" the old one said. "How in the world did he ever get down here by himself?"

"I ask you," the Law said. "I couldn't get nothing out of him except his brother is in Memphis and he wants to get back up there."

"That's right," I said. "I got to git to Memphis today."

"Of course you must," the old one said. "Are you sure you can find your brother when you get to Memphis?"

"I reckon I can," I said. "I ain't got but one and I have knowed him all my life. I reckon I will know him again when I see him."

The old one looked at me. "Somehow he doesn't look like he lives in Memphis," she said.

"He probably don't," the Law said. "You can't tell though. He might live anywhere, overhalls or not. This day and time they get scattered overnight from he – – hope to breakfast; boys and girls, too, almost before they can walk good. He might have been in Missouri or Texas either yestiddy, for all we know. But he don't seem to have any doubt his brother is in Memphis. All I know to do is send him up there and leave him look."

"Yes," the old one said.

The young one set down on the bench by me and opened a hand satchel and taken out a artermatic writing pen and some papers.

"Now, honey," the old one said, "we're going to see that you find your brother, but we must have a case history for our files first. We want to know your name and your brother's name and where you were born and when your parents died."

"I don't need no case history neither," I said. "All I want is to git to Memphis. I got to git there today."

"You see?" the Law said. He said it almost like he enjoyed it. "That's what I told you."

"You're lucky, at that, Mrs. Habersham," the bus feller said. "I don't think he's got a gun on him, but he can open that knife da – – I mean, fast enough to suit any man."

But the old one just stood there looking at me.

"Well," she said. "Well. I really don't know what to do."

"I do," the bus feller said. "I'm going to give him a ticket out of my own pocket, as a measure of protecting the company against riot and bloodshed. And when Mr. Foote tells the city board about it, it will be a civic matter and they will not only reimburse me, they will give me a medal too. Hey, Mr. Foote?"

But nobody paid him no mind. The old one still stood looking down at me. She said, "Well," again. Then she taken a dollar from her purse and give it to the bus feller. "I suppose he will travel on a child's ticket, won't he?"

"Wellum," the bus feller said, "I just don't know what the regulations would be. Likely I will be fired for not crating him and marking the crate Poison. But I'll risk it."

Then they were gone. Then the Law come back with a sandwich and give it to me.

"You're sure you can find that brother?" he said.

"I ain't yet convinced why not," I said. "If I don't see Pete first, he'll see me. He knows me, too."

Then the Law went out for good, too, and I et the sandwich. Then more folks come in and bought tickets, and then the bus feller said it was time to go, and I got into the bus just like Pete done, and we was gone.

I seen all the towns. I seen all of them. When the bus got to going good, I found out I was jest about wore out for sleep. But there was too much I hadn't never saw before. We run out of Jefferson and run past fields and woods, then we would run into another town and out of that un and past fields and woods again, and then into another town with stores and gins [7] and water tanks, and we run along by the railroad for a spell and I seen the signal arm move, and then some more towns, and I was jest about plumb wore out for sleep, but I couldn't resk it. Then Memphis begun. It seemed like, to me, it went on for miles. We would pass a patch of stores and I would think that was sholy it and the bus would even stop. But it wouldn't be Memphis yet and we would go on again past water tanks and smokestacks on top of the mills, and if they was gins and sawmills, I never knowed

---

7. **gins:** machines for separating cotton lint from the seeds.

there was that many and I never seen any that big, and where they got enough cotton and logs to run um I don't know.

Then I seen Memphis. I knowed I was right this time. It was standing up into the air. It looked like about a dozen whole towns bigger than Jefferson was set up on one edge in a field, standing up into the air higher than ara [8] hill in all Yoknapatawpha County. Then we was in it, with the bus stopping ever' few feet, it seemed like to me, and cars rushing past on both sides of it and the streets crowded with folks from ever'where in town that day, until I didn't see how there could 'a' been nobody left in Mis'sippi a-tall to even sell me a bus ticket, let alone write out no case histories. Then the bus stopped. It was another bus dee-po, a heap bigger than the one in Jefferson. And I said, "All right. Where do folks join the Army?"

"What?" the bus feller said.

And I said it again, "Where do folks join the Army?"

"Oh," he said. Then he told me how to get there. I was afraid at first I wouldn't ketch on how to do in a town as big as Memphis. But I caught on all right. I never had to ask but twice more. Then I was there, and I was durn glad to git out of all them rushing cars and shoving folks and all that racket fer a spell, and I thought, it won't be long now, and I thought how if there was any kind of a crowd there that had done already joined the Army, too, Pete would likely see me before I seen him. And so I walked into the room. And Pete wasn't there.

He wasn't even there. There was a soldier with a big arrerhead on his sleeve, writing, and two fellers standing in front of him, and there was some more folks there, I reckon. It seems to me I remember some more folks there.

I went to the table where the soldier was writing, and I said, "Where's Pete?" and he looked up and I said, "My brother. Pete Grier. Where is he?"

"What?" the soldier said. "Who?"

And I told him again. "He joined the Army yestiddy. He's going to Pearl Harbor. So am I. I want to ketch him. Where you-all got him?" Now they were all looking at me, but I never paid them no mind. "Come on," I said. "Where is he?"

The soldier had quit writing. He had both hands spraddled out on the table. "Oh," he said. "You're going, too, hah?"

"Yes," I said. "They got to have wood and water. I can chop it and tote it. Come on. Where's Pete?"

8. **ara:** *dialect,* any.

The soldier stood up. "Who let you in here?" he said. "Go on. Beat it."

"Durn that," I said. "You tell me where Pete—"

I be dog if he couldn't move faster than the bus feller even. He never come over the table, he come around it, he was on me almost before I knowed it, so that I jest had time to jump back and whup out my pocketknife and snap it open and hit one lick, and he hollered and jumped back and grabbed one hand with the other and stood there cussing and hollering.

One of the other fellers grabbed me from behind, and I hit at him with the knife, but I couldn't reach him.

Then both of the fellers had me from behind, and then another soldier come out of a door at the back. He had on a belt with a britching strop [9] over one shoulder.

"What the hell is this?" he said.

"That little kid cut me with a knife!" the first soldier hollered. When he said that I tried to git at him again, but both them fellers was holding me, two against one, and the soldier with the britching strop said, "Here, here. Put your knife up, feller. None of us are armed. A man don't knife-fight folks that are barehanded." I could begin to hear him then. He sounded jest like Pete talked to me. "Let him go," he said. They let me go. "Now what's all the trouble about?" And I told him. "I see," he said. "And you come up to see if he was all right before he left."

"No," I said. "I come to—"

But he had already turned to where the first soldier was wropping a handkerchief around his hand.

"Have you got him?" he said. The first soldier went back to the table and looked at some papers.

"Here he is," he said. "He enlisted yestiddy. He's in a detachment leaving this morning for Little Rock." He had a watch stropped on his arm. He looked at it. "The train leaves in about fifty minutes. If I know country boys, they're probably all down there at the station right now."

"Get him up here," the one with the britching strop said. "Phone the station. Tell the porter to get him a cab. And you come with me," he said.

It was another office behind that un, with jest a table and some chairs. We set there while the soldier smoked, and it wasn't long; I

---

9. **britching strop:** the soldier's Sam Browne belt is mistaken for a breeching strap, that is, part of a harness.

knowed Pete's feet soon as I heard them. Then the first soldier opened the door and Pete come in. He never had no soldier clothes on. He looked jest like he did when he got on the bus yestiddy morning, except it seemed to me like it was at least a week, so much had happened, and I had done had to do so much traveling. He come in and there he was, looking at me like he hadn't never left home, except that here we was in Memphis, on the way to Pearl Harbor.

"What in durnation are you doing here?" he said.

And I told him, "You got to have wood and water to cook with. I can chop it and tote it for you-all."

"No," Pete said. "You're going back home."

"No, Pete," I said. "I got to go too. I got to. It hurts my heart, Pete."

"No," Pete said. He looked at the soldier. "I jest don't know what could have happened to him, lootenant," he said. "He never drawed a knife on anybody before in his life."

He looked at me. "What did you do it for?"

"I don't know," I said. "I jest had to. I jest had to git here. I jest had to find you."

"Well, don't you never do it again, you hear?" Pete said. "You put that knife in your pocket and you keep it there. If I ever again hear of you drawing it on anybody, I'm coming back from wherever I am at and whup the fire out of you. You hear me?"

"I would pure cut a throat if it would bring you back to stay," I said. "Pete," I said. "Pete."

"No," Pete said. Now his voice wasn't hard and quick no more, it was almost quiet, and I knowed now I wouldn't never change him. "You must go home. You must look after maw, and I am depending on you to look after my ten acres. I want you to go back home. Today. Do you hear?"

"I hear," I said.

"Can he get back home by himself?" the soldier said.

"He come up here by himself," Pete said.

"I can get back, I reckon," I said. "I don't live in but one place. I don't reckon it's moved."

Pete taken a dollar out of his pocket and give it to me. "That'll buy your bus ticket right to our mailbox," he said. "I want you to mind the lootenant. He'll send you to the bus. And you go back home and you take care of maw and look after my ten acres and keep that durn knife in your pocket. You hear me?"

"Yes, Pete," I said.

"All right," Pete said. "Now I got to go." He put his hand on my head again. But this time he never wrung my neck. He just laid his hand on my head a minute. And then I be dog if he didn't lean down and kiss me, and I heard his feet and then the door, and I never looked up and that was all, me setting there, rubbing the place where Pete kissed me and the soldier throwed back in his chair, looking out the window and coughing. He reached into his pocket and handed something to me without looking around. It was a piece of chewing gum.

"Much obliged," I said. "Well, I reckon I might as well start back. I got a right fer piece to go."

"Wait," the soldier said. Then he telephoned again and I said again I better start back, and he said again, "Wait. Remember what Pete told you."

So we waited, and then another lady come in, old, too, in a fur coat, too, but she smelled all right, she never had no artermatic writing pen nor no case history neither. She come in and the soldier got up, and she looked around quick until she saw me, and come and put her hand on my shoulder light and quick and easy as maw herself might 'a' done it.

"Come on," she said. "Let's go home to dinner."

"Nome," [10] I said. "I got to ketch the bus to Jefferson."

"I know. There's plenty of time. We'll go home and eat dinner first."

She had a car. And now we was right down in the middle of all them other cars. We was almost under the busses, and all them crowds of people on the street close enough to where I could have talked to them if I had knowed who they was. After a while she stopped the car. "Here we are," she said, and I looked at it, and if all that was her house, she sho had a big family. But all of it wasn't. We crossed a hall with trees growing in it and went into a little room without nothing in it but a Negro dressed up in a uniform a heap shinier than them soldiers had, and the Negro shut the door, and then I hollered, "Look out!" and grabbed, but it was all right; that whole little room jest went right on up and stopped and the door opened and we was in another hall, and the lady unlocked a door and we went in, and there was another soldier, an old feller, with a britching strop, too, and a silver-colored bird on each shoulder.

"Here we are," the lady said. "This is Colonel McKellogg. Now, what would you like for dinner?"

10. **"Nome"**: contraction of "no ma'am."

"I reckon I'll jest have some ham and eggs and coffee," I said.

She had done started to pick up the telephone. She stopped. "Coffee?" she said. "When did you start drinking coffee?"

"I don't know," I said. "I reckon it was before I could remember."

"You're about eight, aren't you?" she said.

"Nome," I said. "I'm eight and ten months. Going on eleven months."

She telephoned then. Then we set there and I told them how Pete had jest left that morning for Pearl Harbor and I had aimed to go with him, but I would have to go back home to take care of maw and look after Pete's ten acres, and she said how they had a little boy about my size, too, in a school in the East. Then a Negro, another one, in a short kind of shirttail coat, rolled a kind of wheelbarrer in. It had my ham and eggs and a glass of milk and a piece of pie, too, and I thought I was hungry. But when I taken the first bite I found out I couldn't swallow it, and I got up quick.

"I got to go," I said.

"Wait," she said.

"I got to go," I said.

"Just a minute," she said. "I've already telephoned for the car. It won't be but a minute now. Can't you drink the milk even? Or maybe some of your coffee?"

"Nome," I said. "I ain't hungry. I'll eat when I git home." Then the telephone rung. She never even answered it.

"There," she said. "There's the car." And we went back down in that 'ere little moving room with the dressed-up Negro. This time it was a big car with a soldier driving it. I got into the front with him. She give the soldier a dollar. "He might get hungry," she said. "Try to find a decent place for him."

"OK, Mrs. McKellogg," the soldier said.

Then we was gone again. And now I could see Memphis good, bright in the sunshine, while we was swinging around it. And the first thing I knowed, we was back on the same highway the bus run on this morning—the patches of stores and them big gins and sawmills, and Memphis running on for miles, it seemed like to me, before it begun to give out. Then we was running again between the fields and woods, running fast now, and except for that soldier, it was like I hadn't never been to Memphis a-tall. We was going fast now. At this rate, before I knowed it we would be home again, and I thought about me riding up to Frenchman's Bend in this big car with a soldier running it, and all of a sudden I begun to cry. I never knowed I was fixing to, and I couldn't stop it. I set there by that soldier, crying. We was going fast.

Meaning

1. How would you describe Pete, his little brother, his father, and his mother? What does the war mean to each of them? Select passages from the story to illustrate your judgments.
2. In how many ways did the different members of the family show love by accepting one another just as they were?
3. How does Pete finally convince his little brother that he has to go home? What difference was there in the way Pete said good-by at home and in Memphis? What was the reason for this difference?
4. Mention the various conflicts the little boy has faced during the story. Why does he finally cry?
5. In what sense are there *two* soldiers in this story?

Method

1. What might be the author's reason for choosing to have the little boy narrate the story of his brother's departure for the war?
2. How does the setting of the story assist in creating characterization? If the people in this story were placed in a different setting—for instance, in a large city—could the same basic plot be used? Explain your answer.
3. How would you describe the tone of this story—the author's attitude toward his subject?
4. How does Faulkner manage to inject humor into this story? Give examples.
5. How are the differences in speech between the boy and Mrs. McKellogg used to characterize them? Why is Pete's speech different from his brother's?

Composition

Pretend you are the boy in the story and that six months have gone by. Write a letter to Pete, telling him the news about school, the town, and, of course, the farm and the parents. Try to imitate the boy's speech and spelling.

Borden Deal

Like "Boy" Sword, the twelve-year-old hero of his novel *The Least One* (1967), Borden Deal knew the difficulties of farm life during the lean years of the 1930's Depression. He was born in Pontotoc, Mississippi, in 1922, to a family of "cotton farmers and storekeepers." In his youth he worked at various jobs around the country—for a circus, the Civilian Conservation Corps, and the Labor Department in Washington.

After serving in the Navy during World War II, he attended the University of Alabama, graduating in 1949. His short story "Exodus" was published in 1948 while he was still in college. Since then he has written more than a hundred short stories and several novels. *Walk Through My Valley* (1956), *Dunbar's Cove* (1957), and *The Insolent Breed* (1959) are regional novels about farm communities. Deal now lives with his wife, Babs, also a writer, and their three children in Sarasota, Florida.

The following short story was a selection in *The Best American Short Stories, 1962.*

Antaeus *

This was during the wartime, when lots of people were coming North for jobs in factories and war industries, when people moved around a lot more than they do now, and sometimes kids were thrown into new groups and new lives that were completely different from anything they had ever known before. I remember this one kid, T. J. his name was, from somewhere down South, whose family moved into our building during that time. They'd come North with everything they owned piled into the back seat of an old-model sedan that you wouldn't expect could make the trip, with T. J. and his three younger sisters riding shakily on top of the load of junk.

---

* **Antaeus:** (an·tē'əs) in Greek mythology, a giant who challenged his enemies to wrestling matches, with the odds always in his favor because each fall to earth renewed his tremendous strength and led to his victory. Antaeus was killed by Hercules, who held him aloft, detached from mother Earth, and strangled him.

"Antaeus" by Borden Deal from *Southwest Review*, Spring 1961, copyright © 1961 by Southern Methodist University Press. Reprinted by permission of the publisher and Paul R. Reynolds Inc., 599 Fifth Avenue, New York, New York 10017.

Our building was just like all the others there, with families crowded into a few rooms, and I guess there were twenty-five or thirty kids about my age in that one building. Of course, there were a few of us who formed a gang and ran together all the time after school, and I was the one who brought T. J. in and started the whole thing.

The building right next door to us was a factory where they made walking dolls. It was a low building with a flat, tarred roof that had a parapet [1] all around it about head-high, and we'd found out a long time before that no one, not even the watchman, paid any attention to the roof because it was higher than any of the other buildings around. So my gang used the roof as a headquarters. We could get up there by crossing over to the fire escape from our own roof on a plank and then going on up. It was a secret place for us, where nobody else could go without our permission.

I remember the day I first took T. J. up there to meet the gang. He was a stocky, robust kid with a shock [2] of white hair, nothing sissy about him except his voice; he talked in this slow, gentle voice like you never heard before. He talked different from any of us and you noticed it right away. But I liked him anyway, so I told him to come on up.

We climbed up over the parapet and dropped down on the roof. The rest of the gang were already there.

"Hi," I said. I jerked my thumb at T. J. "He just moved into the building yesterday."

He just stood there, not scared or anything, just looking, like the first time you see somebody you're not sure you're going to like.

"Hi," Blackie said. "Where are you from?"

"Marion County," T. J. said.

We laughed. "Marion County?" I said. "Where's that?"

He looked at me for a moment like I was a stranger, too. "It's in Alabama," he said, like I ought to know where it was.

"What's your name?" Charley said.

"T. J.," he said, looking back at him. He had pale blue eyes that looked washed-out, but he looked directly at Charley, waiting for his reaction. He'll be all right, I thought. No sissy in him, except that voice. Who ever talked like that?

1. **parapet** (par′ə·pit): a low wall or protecting railing on the edge of a platform, roof, or bridge.
2. **shock**: a thick bushy mass.

"T. J.," Blackie said. "That's just initials. What's your real name? Nobody in the world has just initials."

"I do," he said. "And they're T. J. That's all the name I got."

His voice was resolute with the knowledge of his rightness, and for a moment no one had anything to say. T. J. looked around at the rooftop and down at the black tar under his feet. "Down yonder where I come from," he said, "we played out in the woods. Don't you-all have no woods around here?"

"Naw," Blackie said. "There's the park a few blocks over, but it's full of kids and cops and old women. You can't do a thing."

T. J. kept looking at the tar under his feet. "You mean you ain't got no fields to raise nothing in?—no watermelons or nothing?"

"Naw," I said scornfully. "What do you want to grow something for? The folks can buy everything they need at the store."

He looked at me again with that strange, unknowing look. "In Marion County," he said, "I had my own acre of cotton and my own acre of corn. It was mine to plant and make ever' year."

He sounded like it was something to be proud of, and in some obscure way it made the rest of us angry. Blackie said, "Who'd want to have their own acre of cotton and corn? That's just work. What can you do with an acre of cotton and corn?"

T. J. looked at him. "Well, you get part of the bale offen your acre," he said seriously. "And I fed my acre of corn to my calf."

We didn't really know what he was talking about, so we were more puzzled than angry; otherwise, I guess, we'd have chased him off the roof and wouldn't let him be part of our gang. But he was strange and different, and we were all attracted by his stolid [3] sense of rightness and belonging, maybe by the strange softness of his voice contrasting our own tones of speech into harshness.

He moved his foot against the black tar. "We could make our own field right here," he said softly, thoughtfully. "Come spring we could raise us what we want to—watermelons and garden truck and no telling what all."

"You'd have to be a good farmer to make these tar roofs grow any watermelons," I said. We all laughed.

But T. J. looked serious. "We could haul us some dirt up here," he said. "And spread it out even and water it, and before you know it, we'd have us a crop in here." He looked at us intently. "Wouldn't that be fun?"

"They wouldn't let us," Blackie said quickly.

3. **stolid** (stol'id): unemotional; calm.

"I thought you said this was you-all's roof," T. J. said to me. "That you-all could do anything you wanted to up here."

"They've never bothered us," I said. I felt the idea beginning to catch fire in me. It was a big idea, and it took a while for it to sink in; but the more I thought about it, the better I liked it. "Say," I said to the gang. "He might have something there. Just make us a regular roof garden, with flowers and grass and trees and everything. And all ours, too," I said. "We wouldn't let anybody up here except the ones we wanted to."

"It'd take a while to grow trees," T. J. said quickly, but we weren't paying any attention to him. They were all talking about it suddenly, all excited with the idea after I'd put it in a way they could catch hold of it. Only rich people had roof gardens, we knew, and the idea of our own private domain excited them.

"We could bring it up in sacks and boxes," Blackie said. "We'd have to do it while the folks weren't paying any attention to us, for we'd have to come up to the roof of our building and then cross over with it."

"Where could we get the dirt?" somebody said worriedly.

"Out of those vacant lots over close to school," Blackie said. "No-body'd notice if we scraped it up."

I slapped T. J. on the shoulder. "Man, you had a wonderful idea," I said, and everybody grinned at him, remembering that he had started it. "Our own private roof garden."

He grinned back. "It'll be ourn," he said. "All ourn." Then he looked thoughtful again. "Maybe I can lay my hands on some cotton seed, too. You think we could raise us some cotton?"

We'd started big projects before at one time or another, like any gang of kids, but they'd always petered out for lack of organization and direction. But this one didn't; somehow or other T. J. kept it going all through the winter months. He kept talking about the watermelons and the cotton we'd raise, come spring, and when even that wouldn't work, he'd switch around to my idea of flowers and grass and trees, though he was always honest enough to add that it'd take a while to get any trees started. He always had it on his mind and he'd mention it in school, getting them lined up to carry dirt that afternoon, saying in a casual way that he reckoned a few more weeks ought to see the job through.

Our little area of private earth grew slowly. T. J. was smart enough to start in one corner of the building, heaping up the carried earth two or three feet thick so that we had an immediate result to look at, to contemplate with awe. Some of the evenings T. J. alone was carrying earth up to the building, the rest of the gang distracted by other enterprises or interests, but T. J. kept plugging along on his own, and eventually we'd all come back to him again and then our own little acre would grow more rapidly.

He was careful about the kind of dirt he'd let us carry up there, and more than once he dumped a sandy load over the parapet into the areaway below because it wasn't good enough. He found out the kinds of earth in all the vacant lots for blocks around. He'd pick it up and feel it and smell it, frozen though it was sometimes, and then he'd say it was good growing soil or it wasn't worth anything, and we'd have to go on somewhere else.

Thinking about it now, I don't see how he kept us at it. It was hard work, lugging paper sacks and boxes of dirt all the way up the stairs of our own building, keeping out of the way of the grownups so they wouldn't catch on to what we were doing. They probably wouldn't have cared, for they didn't pay much attention to us, but we wanted to keep it secret anyway. Then we had to go through the trap door to our roof, teeter over a plank to the fire escape, then climb two or three stories to the parapet and drop down onto the roof. All that for a small pile of earth that sometimes didn't seem worth the effort. But T. J. kept the vision bright within us, his words shrewd and calculated toward the fulfillment of his dream; and he worked harder than any of us. He seemed driven toward a goal that we couldn't see, a particular point in time that would be definitely marked by signs and wonders that only he could see.

The laborious earth just lay there during the cold months, inert and lifeless, the clods lumpy and cold under our feet when we walked over it. But one day it rained, and afterward there was a softness in the air, and the earth was live and giving again with moisture and warmth.

That evening T. J. smelled the air, his nostrils dilating with the odor of the earth under his feet. "It's spring," he said, and there was a gladness rising in his voice that filled us all with the same feeling. "It's mighty late for it, but it's spring. I'd just about decided it wasn't never gonna get here at all."

We were all sniffing at the air, too, trying to smell it the way that T. J. did, and I can still remember the sweet odor of the earth under our feet. It was the first time in my life that spring and spring earth had meant anything to me. I looked at T. J. then, knowing in a faint way the hunger within him through the toilsome winter months, knowing the dream that lay behind his plan. He was a new Antaeus, preparing his own bed of strength.

"Planting time," he said. "We'll have to find us some seed."

"What do we do?" Blackie said. "How do we do it?"

"First we'll have to break up the clods," T. J. said. "That won't be hard to do. Then we plant the seeds, and after a while they come up. Then you got you a crop." He frowned. "But you ain't got it raised yet. You got to tend it and hoe it and take care of it, and all the time it's growing and growing, while you're awake and while you're asleep. Then you lay it by when it's growed and let it ripen, and then you got you a crop."

"There's those wholesale seed houses over on Sixth," I said. "We could probably swipe some grass seed over there."

T. J. looked at the earth. "You-all seem mighty set on raising some grass," he said. "I ain't never put no effort into that. I spent all my life trying not to raise grass."

"But it's pretty," Blackie said. "We could play on it and take sunbaths on it. Like having our own lawn. Lots of people got lawns."

"Well," T. J. said. He looked at the rest of us, hesitant for the first time. He kept on looking at us for a moment. "I did have it in mind to raise some corn and vegetables. But we'll plant grass."

He was smart. He knew where to give in. And I don't suppose it made any difference to him, really. He just wanted to grow something, even if it was grass.

"Of course," he said, "I do think we ought to plant a row of watermelons. They'd be mighty nice to eat while we was a-laying on that grass."

We all laughed. "All right," I said. "We'll plant us a row of watermelons."

Things went very quickly then. Perhaps half the roof was covered with the earth, the half that wasn't broken by ventilators, and we swiped pocketfuls of grass seed from the open bins in the wholesale seed house, mingling among the buyers on Saturdays and during the school lunch hour. T. J. showed us how to prepare the earth, breaking up the clods and smoothing it and sowing the grass seed. It looked rich and black now with moisture, receiving of the seed, and it seemed that the grass sprang up overnight, pale green in the early spring.

We couldn't keep from looking at it, unable to believe that we had created this delicate growth. We looked at T. J. with understanding now, knowing the fulfillment of the plan he had carried along within his mind. We had worked without full understanding of the task, but he had known all the time.

We found that we couldn't walk or play on the delicate blades, as we had expected to, but we didn't mind. It was enough just to look at it, to realize that it was the work of our own hands, and each evening the whole gang was there, trying to measure the growth that had been achieved that day.

One time a foot was placed on the plot of ground, one time only, Blackie stepping onto it with sudden bravado.[4] Then he looked at the crushed blades and there was shame in his face. He did not do it again. This was his grass, too, and not to be desecrated.[5] No one said anything, for it was not necessary.

T. J. had reserved a small section for watermelons, and he was still trying to find some seed for it. The wholesale house didn't have any watermelon seeds, and we didn't know where we could lay our hands on them. T. J. shaped the earth into mounds, ready to receive them, three mounds lying in a straight line along the edge of the grass plot.

We had just about decided that we'd have to buy the seeds if we were to get them. It was a violation of our principles, but we were anxious to get the watermelons started. Somewhere or other, T. J. got his hands on a seed catalog and brought it one evening to our roof garden.

"We can order them now," he said, showing us the catalog. "Look!"

We all crowded around, looking at the fat, green watermelons pictured in full color on the pages. Some of them were split open, showing the red, tempting meat, making our mouths water.

"Now we got to scrape up some seed money," T. J. said, looking at us. "I got a quarter. How much you-all got?"

We made up a couple of dollars among us and T. J. nodded his head. "That'll be more than enough. Now we got to decide what kind to get. I think them Kleckley Sweets. What do you-all think?"

He was going into esoteric [6] matters beyond our reach. We hadn't even known there were different kinds of melons. So we just nodded our heads and agreed that yes, we thought the Kleckley Sweets too.

4. **bravado** (brə·vä′dō) : pretense of bravery.
5. **desecrated** (des′ə·krāt·ed) : treated irreverently.
6. **esoteric** (es′ə·ter′ik) : mysterious; understood only by a small group possessing special knowledge.

"I'll order them tonight," T. J. said. "We ought to have them in a few days."

"What are you boys doing up here?" an adult voice said behind us.

It startled us, for no one had ever come up here before in all the time we had been using the roof of the factory. We jerked around and saw three men standing near the trap door at the other end of the roof. They weren't policemen or night watchmen, but three men in plump business suits, looking at us. They walked toward us.

"What are you boys doing up here?" the one in the middle said again.

We stood still, guilt heavy among us, levied [7] by the tone of voice, and looked at the three strangers.

The men stared at the grass flourishing behind us. "What's this?" the man said. "How did this get up here?"

"Sure is growing good, ain't it?" T. J. said conversationally. "We planted it."

The men kept looking at the grass as if they didn't believe it. It was a thick carpet over the earth now, a patch of deep greenness startling in the sterile industrial surroundings.

"Yes, sir," T. J. said proudly. "We toted that earth up here and planted that grass." He fluttered the seed catalog. "And we're just fixing to plant us some watermelon."

The man looked at him then, his eyes strange and faraway. "What do you mean, putting this on the roof of my building?" he said. "Do you want to go to jail?"

T. J. looked shaken. The rest of us were silent, frightened by the authority of his voice. We had grown up aware of adult authority, of policemen and night watchmen and teachers, and this man sounded like all the others. But it was a new thing to T. J.

"Well, you wasn't using the roof," T. J. said. He paused a moment and added shrewdly, "So we just thought to pretty it up a little bit."

"And sag it so I'd have to rebuild it," the man said sharply. He started turning away, saying to another man beside him, "See that all that junk is shoveled off by tomorrow."

"Yes, sir," the man said.

T. J. started forward. "You can't do that," he said. "We toted it up here, and it's our earth. We planted it and raised it and toted it up here."

7. **levied** (lev′ēd): To levy is to impose or collect a tax or a fine by authority or force; here, guilt is established or levied by the man's tone of voice.

The man stared at him coldly. "But it's my building," he said. "It's to be shoveled off tomorrow."

"It's our earth," T. J. said desperately. "You ain't got no right!"

The men walked on without listening and descended clumsily through the trapdoor. T. J. stood looking after them, his body tense with anger, until they had disappeared. They wouldn't even argue with him, wouldn't let him defend his earth-rights.

He turned to us. "We won't let 'em do it," he said fiercely. "We'll stay up here all day tomorrow and the day after that, and we won't let 'em do it."

We just looked at him. We knew there was no stopping it.

He saw it in our faces, and his face wavered for a moment before he gripped it into determination. "They ain't got no right," he said. "It's our earth. It's our land. Can't nobody touch a man's own land."

We kept looking at him, listening to the words but knowing that it was no use. The adult world had descended on us even in our richest dream, and we knew there was no calculating the adult world, no fighting it, no winning against it.

We started moving slowly toward the parapet and the fire escape, avoiding a last look at the green beauty of the earth that T. J. had planted for us, had planted deeply in our minds as well as in our experience. We filed slowly over the edge and down the steps to the plank, T. J. coming last, and all of us could feel the weight of his grief behind us.

"Wait a minute," he said suddenly, his voice harsh with the effort of calling.

We stopped and turned, held by the tone of his voice, and looked up at him standing above us on the fire escape.

"We can't stop them?" he said, looking down at us, his face strange in the dusky light. "There ain't no way to stop 'em?"

"No," Blackie said with finality. "They own the building."

We stood still for a moment, looking up at T. J., caught into inaction by the decision working in his face. He stared back at us, and his face was pale and mean in the poor light, with a bald naked-ness in his skin like cripples have sometimes.

"They ain't gonna touch my earth," he said fiercely. "They ain't gonna lay a hand on it! Come on."

He turned around and started up the fire escape again, almost running against the effort of climbing. We followed more slowly, not knowing what he intended. By the time we reached him, he had seized a board and thrust it into the soil, scooping it up and flinging it over the parapet into the areaway below. He straightened and looked at us.

"They can't touch it," he said. "I won't let 'em lay a dirty hand on it!"

We saw it then. He stooped to his labor again and we followed, the gusts of his anger moving in frenzied labor among us as we scattered along the edge of earth, scooping it and throwing it over the parapet, destroying with anger the growth we had nurtured with such tender care. The soil carried so laboriously upward to the light and the sun cascaded swiftly into the dark areaway, the green blades of grass crumpled and twisted in the falling.

It took less time than you would think; the task of destruction is infinitely easier than that of creation. We stopped at the end, leaving only a scattering of loose soil, and when it was finally over, a stillness stood among the group and over the factory building. We looked down at the bare sterility of black tar, felt the harsh texture of it under the soles of our shoes, and the anger had gone out of us, leaving only a sore aching in our minds like overstretched muscles.

T. J. stood for a moment, his breathing slowing from anger and effort, caught into the same contemplation of destruction as all of us. He stooped slowly, finally, and picked up a lonely blade of grass left trampled under our feet and put it between his teeth, tasting it, sucking the greenness out of it into his mouth. Then he started walking toward the fire escape, moving before any of us were ready to move, and disappeared over the edge.

We followed him, but he was already halfway down to the ground, going on past the board where we crossed over, climbing down into the areaway. We saw the last section swing down with his weight, and then he stood on the concrete below us, looking at the small pile of anonymous earth scattered by our throwing. Then he walked across the place where we could see him and disappeared toward the street without glancing back, without looking up to see us watching him.

They did not find him for two weeks.

Then the Nashville police caught him just outside the Nashville freight yards. He was walking along the railroad track, still heading south, still heading home.

As for us, who had no remembered home to call us, none of us ever again climbed the escapeway to the roof.

Meaning and Method

1. What is the purpose of the opening paragraph?
2. Why does the author have a city boy narrate the story?
3. The city children wanted to plant grass, flowers, and trees, whereas T. J. wanted cotton and watermelon. How do these preferences reflect their lives up to this point?
4. To the narrator the garden represents a new concept of spring. For T. J. the garden is "a bed of strength." Explain the difference in light of what you know of T. J.'s background and the myth of Antaeus. What is the theme of the story?
5. Only a person with leadership ability could accomplish the seemingly impossible task of creating a garden on a tar roof. List what you think are the qualities of an ideal leader and show how T. J. measures up to them. Refer to specific incidents in the story.
6. This story illustrates the vast difference between looking and seeing. How was T. J. able to teach his young friends to *see* the possibilities of his dream? Do the three men ever *see* the roof garden? Explain.
7. What two reactions to the adult world are shown by T. J. and by the other boys when they are ordered off the roof? Why must T. J. destroy the garden?
8. One of the most dramatic scenes in the story takes place when T. J. confronts the three men. Borden Deal could simply have stated that T. J. moved from friendliness to anger. What does he do instead to make this a tense encounter?

Language: Antonyms

The antonym (from Greek *anti*, against, and *onyma*, name) of a word is a word with the opposite meaning. For example, *dark-light*. But note that light can also be an antonym for *heavy*. Some antonyms are formed by using a prefix, as in *active-inactive*, or *natural-unnatural*. For what word is each of the following an antonym?

1. coming
2. different
3. started
4. gentle
5. unknowing
6. gladness

Composition and Discussion

1. The country-born T. J. finds it hard to believe that the "gang" has no woods to play in. Imagine the reverse situation in which a city-born child moves to the country. Write an essay explaining the difficulties he might encounter in adjusting to country life.
2. If you were T. J., how would you answer someone who asked you, "What do you want to grow something for? The folks can buy everything they need at the store." Give some good reasons to support your position. Skim through the story to get a basis for your ideas.

Arthur C. Clarke

Arthur Charles Clarke has been called the "colossus of science fiction." His fiction and nonfiction works number over forty volumes and have sold about five million copies in some thirty languages. His subjects range from electronics and astronomy to space travel and underwater exploration.

One of the many reasons for his large audience is that he reduces complicated technical subjects to layman's terms. At the same time, the accuracy of the scientific facts that he uses in his imaginative stories gives them an air of credibility. His works often have a serious message, pointing the way to the need for more advanced scientific explorations and cautioning man to use his inventions wisely. In this he follows in the tradition of H. G. Wells, who also used science fiction as the vehicle for philosophical ideas.

Clarke was born in Minehead, an English coastal town, in 1917. He became interested in science at an early age, and at thirteen constructed his first telescope from an old lens and a cardboard tube. He attended Huish's Grammar School in Taunton, England, where a teacher encouraged him to write for the school magazine.

In 1936, lacking the money for college, he became an auditor for the British Civil Service. This job, with its short hours and long vacations, enabled him to participate in the activities of the British Interplanetary Society, of which he was subsequently twice chairman. In 1941 he joined the Royal Air Force, where he became a radar instructor and later a technical officer in charge of the first experimental ground-controlled approach unit.

While in the service, Clarke wrote science-fiction stories and articles on electronics. With an ex-serviceman's grant, he entered Kings College, London University, graduating in 1948 with top honors in mathematics and physics. He then began a career as an assistant editor of a scientific journal. By 1951, however, he had found it more profitable to become a full-time author.

Since the mid-1950's, his interest in underwater exploration has taken him to Australia and to Ceylon, where he now makes his home. Among the books which have evolved from his skin-diving adventures are *The Coast of Coral,* a description of his participation in an underwater expedition to the Great Barrier Reef of Australia; and *The Treasure of the Great Reef,* an account of a search made in 1963 for a sunken ship off the coast of Ceylon.

Two of his nonfiction works dealing with space travel are *Interplanetary Flight,* an introduction to astronautics; and *Going Into Space,* an account of the possibilities of travel beyond the earth. He has also written two novels: *Earthlight,* which mixes science fiction and espionage; and *Islands in the Sky,* about a boy who wins a trip to a space station.

During the past thirty years he has written nearly a hundred short stories. His favorite stories have been collected in *The Nine Billion Names of God,* in which "Dog Star," written in the early 1960's, appears.

Dog Star *

When I heard Laika's [1] frantic barking, my first reaction was one of annoyance. I turned over in my bunk and murmured sleepily, "Shut up." That dreamy interlude lasted only a fraction of a second; then consciousness returned—and with it, fear. Fear of loneliness and fear of madness.

For a moment I dared not open my eyes; I was afraid of what I might see. Reason told me that no dog had ever set foot upon this world, that Laika was separated from me by a quarter of a million miles of space—and, far more irrevocably,[2] five years of time.

"You've been dreaming," I told myself angrily. "Stop being a fool —open your eyes! You won't see anything except the glow of the wall paint."

That was right, of course. The tiny cabin was empty, the door tightly closed. I was alone with my memories, overwhelmed by the transcendental [3] sadness that often comes when some bright dream fades into drab reality. The sense of loss was so desolating that I longed to return to sleep. It was well that I failed to do so, for at that

---

* **Dog Star:** another name for the star Sirius (sir′ē·əs), the brightest star in the heavens, located in the constellation Canis Major (the Great Dog).
1. **Laika's** (lī′kəs): Laïka is the name of the dog in this story. A Laika is also a breed of dog. In November 1957, a Laika was sent aloft in Russia's second earth satellite, Sputnik II.
2. **irrevocably** (i·rev′ə·kə·blē): unalterably; without possibility of change.
3. **transcendental** (tran′sen·den′tal): profound, intuitive, beyond human understanding.

moment sleep would have been death. But I did not know this for another five seconds, and during that eternity I was back on Earth, seeking what comfort I could from the past.

No one ever discovered Laika's origin, though the Observatory staff made a few inquiries and I inserted several advertisements in the Pasadena [4] newspapers. I found her, a lost and lonely ball of fluff, huddled by the roadside one summer evening when I was driving up to Palomar.[5] Though I have never liked dogs, or indeed any animals, it was impossible to leave this helpless little creature to the mercy of the passing cars. With some qualms, wishing that I had a pair of gloves, I picked her up and dumped her in the baggage compartment. I was not going to hazard the upholstery of my new '92 Vik, and felt that she could do little damage there. In this, I was not altogether correct.

When I had parked the car at the Monastery—the astronomers' residential quarters, where I'd be living for the next week—I inspected my find without much enthusiasm. At that stage, I had intended to hand the puppy over to the janitor; but then it whimpered and opened its eyes. There was such an expression of helpless trust in them that—well, I changed my mind.

Sometimes I regretted that decision, though never for long. I had no idea how much trouble a growing dog could cause, deliberately and otherwise. My cleaning and repair bills soared; I could never be sure of finding an unravaged pair of socks or an unchewed copy of the *Astrophysical* [6] *Journal*. But eventually Laika was both house-trained and Observatory-trained: she must have been the only dog ever to be allowed inside the two-hundred-inch dome. She would lie there quietly in the shadows for hours, while I was up in the cage making adjustments, quite content if she could hear my voice from time to time. The other astronomers became equally fond of her (it was old Dr. Anderson who suggested her name), but from the beginning she was my dog, and would obey no one else. Not that she would always obey me.

4. **Pasadena** (pas′ə·dē·nə): a city in southern California near Los Angeles.
5. **Palomar** (pal′ə·mär): Mount Palomar, an astronomical observatory near San Diego, California, having a 200-inch reflecting telescope, at present the largest in existence. Powerful telescopes are used in *astronomy*, the scientific study of the motions, distributions and arrangements, and make-up of the sun, the moon, the planets, the stars, and the earth. Astronomy comes from two Greek words, *astron* (star), and *nemein* (to distribute, arrange).
6. **Astrophysical** (as′trō·fiz′i·kəl): pertaining to *astrophysics*, the branch of astronomy that treats of the physical make-up of the stars and the heavenly bodies, especially as revealed by spectrum analysis (see footnote 8 on p. 276).

She was a beautiful animal, about ninety-five per cent Alsatian.[7] It was that missing five percent, I imagine, that led to her being abandoned. (I still feel a surge of anger when I think of it, but since I shall never know the facts, I may be jumping to false conclusions.) Apart from two dark patches over the eyes, most of her body was a smoky gray, and her coat was soft as silk. When her ears were pricked up, she looked incredibly intelligent and alert; sometimes I would be discussing spectral [8] types or stellar evolution [9] with my colleagues, and it would be hard to believe that she was not following the conversation.

Even now, I cannot understand why she became so attached to me, for I have made very few friends among human beings. Yet when I returned to the Observatory after an absence, she would go almost frantic with delight, bouncing around on her hind legs and putting her paws on my shoulders—which she could reach quite easily—all the while uttering small squeaks of joy which seemed highly inappropriate from so large a dog. I hated to leave her for more than a few days at a time, and though I could not take her with me on overseas trips, she accompanied me on most of my shorter journeys. She was with me when I drove north to attend that ill-fated seminar at Berkeley.[10]

We were staying with university acquaintances; they had been polite about it, but obviously did not look forward to having a monster in the house. However, I assured them that Laika never gave the slightest trouble, and rather reluctantly they let her sleep in the living room. "You needn't worry about burglars tonight," I said. "We don't have any in Berkeley," they answered, rather coldly.

In the middle of the night, it seemed that they were wrong. I was awakened by a hysterical, high-pitched barking from Laika which I had heard only once before—when she had first seen a cow and did not know what on earth to make of it. Cursing, I threw off the sheets and stumbled out into the darkness of the unfamiliar house. My main thought was to silence Laika before she roused my hosts—

7. **Alsatian** (al·sā′shən): a German shepherd dog, also called a police dog. This breed has a large, strong body, a thick, smooth coat, and great intelligence.
8. **spectral:** pertaining to or made by a spectrum. A *spectrum* is the band of color or pattern of lines observed when light from a source is separated into wavelengths. Astronomers study the colors contained in a star's light to determine its composition and to measure its motion toward or away from the earth. (*Spectral* can also refer to a specter or ghost.)
9. **stellar evolution:** the complex movements or formations of the stars. Stellar comes from the Latin word *stella* (star).
10. **Berkeley:** a city near San Francisco, California, and the site of the University of California at Berkeley.

assuming that this was not already far too late. If there had been an intruder, he would certainly have taken flight by now. Indeed, I rather hoped that he had.

For a moment I stood beside the switch at the top of the stairs, wondering whether to throw it. Then I growled, "Shut up, Laika!" and flooded the place with light.

She was scratching frantically at the door, pausing from time to time to give that hysterical yelp. "If you want out," I said angrily, "there's no need for all that fuss." I went down, shot the bolt, and she took off into the night like a rocket.

It was very calm and still, with a waning moon struggling to pierce the San Francisco fog. I stood in the luminous haze, looking out across the water to the lights of the city, waiting for Laika to come back so that I could chastise her suitably. I was still waiting when, for the second time in the twentieth century, the San Andreas Fault [11] woke from its sleep.

Oddly enough, I was not frightened—at first. I can remember that two thoughts passed through my mind, in the moment before I realized the danger. Surely, I told myself, the geophysicists [12] could have given us some warning. And then I found myself thinking, with great surprise, "I'd no idea that earthquakes make so much noise!"

It was about then that I knew that this was no ordinary quake; what happened afterward, I would prefer to forget. The Red Cross did not take me away until quite late the next morning, because I refused to leave without Laika. As I looked at the shattered house containing the bodies of my friends, I knew that I owed my life to her; but the helicopter pilots could not be expected to understand that, and I cannot blame them for thinking that I was crazy, like so many of the others they had found wandering among the fires and the debris.

After that, I do not suppose we were ever apart for more than a few hours. I have been told—and I can well believe it—that I became less and less interested in human company, without being actively

11. **San Andreas Fault:** San Andreas is a village in central California. A *fault* is a break in the rock layers beneath the earth's crust, caused by the shifting of the crust, a movement usually associated with earthquakes. A zone of faults, called the San Andreas Fault, extends along the coast of northern California. The fault line is traceable over a distance of more than 270 miles. A movement along a part of this zone caused the highly destructive San Francisco earthquake of 1906.
12. **geophysicists** (jē′ō·fiz′i·sists): experts in geophysics. *Physics* is the scientific study of matter, energy, motion, and their interrelations, including mechanics, heat, sound, light, electricity, and magnetism. *Geophysics* is the study of the physics of the earth including its magnetism, volcanoes, and air and water movements.

unsocial or misanthropic.[13] Between them, the stars and Laika filled all my needs. We used to go for long walks together over the mountains; it was the happiest time I have ever known. There was only one flaw; I knew, though Laika could not, how soon it must end.

We had been planning the move for more than a decade. As far back as the nineteen-sixties it was realized that Earth was no place for an astronomical observatory. Even the small pilot instruments on the moon had far outperformed all the telescopes peering through the murk and haze of the terrestrial[14] atmosphere. The story of Mount Wilson,[15] Palomar, Greenwich, and the other great names was coming to an end; they would still be used for training purposes, but the research frontier must move out into space.

I had to move with it; indeed, I had already been offered the post of Deputy Director, Farside Observatory. In a few months, I could hope to solve problems I had been working on for years. Beyond the atmosphere, I would be like a blind man who has suddenly been given sight.

It was utterly impossible, of course, to take Laika with me. The only animals on the Moon were those needed for experimental purposes; it might be another generation before pets were allowed, and even then it would cost a fortune to carry them there—and to keep them alive. Providing Laika with her usual two pounds of meat a day would, I calculated, take several times my quite comfortable salary.

The choice was simple and straightforward. I could stay on Earth and abandon my career. Or I could go to the Moon—and abandon Laika.

After all, she was only a dog. In a dozen years, she would be dead, while I should be reaching the peak of my profession. No sane man would have hesitated over the matter; yet I did hesitate, and if by now you do not understand why, no further words of mine can help.

In the end, I let matters go by default. Up to the very week I was due to leave, I had still made no plans for Laika. When Dr. Anderson volunteered to look after her, I accepted numbly, with scarcely a word of thanks. The old physicist and his wife had always been fond

13. **misanthropic** (mis'ən·throp'ik): marked by hatred or contempt for one's fellow man.
14. **terrestrial** (tə·res'trē·əl): of, belonging to, or representing the earth. This word comes from the Latin word *terra* (land).
15. **Mount Wilson:** an astronomical observatory near Pasadena, California. It has a 100-inch telescope. **Greenwich** was formerly the site of the Royal Observatory at Greenwich, near London, established by King Charles II in 1675.

of her, and I am afraid that they considered me indifferent and heart-less—when the truth was just the opposite. We went for one more walk together over the hills; then I delivered her silently to the Andersons, and did not see her again.

Takeoff was delayed almost twenty-four hours, until a major flare storm had cleared the Earth's orbit; even so, the Van Allen belts [16] were still so active that we had to make our exit through the North Polar Gap.[17] It was a miserable flight; apart from the usual trouble with weightlessness, we were all groggy with antiradiation drugs. The ship was already over Farside before I took much interest in the pro-ceedings, so I missed the sight of Earth dropping below the horizon. Nor was I really sorry; I wanted no reminders, and intended to think only of the future. Yet I could not shake off that feeling of guilt; I had deserted someone who loved and trusted me, and was no better than those who had abandoned Laika when she was a puppy, beside the dusty road to Palomar.

The news that she was dead reached me a month later. There was no reason that anyone knew; the Andersons had done their best, and were very upset. She had just lost interest in living, it seemed. For a while, I think I did the same; but work is a wonderful anodyne,[18] and my program was just getting under way. Though I never forgot Laika, in a little while the memory ceased to hurt.

Then why had it come back to haunt me, five years later, on the far side of the Moon? I was searching my mind for the reason when the metal building around me quivered as if under the impact of a heavy blow. I reacted without thinking, and was already closing the helmet of my emergency suit when the foundations slipped and the wall tore open with a short-lived scream of escaping air. Because I had automatically pressed the General Alarm button, we lost only two men, despite the fact that the tremor—the worst ever recorded on Farside—cracked all three of the Observatory's pressure domes.

It is hardly necessary for me to say that I do not believe in the supernatural; everything that happened has a perfectly rational ex-planation, obvious to any man with the slightest knowledge of psy-

16. **Van Allen belts:** belts of radiation surrounding the earth. Charged atomic particles are believed to circle the earth in an inner and outer belt conforming to the earth's magnetic field. They are named after their discoverer, James A. Van Allen, a United States physicist born in 1914.
17. **North Polar Gap:** probably an opening or gap in the Van Allen belts at the North Pole, the northernmost point of the earth's axis, where the radiation would be less intense.
18. **anodyne** (an′ə·dīn): pain-reliever.

chology. In the second San Francisco earthquake, Laika was not the only dog to sense approaching disaster; many such cases were reported. And on Farside, my own memories must have given me that heightened awareness, when my never-sleeping subconscious detected the first faint vibrations from within the Moon.

The human mind has strange and labyrinthine [19] ways of going about its business; it knew the signal that would most swiftly rouse me to the knowledge of danger. There is nothing more to it than that; though in a sense one could say that Laika woke me on both occasions, there is no mystery about it, no miraculous warning across the gulf that neither man nor dog can ever bridge.

Of that I am sure, if I am sure of anything. Yet sometimes I wake now, in the silence of the Moon, and wish that the dream could have lasted a few seconds longer—so that I could have looked just once more into those luminous brown eyes, brimming with an unselfish, undemanding love I have found nowhere else on this or any other world.

19. **labyrinthine** (lab′ə·rin′thin) : like a labyrinth or maze; intricate; involved.

Meaning and Method

1. Twice in this story the narrator finds himself in a dangerous situation. How are the situations similar? Describe the situations and the narrator's reactions. In each case, how does the narrator account for his being saved?

2. The story opens with a situation that seems to contradict reason. The author then proceeds to use the flashback technique to provide necessary background information before returning to the danger he is facing. What effect does this have on the element of suspense?

3. The narrator has to choose between Laika and his career. What inner conflicts make this choice difficult for him?

4. Does this story have more than one level of interpretation? In giving the reasons for your answer, consider the narrator's explanation of why Laika died.

5. *Science fiction* is a blend of both science and fiction. The writer begins with known scientific facts and principles and the real experiences of men in the past and the present. He then projects his knowledge of scientific theory and human nature into the future. The result is a plausible blend of fact and fancy.

   What scientific facts and theories are used to make key events and decisions in this story seem real and convincing? Give examples to illustrate your answers.

6. This story takes place in California and on the moon. Are both of

these settings essential to the plot? Do they add anything to the story? Explain your answers.

7. Reread the discussion of tone on page 6. What would you say is the tone of "Dog Star?" How does the author make you feel the way you do about the scientist and his dog—that is, how does Clarke convey his tone?

8. Both H. G. Wells and Arthur C. Clarke are science-fiction writers. Are their stories, "The Magic Shop" and "Dog Star," similar in any way? Give reasons for your answers.

Composition

1. Scientists feel that men from earth cannot only visit the moon but will travel to Mars and Venus. Write a composition in which you give reasons why you would or would not like to be involved in the exploratory flights. Include your opinions on what you believe are the advantages (or disadvantages) of interplanetary travel.

2. Write a narrative about your dog—or someone else's dog—telling how the animal helped to save a life.

Stephen Vincent Benét

Duty, integrity, patriotism, and honor were qualities Stephen Vincent Benét learned at an early age from his father, a West Point graduate and a career army officer. The father was also a cultivated and widely-read man who filled the house with books, read poetry aloud to his three children, and instilled in them a lasting interest in literature and writing. Stephen's older brother, William Rose, became a poet and critic, and his sister, Laura, began serious writing while in college. Stephen was thirteen when he won his first literary prize, in a poetry contest for a juvenile magazine, and seventeen when his first book, *Five Men and Pompey*, was published.

The Benét family moved constantly to different army posts throughout the country as the father received new assignments. Stephen was born in Bethlehem, Pennsylvania in 1898. He received his secondary education at schools in California and Georgia and then attended Yale. When he was twenty-two he was awarded a Yale fellowship for study at the Sorbonne, and left for France. While in Paris he met his future wife, Rosemary Carr, also a writer, with whom he later collaborated on the volume of verse *A Book of Americans* (1933).

In his early career, Stephen Vincent Benét supported his family by writing several novels and stories for popular magazines. In 1926, he won a Guggenheim fellowship which enabled him to return to Paris, where he wrote *John Brown's Body*, awarded the Pulitzer prize in 1929.

During World War II he worked long hours on radio scripts and speeches to rally support for the American cause. He never accepted money for such government assignments and summed up his sense of obligation with the words, "We Benéts are an army family." Weakened by overwork and poor health, he died suddenly of a heart attack in 1943.

The collected edition of Benét's prose divides his short stories into three categories: Stories of American History, Tales of Our Time, and Fantasies and Prophecies. To this last category belongs "By the Waters of Babylon."

By the Waters of Babylon

(The title of this selection is allusive, not literal. Babylon, a mighty city of ancient times, situated between the Tigris and the Euphrates rivers, was noted for its wealth, luxury, and wickedness. In the early part of the sixth century B.C., *the Babylonians attacked and destroyed Jerusalem and deported thousands of Jews to Babylon, where they were held for over fifty years. In the Old Testament Book of Psalms (137:1), a psalm or lyric sung in memory of that exile and captivity begins, "By the waters of Babylon, there we sat down and wept, when we remembered Zion." Zion, the hill in Jerusalem that was the site of the Temple, is regarded as a symbol for the center of Jewish national culture and religion.*

In this story, the ruined city of the dead gods is also situated between two rivers, the Ou-dis-sun and another, unnamed, river.)

The north and the west and the south are good hunting ground, but it is forbidden to go east. It is forbidden to go to any of the Dead Places [1] except to search for metal and then he who touches the metal must be a priest or the son of a priest. Afterward, both the man and the metal must be purified. These are the rules and the laws; they are well made. It is forbidden to cross the great river and look upon the place that was the Place of the Gods—this is most strictly forbidden. We do not even say its name though we know its name. It is there that spirits live, and demons—it is there that there are the ashes of the Great Burning.[2] These things are forbidden—they have been forbidden since the beginning of time.

My father is a priest; I am the son of a priest. I have been in the Dead Places near us, with my father. At first, I was afraid. When my father went into the house to search for the metal,[3] I stood by the door and my heart felt small and weak. It was a dead man's house, a spirit house. It did not have the smell of man, though there were old bones in a corner. But it is not fitting that a priest's son should show fear. I looked at the bones in the shadow and kept my voice still.

Then my father came out with the metal—a good, strong piece. He

1. **Dead Places:** the remains of cities and towns of past civilizations.
2. **the Great Burning:** a reference to how the city was destroyed.
3. **metal:** important to a primitive people for tools and weapons.

"By the Waters of Babylon" from *Selected Works of Stephen Vincent Benét*, Holt, Rinehart and Winston, Inc., copyright 1937 by Stephen Vincent Benét, copyright renewed © 1964 by Thomas C. Benét, Stephanie B. Mahin, and Rachel Benét Lewis. Reprinted by permission of Brandt & Brandt.

looked at me with both eyes but I had not run away. He gave me the metal to hold—I took it and did not die. So he knew that I was truly his son and would be a priest in my time. That was when I was very young—nevertheless my brothers would not have done it, though they are good hunters. After that, they gave me the good piece of meat and the warm corner by the fire. My father watched over me— he was glad that I should be a priest. But when I boasted or wept without a reason, he punished me more strictly than my brothers. That was right.

After a time, I myself was allowed to go into the dead houses and search for metal. So I learned the ways of those houses—and if I saw bones, I was no longer afraid. The bones are light and old—sometimes they will fall into dust if you touch them. But that is a great sin.

I was taught the chants and the spells—I was taught how to stop the running of blood from a wound, and many secrets. A priest must know many secrets—that was what my father said. If the hunters think we do all things by chants and spells, they may believe so—it does not hurt them. I was taught how to read in the old books and how to make the old writings—that was hard and took a long time. My knowledge made me happy—it was like a fire in my heart. Most of all, I liked to hear of the Old Days and the stories of the gods. I asked myself many questions that I could not answer, but it was good to ask them. At night, I would lie awake and listen to the wind—it seemed to me that it was the voice of the gods as they flew through the air.

We are not ignorant like the Forest People—our women spin wool on the wheel, our priests wear a white robe. We do not eat grubs [4] from the tree, we have not forgotten the old writings, although they are hard to understand. Nevertheless, my knowledge and my lack of knowledge burned in me—I wished to know more. When I was a man at last, I came to my father and said, "It is time for me to go on my journey. Give me your leave."

He looked at me for a long time, stroking his beard, then he said at last, "Yes. It is time." That night, in the house of the priesthood, I asked for and received purification. My body hurt but my spirit was a cool stone. It was my father himself who questioned me about my dreams.

He bade me look into the smoke of the fire and see—I saw and told what I saw. It was what I have always seen—a river, and, beyond it, a

4. **grubs:** the larva of certain insects.

great Dead Place, and in it the gods walking. I have always thought about that. His eyes were stern when I told him—he was no longer my father but a priest. He said, "This is a strong dream."

"It is mine," I said, while the smoke waved and my head felt light. They were singing the Star song in the outer chamber and it was like the buzzing of bees in my head.

He asked me how the gods were dressed and I told him how they were dressed. We know how they were dressed from the book, but I saw them as if they were before me. When I had finished, he threw the sticks three times and studied them as they fell.

"This is a very strong dream," he said. "It may eat you up."

"I am not afraid," I said and looked at him with both my eyes. My voice sounded thin in my ears but that was because of the smoke.

He touched me on the breast and the forehead. He gave me the bow and the three arrows.

"Take them," he said. "It is forbidden to travel east. It is forbidden to cross the river. It is forbidden to go to the Place of the Gods. All these things are forbidden."

"All these things are forbidden," I said, but it was my voice that spoke and not my spirit. He looked at me again.

"My son," he said. "Once I had young dreams. If your dreams do not eat you up, you may be a great priest. If they eat you, you are still my son. Now go on your journey."

I went fasting, as is the law. My body hurt but not my heart. When the dawn came, I was out of sight of the village. I prayed and purified myself, waiting for a sign. The sign was an eagle. It flew east.

Sometimes signs are sent by bad spirits. I waited again on the flat rock, fasting, taking no food. I was very still—I could feel the sky above me and the earth beneath. I waited till the sun was beginning to sink. Then three deer passed in the valley, going east—they did not wind [5] me or see me. There was a white fawn with them—a very great sign.

I followed them at a distance, waiting for what would happen. My heart was troubled about going east, yet I knew that I must go. My head hummed with my fasting—I did not even see the panther spring upon the white fawn. But before I knew it, the bow was in my hand. I shouted and the panther lifted his head from the fawn. It is not easy to kill a panther with one arrow but the arrow went through his eye and into his brain. He died as he tried to spring—he rolled over, tearing at the ground. Then I knew I was meant to go east—I knew

5. **wind:** in this context, smell or get the scent of.

that was my journey. When the night came, I made my fire and roasted meat.

It is eight suns' journey to the east, and a man passes by many Dead Places. The Forest People are afraid of them, but I am not. Once I made my fire on the edge of a Dead Place at night and next morning, in the dead house, I found a good knife, little rusted. That was small to what came afterward but it made my heart feel big. Always when I looked for game, it was in front of my arrow, and twice I passed hunting parties of the Forest People without their knowing. So I knew my magic was strong and my journey clean, in spite of the law.

Toward the setting of the eighth sun, I came to the banks of the great river. It was half-a-day's journey after I had left the god-road—we do not use the god-roads now, for they are falling apart into great blocks of stone, and the forest is safer going. A long way off I had seen the water through trees but the trees were thick. At last I came out upon an open place at the top of a cliff. There was the great river below, like a giant in the sun. It is very long, very wide. It could eat all the streams we know and still be thirsty. Its name is Ou-dis-sun, the Sacred, the Long. No man of my tribe had seen it, not even my father, the priest. It was magic and I prayed.

Then I raised my eyes and looked south. It was there, the Place of the Gods.

How can I tell what it was like—you do not know. It was there, in the red light, and they were too big to be houses. It was there, with the red light upon it, mighty and ruined. I knew that in another moment the gods would see me. I covered my eyes with my hands and crept back into the forest.

Surely that was enough to do, and live. Surely it was enough to spend the night upon the cliff. The Forest People themselves do not come near. Yet, all through the night, I knew that I should have to cross the river and walk in the Place of the Gods, although the gods ate me up. My magic did not help me at all and yet there was a fire in my bowels, a fire in my mind. When the sun rose, I thought, "My journey has been clean. Now I will go home from my journey." But, even as I thought so, I knew I could not. If I went to the Place of the Gods, I would surely die, but if I did not go I could never be at peace with my spirit again. It is better to lose one's life than one's spirit, if one is a priest and the son of a priest.

Nevertheless, as I made the raft, the tears ran out of my eyes. The Forest People could have killed me without fight, if they had come upon me then, but they did not come. When the raft was made, I said the sayings for the dead and painted myself for death. My heart was cold as a frog and my knees like water, but the burning in my mind would not let me have peace. As I pushed the raft from the shore, I began my death song—I had the right. It was a fine song.

"I am John, son of John," I sang. "My people are the Hill People. They are the men.
I go into the Dead Places but I am not slain.
I take the metal from the Dead Places but I am not blasted.
I travel upon the god-roads and am not afraid. E-yah! I have killed the panther, I have killed the fawn!
E-yah! I have come to the great river. No man has come there before.

It is forbidden to go east, but I have gone, forbidden to go on the great river, but I am there.
Open your hearts, you spirits, and hear my song.
Now I go to the Place of the Gods; I shall not return.
My body is painted for death and my limbs weak, but my heart is big as I go to the Place of the Gods!"

All the same, when I came to the Place of the Gods, I was afraid, afraid. The current of the great river is very strong—it gripped my raft with its hands. That was magic, for the river itself is wide and calm. I could feel evil spirits about me, in the bright morning; I could feel their breath on my neck as I was swept down the stream. Never have I been so much alone—I tried to think of my knowledge, but it was a squirrel's heap of winter nuts. There was no strength in my knowledge any more, and I felt small and naked as a new-hatched bird—alone upon the great river, the servant of the gods.

Yet after awhile my eyes were opened, and I saw. I saw both banks of the river—I saw that once there had been god-roads across it, though now they were broken and fallen like broken vines. Very great they were, and wonderful and broken—broken in the time of the Great Burning when the fire fell out of the sky. And always the current took me nearer to the Place of the Gods, and the huge ruins rose before my eyes.

I do not know the customs of rivers—we are the People of the Hills. I tried to guide my raft with the pole but it spun around. I thought the river meant to take me past the Place of the Gods and out into the Bitter Water of the legends. I grew angry then—my heart felt strong. I said aloud, "I am a priest and the son of a priest!" The gods heard me—they showed me how to paddle with the pole on one side of the raft. The current changed itself—I drew near to the Place of the Gods.

When I was very near, my raft struck and turned over. I can swim in our lakes—I swam to the shore. There was a great spike of rusted metal sticking out into the river—I hauled myself up upon it and sat there, panting. I had saved my bow and two arrows and the knife I found in the Dead Place but that was all. My raft went whirling downstream toward the Bitter Water. I looked after it, and thought if it had trod me under, at least I would be safely dead. Nevertheless, when I had dried my bowstring and restrung it, I walked forward to the Place of the Gods.

It felt like ground underfoot; it did not burn me. It is not true what some of the tales say, that the ground there burns forever, for I have been there. Here and there were the marks and stains of the Great Burning, on the ruins, that is true. But they were old marks and old stains. It is not true either, what some of our priests say, that it is an island covered with fogs and enchantments. It is not. It is a great Dead Place—greater than any Dead Place we know. Everywhere in it there are god-roads, though most are cracked and broken. Everywhere there are the ruins of the high towers of the gods.

How shall I tell what I saw? I went carefully, my strung bow in my hand, my skin ready for danger. There should have been the wailings of spirits and the shrieks of demons, but there were not. It was very silent and sunny where I had landed—the wind and the rain and the birds that drop seeds had done their work—the grass grew in the cracks of the broken stone. It is a fair island—no wonder the gods built there. If I had come there, a god, I also would have built.

How shall I tell what I saw? The towers are not all broken—here and there one still stands, like a great tree in a forest, and the birds nest high. But the towers themselves look blind, for the gods are gone. I saw a fish hawk, catching fish in the river. I saw a little dance of white butterflies over a great heap of broken stones and columns. I went there and looked about me—there was a carved stone with cut letters, broken in half. I can read letters but I could not understand these. The said UBTREAS. There was also the shattered image of a man or a god. It had been made of white stone and he wore his hair tied back like a woman's. His name was ASHING, as I read on the cracked half of a stone. I thought it wise to pray to ASHING, though I do not know that god.

How shall I tell what I saw? There was no smell of man left, on stone or metal. Nor were there many trees in that wilderness of stone. There are many pigeons, nesting and dropping in the towers—the gods must have loved them, or perhaps they used them for sacrifices. There are wild cats that roam the god-roads, green-eyed, unafraid of man. At night they wail like demons but they are not demons. The wild dogs are more dangerous, for they hunt in a pack, but them I did not meet till later. Everywhere there are the carved stones, carved with magical numbers or words.

I went north—I did not try to hide myself. When a god or a demon saw me, then I would die, but meanwhile I was no longer afraid. My hunger for knowledge burned in me—there was so much that I could not understand. After awhile, I knew that my belly was hungry. I could have hunted for my meat, but I did not hunt. It is known that the gods did not hunt as we do—they got their food from enchanted boxes and jars. Sometimes these are still found in the Dead Places— once, when I was a child and foolish, I opened such a jar and tasted it and found the food sweet. But my father found out and punished me for it strictly, for often that food is death. Now, though, I had long gone past what was forbidden, and I entered the likeliest towers, looking for the food of the gods.

I found it at last in the ruins of a great temple in the mid-city. A mighty temple it must have been, for the roof was painted like the sky at night with its stars—that much I could see, though the colors were faint and dim. It went down into great caves and tunnels— perhaps they kept their slaves there. But when I started to climb down, I heard the squeaking of rats, so I did not go—rats are unclean, and there must have been many tribes of them, from the squeaking. But near there I found food, in the heart of a ruin, behind a door that still opened. I ate only the fruits from the jars—they had a very sweet taste. There was drink, too, in bottles of glass—the drink of the gods was strong and made my head swim. After I had eaten and drunk, I slept on the top of a stone, my bow at my side.

When I woke, the sun was low. Looking down from where I lay, I saw a dog sitting on his haunches. His tongue was hanging out of his mouth; he looked as if he were laughing. He was a big dog, with a gray-brown coat, as big as a wolf. I sprang up and shouted at him but he did not move—he just sat there as if he were laughing. I did not like that. When I reached for a stone to throw, he moved swiftly out of the way of the stone. He was not afraid of me; he looked at me as if I were meat. No doubt I could have killed him with an arrow, but I did not know if there were others. Moreover, night was falling.

I looked about me—not far away there was a great, broken god-road, leading north. The towers were high enough, but not so high, and while many of the dead-houses were wrecked, there were some that stood. I went toward this god-road, keeping to the heights of the ruins, while the dog followed. When I had reached the god-road, I saw that there were others behind him. If I had slept later, they would have come upon me asleep and torn out my throat. As it was, they were sure enough of me; they did not hurry. When I went into the dead-house, they kept watch at the entrance—doubtless they thought they would have a fine hunt. But a dog cannot open a door, and I knew, from the books, that the gods did not like to live on the ground but on high.

I had just found a door I could open when the dogs decided to rush. Ha! They were surprised when I shut the door in their faces—it was a good door, of strong metal. I could hear their foolish baying beyond it but I did not stop to answer them. I was in darkness—I found stairs and climbed. There were many stairs, turning around till my head was dizzy. At the top was another door—I found the knob and opened it. I was in a long, small chamber—on one side of it was a bronze door that could not be opened, for it had no handle. Perhaps there was a magic word to open it but I did not have the word. I turned to the door in the opposite side of the wall. The lock of it was broken and I opened it and went in.

Within, there was a place of great riches. The god who lived there must have been a powerful god. The first room was a small anteroom —I waited there for some time, telling the spirits of the place that I came in peace and not as a robber. When it seemed to me that they had had time to hear me, I went on. Ah, what riches! Few, even, of the windows had been broken—it was all as it had been. The great windows that looked over the city had not been broken at all, though they were dusty and streaked with many years. There were coverings on the floors, the colors not greatly faded, and the chairs were soft and deep. There were pictures upon the walls, very strange, very wonderful—I remember one of a bunch of flowers in a jar—if you came close to it, you could see nothing but bits of color, but if you stood away from it, the flowers might have been picked yesterday. It made my heart feel strange to look at this picture—and to look at the figure of a bird, in some hard clay, on a table and see it so like our birds. Everywhere there were books and writings, many in tongues that I could not read. The god who lived there must have been a wise god and full of knowledge. I felt I had right there, as I sought knowledge also.

Nevertheless, it was strange. There was a washing-place but no water—perhaps the gods washed in air. There was a cooking-place but no wood, and though there was a machine to cook food, there was no place to put fire in it. Nor were there candles or lamps—there were things that looked like lamps but they had neither oil nor wick. All these things were magic, but I touched them and lived—the magic had gone out of them. Let me tell one thing to show. In the washing-place, a thing said "Hot" but it was not hot to the touch—another thing said "Cold" but it was not cold. This must have been a strong magic but the magic was gone. I do not understand—they had ways —I wish that I knew.

It was close and dry and dusty in their house of the gods. I have said the magic was gone but that is not true—it had gone from the magic things but it had not gone from the place. I felt the spirits about me, weighing upon me. Nor had I ever slept in a Dead Place before—and yet tonight I must sleep there. When I thought of it, my tongue felt dry in my throat, in spite of my wish for knowledge. Almost I would have gone down again and faced the dogs, but I did not.

I had not gone through all the rooms when the darkness fell. When it fell, I went back to the big room looking over the city and made fire. There was a place to make fire and a box with wood in it, though I do not think they cooked there. I wrapped myself in a floor-covering and slept in front of the fire—I was very tired.

Now I tell what is very strong magic. I woke in the midst of the night. When I woke, the fire had gone out and I was cold. It seemed to me that all around me there were whisperings and voices. I closed my eyes to shut them out. Some will say that I slept again, but I do not think that I slept. I could feel the spirits drawing my spirit out of my body as a fish is drawn on a line.

Why should I lie about it? I am a priest and the son of a priest. If there are spirits, as they say, in the small Dead Places near us, what spirits must there not be in that great Place of Gods? And would not they wish to speak? After such long years? I know that I felt myself drawn as a fish is drawn on a line. I had stepped out of my body—I could see my body asleep in front of the cold fire, but it was not I. I was drawn to look out upon the city of the gods.

It should have been dark, for it was night, but it was not dark. Everywhere there were lights—lines of light—circles and blurs of light—ten thousand torches would not have been the same. The sky itself was alight—you could barely see the stars for the glow in the sky. I thought to myself "This is strong magic" and trembled. There was a roaring in my ears like the rushing of rivers. Then my eyes grew used to the light and my ears to the sound. I knew that I was seeing the city as it had been when the gods were alive.

That was a sight indeed—yes, that was a sight: I could not have seen it in the body—my body would have died. Everywhere went the gods, on foot and in chariots—there were gods beyond number and counting and their chariots blocked the streets. They had turned night to day for their pleasure—they did not sleep with the sun. The noise of their coming and going was the noise of many waters. It was magic what they could do—it was magic what they did.

I looked out of another window—the great vines of their bridges were mended and the god-roads went east and west. Restless, restless, were the gods and always in motion! They burrowed tunnels under rivers—they flew in the air. With unbelievable tools they did giant works—no part of the earth was safe from them, for, if they wished for a thing, they summoned it from the other side of the world. And always, as they labored and rested, as they feasted and made love, there was a drum in their ears—the pulse of the giant city, beating and beating like a man's heart.

Were they happy? What is happiness to the gods? They were great, they were mighty, they were wonderful and terrible. As I looked upon them and their magic, I felt like a child—but a little more, it seemed to me, and they would pull down the moon from the sky. I saw them with wisdom beyond wisdom and knowledge beyond knowledge. And yet not all they did was well done—even I could see that—and yet their wisdom could not but grow until all was peace.

Then I saw their fate come upon them and that was terrible past speech. It came upon them as they walked the streets of their city. I have been in the fights with the Forest People—I have seen men die. But this was not like that. When gods war with gods, they use weapons we do not know. It was fire falling out of the sky and a mist that poisoned. It was the time of the Great Burning and the Destruction. They ran about like ants in the streets of their city—poor gods, poor gods! Then the towers began to fall. A few escaped—yes, a few. The legends tell it. But even after the city had become a Dead Place, for many years the poison was still in the ground. I saw it happen, I saw the last of them die. It was darkness over the broken city and I wept.

All this I saw. I saw it as I have told it, though not in the body. When I woke in the morning I was hungry, but I did not think first of my hunger, for my heart was perplexed and confused. I knew the reason for the Dead Places but I did not see why it had happened. It seemed to me it should not have happened, with all the magic they had. I went through the house looking for an answer. There was so much in the house I could not understand—and yet I am a priest and the son of a priest. It was like being on one side of the great river, at night, with no light to show the way.

Then I saw the dead god. He was sitting in his chair by the window, in a room I had not entered before, and for the first moment I thought that he was alive. Then I saw the skin on the back of his hand—it was like dry leather. The room was shut, hot, and dry—no doubt that had kept him as he was. At first I was afraid to approach him—then the fear left me. He was sitting looking out over the city —he was dressed in the clothes of the gods. His age was neither young nor old—I could not tell his age. But there was wisdom in his face and great sadness. You could see that he would not have run away. He had sat at his window, watching his city die—then he himself had died. But it is better to lose one's life than one's spirit—and you could see from the face that his spirit had not been lost. I knew that if I touched him, he would fall into dust—and yet, there was something unconquered in the face.

That is all of my story, for then I knew he was a man—I knew then that they had been men, neither gods nor demons. It is a great knowledge, hard to tell and believe. They were men—they went a dark road, but they were men. I had no fear after that—I had no fear going home, though twice I fought off the dogs and once I was hunted for two days by the Forest People. When I saw my father again, I prayed and was purified. He touched my lips and my breast; he said, "You went away a boy. You come back a man and a priest." I said, "Father, they were men! I have been in the Place of the Gods and seen it! Now slay me, if it is the law—but still I know they were men."

He looked at me out of both eyes. He said, "The law is not always the same shape—you have done what you have done. I could not have done it in my time, but you come after me. Tell!"

I told and he listened. After that, I wished to tell all the people but he showed me otherwise. He said, "Truth is a hard deer to hunt. If you eat too much truth at once, you may die of the truth. It was not idly that our fathers forbade the Dead Places." He was right—it is better the truth should come little by little. I have learned that, being a priest. Perhaps, in the old days, they ate knowledge too fast.

Nevertheless, we make a beginning. It is not for the metal alone we go to the Dead Places now—there are the books and the writings. They are hard to learn. And the magic tools are broken—but we can look at them and wonder. At least, we make a beginning. And when I am chief priest we shall go beyond the great river. We shall go to the Place of the Gods—the place new-york—not one man but a company. We shall look for the images of the gods and find the god ASHING and the others—the gods Lincoln and Biltmore and Moses. But they were men who built the city, not gods or demons. They were men. I remember the dead man's face. They were men who were here before us. We must build again.

Meaning

1. The setting of the story is not revealed until the last paragraph, when the Place of the Gods is identified as New York City. But there are previous clues, such as *Ubtreas* for *Subtreasury* and *Ashing* for *Washington*. To what do the following refer: (a) the Ou-dis-san River, (b) the cliff next to it, (c) the Bitter Waters into which the river threatened to take the boy, and (d) the great underground caves and tunnels?

2. When does John know he is to be a priest? What traits of character does he have?

3. When John first sees the Place of the Gods, he is reluctant to continue. Explain both the external and internal conflict that he faces, and his words, "It is better to lose one's life than one's spirit."

4. The climax of the story is reached when John has a vision of the city before its destruction. Give examples of the things the gods had created that he admired. What words does he use that sum up what the gods possessed and also what he is searching for? What puzzles him about the fate of the great city?

5. What is meant by "fire falling out of the sky"? "a mist that poisoned"? "the Great Burning"? What is your interpretation of how the city met its end?

6. What is the most important discovery the young priest makes in the Place of the Gods? Why do the words he used earlier in the story, "It is better to lose one's life than one's spirit" once again have meaning for him?

7. The young priest broke the law of his tribe by visiting the Dead Places and is ready to receive the death penalty. What reason does the father give for not punishing him? Explain the father's words, "The law is not always the same shape—you have done what you

have done. I could not have done it in my time." Point out other references to law in the story.

8. What does John learn about the relationship between knowledge and the use of knowledge? Had the gods known this difference? What would you say is the theme of the story?

Method

1. Why does Benét use some rather primitive customs and beliefs for the story? What contrast do they provide? Why do they help to provide a high-level interest for the story?
2. What values does the author, through the narrator, seem to hold the highest? What reasons can you give for the author's choice of a young priest as narrator?
3. What element does the author consider more important than the adventure element in this story?
4. Examine the language and sentence structure in the story. What obvious reason is there for having John use such a simple vocabulary?

Language: Similes and Metaphors

A study of the similes in this story will show that sometimes a writer explicitly states in the simile that quality which the two compared things have in common. At other times he leaves it to his reader to work out the comparison. For example, look at "My heart was cold as a frog. . . ." and "My knowledge made me happy—it was like a fire in my heart." In the first simile the quality of coldness is expressed; in the second simile it is for you to make the relationship between knowledge and fire. Now compare the two following similes. ". . . I felt small and naked as a new-hatched bird." "The towers are not all broken—here and there one still stands, like a great tree in a forest, . . ." In which of these is the similarity of the two things stated directly?

Benét also uses metaphors in his story. Explain the comparisons used here. "My body hurt but my spirit was a cool stone." "Never have I been so much alone—I tried to think of my knowledge, but it was a squirrel's heap of winter nuts."

Composition

How can modern man prevent the "Great Burning and the Destruction" prophesied in the story? In an essay, offer specific suggestions on some ways to control and use positively for the benefit of mankind the fruits of knowledge, especially scientific and technical knowledge.

A Glossary
of Literary Terms

Abstract and Concrete Terms: *abstract terms* are words and phrases that refer to ideas, characteristics, or intangible qualities. Abstractions have little or no appeal to any of the senses. Examples of abstract terms are *democracy, strength, brightness,* and *realism. Concrete terms* stand for objects that can be perceived by the senses or imagined vividly. Examples of concrete terms are *grass, smoke, guitar,* and *hat.*

Allegory: a narrative in verse or prose in which concrete characters and actions represent abstract ideas or moral qualities. An allegory carries both literal, or real, and symbolic levels of meaning.

An example of an allegory is the play *Everyman,* written in the fifteenth century. Among the characters whom Everyman meets are Fellowship, Knowledge, and Good Deeds. (See also **Symbol.**)

Alliteration: the repetition of the same consonant sound, usually at the beginnings of words, in the same line or successive lines. Although mainly a poetic device, alliteration is sometimes used in prose, as in this excerpt from Mark Twain's *Life on the Mississippi:*

". . . the white town drowsing in the sunshine of a summer's morning; . . . the great Mississippi, the majestic, the magnificent Mississippi, rolling its mile-wide tide along, shining in the sun; . . ."

Allusion: a casual reference to a person, place, event, or artistic work that the author expects the reader to recognize. An allusion may be drawn from literature, history, geography, scripture, or mythology. For example, if a writer says that a character faces an "Augean task" he means that the character is confronted with a huge and seemingly impossible undertaking. The author is alluding to one of the labors that the Greek hero Hercules, noted for his amazing strength, set out to accomplish in the kingdom of Augeas. According to Greek mythology, Hercules had to clean the stables of King Augeas, which housed 3,000 cattle and had not been touched in thirty years. Hercules, realizing that success was impossible by ordinary means, turned the waters of a neighboring river, the Alpheus, into the stables.

Ambiguity: in its general sense, ambiguity results when a word that has two or more meanings is used in such a way that its meaning in context is not readily understandable. An author may deliberately use ambiguity, or double meaning, to produce subtle or multiple variations in meaning. To understand the full significance of its usage in context, the reader must search for the other sense (or senses) of the word.

Analogy: a form of comparison which points out the likenesses between two dissimilar things; it attempts to use a familiar object or idea to illustrate or to introduce one that is unfamiliar.

Anecdote: a brief account, sometimes biographical, of an interesting or entertaining incident. In writing an essay, a writer may use an anecdote to introduce or illustrate his topic.

Antagonist: the character who opposes the **Protagonist;** a rival of the hero or heroine.

Antonym: a word having a meaning or meanings opposite to another word or words in the same language. For the word *failure*, for example, the following nouns are antonyms: *success, accomplishment*, and *victory*.

Argumentation: a type of writing that attempts to convince the reader of the logic and the merits of a particular viewpoint (especially by giving specific reasons and examples), or that attempts to persuade the reader to accept a particular belief or opinion.

Atmosphere: the prevailing mental and emotional climate of a story. **Setting** and **Mood** help to create and heighten atmosphere.

Autobiography and Biography: attempts to present an account of a person's life, usually in a systematic and chronological order, using whatever facts, events, and other evidence are available. The *autobiography* is an account written by the individual himself; the *biography* is written by another person.

Character: a person (sometimes a group of people, an animal, or a physical force) invented by an author.

Character foil: a character who serves by contrast to set off the qualities of another character. For example, the appearance of a particularly dull, slow-witted, unimaginative character will strengthen the reader's impression of an amusing, witty, expressive character.

Characterization: the techniques an author uses to develop the personality of his fictional characters so that they seem believable, act consistently, and speak naturally. These methods include presenting a character's actions and showing how others react to his behavior; revealing his thoughts and motives through either dialogue or description or both; and contrasting one character's attitudes or actions with those of other characters in the story. (See also the discussions of *Character Portrayal* in the Introduction, page 4 and in the Story Analysis, page 28).

Cliché: any trite or commonplace expression that is no longer fresh or effective because it has been used too often. The following are examples of clichés that have been used *year in and year out: light as* *a feather, acting like a fool, radiantly happy,* and *you could have heard a pin drop.*

Climax: the point of greatest intensity of action, interest, emotion, or suspense in a story. The climax normally follows a buildup through successive narrative incidents. It usually occurs at the narrative's turning point and is sometimes coincidental with the dénouement (*French* for "unknotting") or final unravelling of the **Plot.**

Coherence: the logical and clear relationship of one sentence to another within a paragraph and of one paragraph to another within a composition. Coherence is the quality in writing that links and binds the related parts of the composition into a unified whole. It is achieved through the use of transitional words and phrases (*accordingly, on the contrary, first, finally, however, nevertheless*); linking expressions (*this, these, they, it, that, he*); the repetition of key terms; synonyms; and the use of identical grammatical constructions ("By his words . . . By his deeds. . . ." or "At the beginning . . . At the end. . . ."). **Unity** and **Emphasis** are also necessary for effective writing.

Commercial or Craft Story: a story that follows a set pattern or formula using trite situations (the foreclosed mortgage, the romantic scenes in the countryside), contrived plots (the important letter that slips by accident into the wastepaper basket), stereotyped characters, excesses of sentimentality or emotion, and commonplace, conventional themes (see the discussion on **Theme**). The emphasis is usually placed on the course of events, rather than on the development of lifelike characters or thought-provoking themes, as found in the *quality* story.

Comparison and Contrast: in writing, a method used to clarify and illustrate a subject. *Comparison* shows the similarities between two things, and *contrast* details the differences between things. They are often used together, but can be used separately. (See **Contrast**.)

Concrete Terms: see **Abstract and Concrete Terms.**

Conflict: the clash between opposing forces. It may be man versus himself (inner conflict), man versus man, man versus nature, man versus society, or a combination of one or more of these. Conflict may be external (a struggle with physical or outside forces) or internal (a struggle that takes place within the mind of a character). The forces in opposition are labeled protagonist and antagonist.

Connotation: the associated or suggested meanings of a word, in addition to its literal meaning (see **Denotation**). The word *summer,* for example, implies additional meanings beyond its literal meaning as "the warmest season of the year."

Context: for a word, the other words and phrases so closely surrounding it that they affect its meaning or use.

Context often determines a word's meaning, as in the following:

"The customer refused to buy the table because the edges were too *rough*."

"The students felt that the last two questions were too *rough*."

For an event or incident, *context* is the combination of circumstances that surround the event; we often speak of a specific event in its historical context.

Contrast: a striking difference between two things. An author, to heighten or clarify a situation, may contrast ideas, personalities, or images. (See also **Comparison and Contrast.**)

Denotation: the literal or "dictionary" meaning or meanings of a word. (See also **Connotation.**)

Description: the purpose of description is to make the reader share as intensely as possible in the sensory experiences of the writer; that is, the writer wants his audience to see, hear, smell, taste, or touch, in imagination, those things which he describes.

In composition writing, an image or mental picture of a person, place, object, or action can be achieved through an enumeration of physical details, particulars, and sensory impressions.

Dialect: the speech that is characteristic of a particular group or of the inhabitants of a specific geographical region. In literature, dialect can be used as part of a characterization.

Dialogue: the conversation carried on by two or more characters. A monologue or *soliloquy* is the speech of a single person, as that of someone thinking aloud.

Diction: in writing and speaking, the choice, arrangement, and use of words. In literature, the diction will vary according to the literary form, the subject matter, the style of the writer, and the historical, cultural, and social context in which he writes. Effective diction results when ideas or impressions are conveyed clearly, accurately, and forcefully.

Emphasis: in writing, stressing what is important in the right places. It is achieved through the effective order and arrangement of words, sentences, paragraphs, and sections of a composition. **Unity** (sticking to the topic) and **Coherence** (logically relating all parts of a composition) are also essential for effective writing (see entries for each).

Episode: one of a progressive series of occurrences or significant events in a story.

Exposition: in fiction, that part where the author conveys the background material which the reader must know about the characters and events in order to understand the problem to be solved.

In essay writing, the purpose of exposition is to give information, explain something, or develop an idea. When doing an expository composition, the writer should introduce each paragraph with a topic sentence and use one or more of the methods of paragraph development.

Fable: a brief narrative in prose or verse intended to teach a moral lesson. Many fables, such as those of the Greek writer Aesop, are beast fables, in which animals speak and act as if they were human. A writer of modern fables was the late James Thurber.

Fantasy: a work that deliberately employs unrealistic, highly imaginative, or unbelievable elements. It departs from reality as the reader has experienced it. A fantasy might take place in a dreamlike world, such as that of *Alice in Wonderland*, or present unreal characters, such as giants, or project scientific principles into the future, as in science fiction. A fantasy can be a whimsical form of entertainment, or can offer a serious comment on reality.

Figurative Language: language that gives new shape or form to the standard or literal manner of expression by means of imaginative devices called *figures of speech. Simile, metaphor, personification,* and *irony* are among the most common figures of speech (see entries for each).

Flashback: a device by which an author interrupts the logical time sequence of a story or play to relate an episode or scene that occurred prior to the opening situation.

Foreshadowing: hints or clues; a shadow of things to come. Foreshadowing may be indicated by a word, a phrase, or a sentence, usually early in the story, to indicate what is going to occur. The use of foreshadowing stimulates reader interest, adds suspense, and helps prepare the reader for the outcome.

Form and Content: in literature, *form* is the structure, pattern, or organization of a piece of writing that gives it a particular appearance or aspect. A short story is one form of fiction; the sonnet is one form of poetry. *Content* refers to the subject matter, ideas, or impressions shaped or governed by the form of the work.

For purposes of discussion, content (what is said) may be distinguished from form (how it is said), but the overall meaning and effect of a piece of work stems from the successful fusion of both form and content.

Frame story: a story placed within the framework of another story; a story within a story. The outer story embodies the reason for the inner story, which is usually the more significant of the two.

Homonym: a word that is distinct in meaning from, but has the same spelling and pronunciation as another word. *Peer* meaning "look closely" and *peer* meaning "an equal" are true homonyms. They are the same in spelling and pronunciation, but different in meaning, function, and origin. *Peer* and *pier*, however, are not true homonyms. They are alike only in pronunciation.

Hyperbole (hī·pûr′bə·lē): a deliberate exaggeration for the purpose of emphasis or humor; overstatement. "He always has a million excuses," is an example of hyperbole.

Imagery: the collective *images*, or pictures and impressions, made with words. Although most imagery makes the reader mentally *see* things, some appeals to the senses of touch, taste, smell, and hearing as well. Imagery results from the use of figurative language and vivid description.

Immediacy: the quality in writing which makes the reader feel that he is directly involved in the action of the story, not just reading about it. Immediacy is closely related to atmosphere and setting.

Irony: a figure of speech, humorous or sarcastic, in which the writer's words really mean the opposite of what they seem to say. When Mark Twain makes the following statement about his father, his real meaning is quite different from his surface meaning:

"When I was a boy of fourteen, my father was so ignorant I could hardly stand to have the old man around. But when I got to be twenty-one, I was astonished at how much the old man had learned in seven years."

A situation may also be ironic when an event takes place that turns out to be the opposite of what the reader expected. An example is found in the outcome of the poem "Richard Cory" by Edwin Arlington Robinson. In the last two lines the reader learns that Richard Cory, a rich, well-educated, respected, and envied gentleman ". . . one calm summer night,/ Went home and put a bullet through his head."

Legend: a story about a national hero, folk hero, saint, tribe, people, or historical event that has been handed down from the past, usually by word of mouth. Although they are popularly regarded as historical, legends contain facts that have been exaggerated or changed to suit each storyteller's purpose. The Pied Piper of Hamelin, Robin Hood, and Paul Bunyan are legendary heroes.

Local Color: concrete details of dress, speech, locale, customs, and traditions which give an impression of the local "atmosphere" of a particular place.

Stories of "local color" flourished in American literature in the years following the War Between the States. Among authors who wrote about specific regions of the United States were Bret Harte, the West; Mark Twain, California and the Mississippi region; and Sarah Orne Jewett, the Maine coast. An attempt was made to copy local dialects and to depict the characteristic appearance, mannerisms, and customs of the people and the period.

Metaphor: a likeness expressed in figurative language in which one thing is compared to another without using *like* or *as*. For example:

"Language is the dress of thought."—Samuel Johnson, *Lives of the English Poets*

Metaphor is often expressed by the verb of a statement, as:

"Hope springs eternal in the human breast."—Alexander Pope, *An Essay on Man*

Mood: the overall emotional atmosphere or feeling created in a literary work by its tone or tones. (See also **Atmosphere, Setting,** and **Tone.**)

Motivation: the force which drives a character to some action; the grounds for his behavior. Outside events and environmental influences may cause a character to act as he does, or his action may stem from a need, an inclination, a goal, or a fear within himself.

Myth: a tale or story, related to *legend*, usually focusing on the deeds of gods or superhuman heroes. Myths are the imaginative part of legends and played an important role in ancient cultures by helping to explain or justify the mysteries of nature and the universe, such as the origin of fire. As a loose term, *myth* can denote any invented or grossly exaggerated story.

Narrative: the telling of an event or series of incidents that together make up a meaningful action; a story.

Narrator: one who narrates, or relates, a true or fictional story. The narrator may be a major or minor participant in the action of the narrative, or he may simply be an observer of the action.

Objectivity: the quality in writing that is free from the expression of the author's personal sentiments, partialities, feelings, and opinions.

Onomatopoeia (on′ə·mat′ə·pē′ə): the use of words that imitate the sound, action, or idea they represent. "The girl campers *chitchatted* as they clustered around the fire."

Paragraph Development, Methods of: there are several ways of developing a paragraph after introducing the main subject or idea in a topic sentence. The methods include (a) giving many details and particulars, (b) giving specific examples and illustrations, (c) telling an incident or anecdote, (d) offering reasons, and (e) drawing comparison or showing contrast, or both.

Paraphrase: the restatement of a line, passage, or entire work, giving the meaning in another form, usually to clarify or amplify the original.

Personification: a figure of speech in which a nonhuman or inanimate object, quality, or idea is given human characteristics or powers. For instance:

> "How sweet the moonlight sleeps upon this bank!"—William Shakespeare, *The Merchant of Venice*

Plot: the plan and arrangement of related incidents, details, and elements of conflict in a story. Plot incorporates the situation or problem in which a narrative commences, the resulting complications, the rising action toward the climax, and the dénouement or final outcome.

Point of View: the manner in which the author presents the events and views the characters in his story. There are two basic points of view:

(a) *first-person narrator* (author participant). The narrative is told by a major or minor character in his or her own words. The author through this "I" narrator is limited to his or her scope of knowledge, degree of involvement, and powers of observation and expression.

(b) *third-person narrator* (author omniscient). The author serves as an unrestricted, all-knowing observer who describes and comments upon the characters and action in a narrative. The omniscient author knows everything there is to know about the characters—their thoughts, motives, actions, and reactions.

Sometimes an author narrating in the third person does not wish to indicate that he has any special knowledge about his characters and their behavior. He attempts to keep his personal feelings *objective*, or impartial and detached. In contrast, when the author's opinions about the characters or events in the story are obvious, the writing is called *subjective*.

Protagonist: the character in a story or drama in whom the action centers; the hero or heroine who is confronted with a problem. The word was originally used to designate the actor who played the chief role in a Greek drama. It comes from the Greek *prōtos* meaning "first" and *agōnistēs* meaning "contestant, actor." (See also **Antagonist**.)

Quality or Literary Story: a "significant" story that reveals the author's originality and imagination in creating natural and interesting characters, realistic situations, and meaningful themes. It is usually written for those whose tastes are inclined toward "serious" literature. No set formula is followed in writing the quality story, in contrast to the *commercial* or *craft* story.

Realism: the attempt to present life as it actually is without distortion or idealization. It is often used to depict the everyday life and speech of ordinary people. A literary movement called realism began in America in the late 1800's with the works of William Dean Howells.

Repetition: the use of the same word, phrase, sentence, idea (or some slight variation of these) to achieve emphasis. Some repetition is found in prose (see the short stories of Pearl S. Buck and Saki in this book), but it is most often used in poetry.

Rhythm: in poetry, the regular and harmonious rise and fall of stress. (As the stress becomes more and more fixed and systematized, it approaches *meter*.) In prose, although rhythm is always present, it is irregular and approximate; prose rhythm is the effective and pleasing arrangement of meaningful sounds in a sentence.

Romanticism: the attempt to present life as it should be or as the writer (and his readers) would like it to be; it pictures life in a picturesque, fanciful, exotic, emotional, or imaginative manner. Romanticism often reflects the writer's strong interest in nature and his love of the strange and the supernatural. It is the opposite of *realism*, which treats the ordinary events of everyday life in an unsentimental and factual manner.

A literary movement called romanticism, which flourished in English literature in the early nineteenth century, was exemplified in the works of writers such as Wordsworth, Coleridge, Byron, Shelley, and Keats, and in American literature in the middle-nineteenth century in the works of authors such as Longfellow, Hawthorne, and Melville.

Satire: the use of ridicule, sarcasm, wit, or irony to expose, set right, or destroy a vice, folly, breach of good taste, or social evil.

The American novelist Sinclair Lewis satirized many elements of American society. Various aspects of the medical profession come under attack in his novel *Arrowsmith*. For example, Lewis felt that public health campaigns can become somewhat ridiculous, especially when they are directed by a pompous and ill-qualified doctor like Dr. Almus Pickerbough, the head of the Department of Public Health. The following excerpt from the novel satirizes Pickerbough's activities:

"No organization could rival Almus Pickerbaugh in the invention of Weeks.

"He started in January with a Better Babies Week, and a very good Week it was, but so hotly followed by Banish the Booze Week, Tougher Teeth Week, and Stop the Spitter Week that people who lacked his vigor were heard groaning, 'My health is being ruined by all this fretting over health.'"

Science Fiction: a type of *fantasy* that combines man's real knowledge of scientific facts and principles with his imaginative speculations as to what life will be like in the future, or on another planet.

Some science fiction has actually become fact. H. G. Wells, for example, in *The War of the Worlds* (1898) and *The Shape of Things to Come* (1933) "predicted" tanks, air combat, and the atomic bomb.

Sentiment and Sentimentality: *sentiment* is a true, noble, or elevated feeling; an honest emotion. *Sentimentality* is an excess of sentiment or feeling; an artificial emotion.

Setting: the time and place of the events in a story; the physical background. The importance of setting as a story element depends on the extent of its contribution to characterization, plot, theme, and atmosphere. (See **Atmosphere**.)

Simile: a stated comparison or likeness expressed in figurative language and introduced by such terms as *like, as, so, as if, as though.* For example:

"It [the beating of the old man's heart] increased my fury, as the beating of a drum stimulates the soldier into courage."—Edgar Allan Poe, "The Tell-Tale Heart"

Sketch: a short, simply constructed work, usually about a single character, locale, or incident. A *character sketch*, for example, may be a brief study of a person's characteristics and personality. As in art, a sketch may also be a "rough" or preliminary draft for a longer, more complex work.

Soliloquy: in drama, a speech delivered by a character alone on the stage or apart from the other characters. As a literary device, it is used to reveal character or give information to the reader or the audience. It is similar to a character talking to himself and revealing his thoughts and problems.

Stereotype (Stock Character): a commonplace character who always behaves in the same way and shows the same traits of character; also, a character who lacks real personality because he possesses or is believed to possess the characteristics of a particular group or class. Examples are the temperamental movie star, the talkative cab driver, and the shrewd, cigar-smoking politician.

Stream of Consciousness: in fiction, a literary technique by which characters and actions are presented through the flow of thoughts, feelings, reflections, memories, and mental images of one or more characters.

Style: a writer's distinctive or characteristic form of expression; the means he uses to express his thoughts effectively. Style is determined by the choice and arrangement of words, sentence structure, the use of figurative language, rhythm, and tone.

Subjectivity: the quality of writing in which the author's opinions, sympathies, personal beliefs, or tastes are obvious and sometimes even dominate his work. O. Henry is an example of an author who introduces his own opinions into a story. See "The Gift of the Magi."

Surprise Ending: an unexpected twist of plot at the conclusion of a story; a trick ending. It should be carefully foreshadowed to produce its striking effect. Both O. Henry and Saki wrote stories with surprise endings.

Saki's "The Interlopers" has a horrifying surprise ending. At the conclusion of the story, two disabled men, trapped in the forest, suddenly realize that the approaching figures, whom they had assumed to be their rescuers, are not men at all. They are—as stated in the last line—"*Wolves.*"

Suspense: the uncertainty, expectancy, or tension that builds up as the climax of a narrative approaches; curiosity regarding the outcome of a narrative.

Symbol: a person, place, event, or object that exists and has meaning in itself and also suggests something further, as an attitude or a value. For example, the poppy is both a flower and a symbol of peace, rest, and sleep (especially when displayed on Memorial Day).

In literature, characters or concrete objects may be so used that they come to symbolize or represent abstract ideas. In Tennessee Williams' play *The Glass Menagerie,* the menagerie is first of all itself—a collection of small, delicate glass animals carefully taken care of by Laura, a shy, withdrawn young girl. Second, it symbolizes Laura's means of escape from the actual world, with all its difficult problems, into a world of illusion and make-believe.

Synonym: a word having the same or approximately the same meaning or meanings as another word or words in the same language. Most synonyms are interchangeable but at the same time vary widely in connotation. A standard dictionary of synonyms is Roget's *Thesaurus.* For the word *warning,* for example, Roget's lists the following nouns as synonyms: caution, caveat; advice, aviso; admonition, monition, admonishment, exhortation; notice, notification; word to the wise, *verbum sapienti* (Latin), word in the ear, flea in the ear (colloquial); lesson, example, deterrent example, warning piece; warning voice; alarm; threat.

Theme: the main idea of a literary work; the statement about the meaning of life that the author wishes to make. The theme of most short stories is, or can be, expressed in a single sentence.

An unconventional theme is a statement about life that may be contradictory to conventional or established beliefs and customs. For example, a *conventional* or traditional theme might be that true happiness is more important than money or wealth. An *unconven-*

tional theme might be that real happiness is not possible where poverty exists.

In an essay, the theme is the basic idea, major premise, or topic to be discussed; the main point. A *statement of theme* usually appears near the beginning of the discussion.

Tone: the attitude of the writer toward his subject, his characters, and his readers. He may love his subject or be highly amused by his characters. He may wish to anger his readers or to amuse them. The author conveys his feelings through his choice of words and his arrangement of words and sentences.

Topic Sentence: a clear, brief statement of what will be discussed in the paragraph; it is usually placed at the beginning of the paragraph. (See also **Paragraph Development, Methods of.**)

Understatement: the representation of something as less than it really is for the purpose of emphasis or humor. The man who casually remarks, "I've had a little luck" after he has won a top sweepstake prize is playing down or understating the true extent of his good fortune.

Unity: in writing, the organizing principle that links together all the parts of a work. In essay writing, this means the singleness of purpose, theme, or topic (or all three) that links all the subordinate parts of a composition into a whole. See also **Coherence** and **Emphasis.** In fiction writing, unity means that all the elements of a narrative relate to a single controlling idea.

The
Language Arts
Program

Throughout the text, language arts have been integrated with the presentation of literature. The majority of language-arts activities appear in the end-of-selection questions and assignments under the headings **Meaning**, **Method**, **Language**, **Composition**, and **Composition and Discussion**. Others are introduced and discussed in the general introductions, and still others, especially those concerning word origins and derivations, are covered in text footnotes.

The following indexes are intended to serve as guidelines to specific aspects of the language-arts program in A *Book of Short Stories—1*.

Literary Terms and Types

Vocabulary Development

Speaking and Listening

Reading final paragraph of story aloud (page 100, Pearl S. Buck)

Discussing student problems—past and present (121, MacKinlay Kantor, assignment 1)

Reading contrasting sentences aloud to show effects of rewriting (137, Elizabeth Enright)

Panel or open-class discussion of Sandburg's poem "Happiness" (138, Enright, 2)

Discussing problems of the "generation gap" (160, Jesse Stuart, 2)

Supporting with reasons and examples your position on the value of studying "nonessentials" (160, Stuart, 3)

Discussing changes in the high school curriculum (160, Stuart, 4)

Panel discussion or debate on voting requirements (190, Junius Edwards, 3)

Discussing author's objective and

straightforward presentation of his story (221, Guy de Maupassant, 1)

Discussing author's creation of a "certain combination of circumstances" to make the irony in his story effective (221, Maupassant, 2)

Panel discussion on problem solving (245, William Melvin Kelley, 2)

Supporting with reasons and references from story your position on "growing something" (273, Bordon Deal, 2)

Composition

Narration:

Writing a short story of a daydream (page 79, James Thurber, assignment 1)

An account of a humorous incident (79, Thurber, 2)

A personal essay or narrative on "Gift-giving" or "Christmastime" (87, O. Henry)

A narrative about a dog who helped to save a life (281, Arthur C. Clarke, 2)

Description:

Character sketch using as a guide an author's methods of characterization (54, Richard Connell, 2; 236, Selma Lagerlöf)

Setting, through words rich in their power of suggestion, the mood and atmosphere for conveying a strong single effect (169, Edgar Allan Poe)

Exposition:

Explaining the meaning of similes and metaphors in a story (54, Richard Connell, 1)

Comparing and contrasting conflicts of two characters (71, Jack London, 1)

Explaining the conflict of man versus nature and justifying its resolution (71, London, 2)

Using details and particulars and examples to explain the qualifications for a missionary or peace corps worker (101, Pearl S. Buck)

Developing one or two topic sentences by using examples from reading or personal experiences (121, MacKinlay Kantor, 3)

Comparing and contrasting the "secret lives" of two characters (138, Elizabeth Enright, 1)

Comparing and contrasting understanding and sympathetic natures of two characters (160, Jesse Stuart, 1)

Explaining procedure (189, Junius Edwards, 1)

Giving possible reasons why children lose their sense of wonder as they grow into adulthood (203, H. G. Wells, 1)

Comparing and contrasting "imaginary" settings (203, Wells, 2)

Explaining, by referring to specific techniques, author's use of satire (211, Saki)

Explaining, by analyzing the "certain combination of circumstances," author's use of irony (221, Guy de Maupassant, 2)

Explaining conflict of man versus society (245, William Melvin Kelley, 1)

Explaining difficulties of adjusting to country life (272, Bordon Deal, 1)

Developing idea expressed in story by offering specific suggestions on ways to control and use scientific data (295, Stephen Vincent Benét)

Argumentation:

Using details and particulars and examples to support your point of view about the behavior of characters in a story (146, Morley Callaghan, 1)

Supporting with facts, examples, and incidents your viewpoint, pro or con, on one of two topics (222, Guy de Maupassant, 4)

Supporting with reasons a character's standpoint on "growing something" (272, Bordon Deal, 2)

Combined Forms of Discourse:

Supporting with reasons and examples your choice of the most important problem facing high school students today (146, Morley Callaghan, 2)

Analyzing a character's past reactions as a guide for supporting your opinion of her chances for happiness "had she not lost the necklace" (222, Guy de Maupassant, 3)

Presenting reasons for [not] becoming involved in exploratory space flights and the advantages [or disadvantages] of interplanetary travel (281, Arthur C. Clarke, 1)

Newspaper Reporting:

Using obituary page of local newspaper as guide for writing obituary-feature of a character, including quotations from teachers and students and the 5 W's and H (121, MacKinlay Kantor, 2)

Book Review:

Using suggested outline as guide for a written review of Junius Edwards's novel *If We Must Die*, including description of events and discussion of author's attitude (190, Junius Edwards, 2)

Letter Writing:

Imitating speech and spelling of boy in "Two Soldiers," in letter telling news of family and town (261, William Faulkner)